6/-
6810

elements of
materials science

elements of
materials science

AN INTRODUCTORY TEXT FOR ENGINEERING STUDENTS

by

LAWRENCE H. VAN VLACK

Department of Chemical and Metallurgical Engineering
The University of Michigan

SECOND EDITION

ADDISON-WESLEY PUBLISHING COMPANY, INC.

Reading, Massachusetts · Menlo Park, California · London · Sydney · Manila

THIS BOOK IS AN ADDISON-WESLEY
WORLD STUDENT SERIES EDITION

FOURTH PRINTING 1968

A complete and unabridged reprint of the original American
textbook, this World Student Series edition may be sold only in those
countries to which it is consigned by Addison-Wesley or its
authorized trade distributors. It may not be re-exported from the
country to which it has been consigned, and it may not be sold in
the United States of America or its possessions.

*Dedicated to today's students
and tomorrow's engineers*

by L., F., L., *and* B.

preface

Before the first edition of this text was published, the subject matter taught in Engineering Materials courses had for some time been changing rapidly. Empirical presentations and descriptions of materials and their properties were being replaced by more systematic approaches and analyses. A science of materials, based on the physics and chemistry of the internal structures of materials, was developing. The first edition of this textbook attempted to present to engineering students the basic principles of this new science in an introductory manner. Although the book's approach was considered to be successful, additional classroom usage indicated desirable modifications, additions, and deletions. Furthermore, there have been recent advances in the science of materials which could not go unnoticed. The above factors led to this revision of *Elements of Materials Science*.

Before attempting a revision, the author discussed, with many other engineers and engineering instructors, the best way to teach Materials Science to engineering students. Should there be a general course on the subject taught to all engineers, or should there be a separate materials course tailored to each engineering curriculum? These discussions, reinforced by the author's teaching experience, led to the conclusion that a general materials course is advantageous in many schools and departments. Assuming that the course is analytical, the same arguments can be used in favor of a general course to introduce materials as are used for a general course to introduce chemistry or physics. No one suggests that electrical, mechanical, or other types of engineers need separate and differing courses in chemistry and physics. This same conclusion applied to a general materials course has one logical exception. If an individual curriculum requires additional basic sciences, such as physical chemistry or modern physics, it may be desirable to tailor the materials course to make use of this enriched background.

The second edition of this text, like the first, is directed specifically to the undergraduate engineering student who has had general chemistry and who is concurrently taking general physics. Although the text does not use the rigor usually encountered in solid-state physics courses, it attempts to be systematic in its approach.

Chapter 1, here as in the previous edition, is an introduction designed to orient the reader in the study of this engineering science and to acquaint him with the engineering terminology applicable to properties of materials. Succeeding chapters are concerned with the internal structure of materials and with the dependence of properties on these structures. A given sequence proceeds from atomic structures to coarser structures, from the simple to the more complex. This sequence—from atoms to crystals, to phases, to microstructures, and finally to macrostructures—is logical both scientifically and pedagogically, since the grosser structures and properties depend on the finer structural characteristics.

There is new material in the previously neglected area of structural imperfections and atom movements, and there are two major rearrangements of subject matter: (a) Electrical behavior is introduced earlier in this edition than in the first, which permits attention to electrical properties concurrently with mechanical properties when metals, polymers, and ceramics are introduced in Chapters 6, 7, and 8. (b) Service behavior, which occupied the final five chapters of the first edition, has been consolidated with part of the material covered in a chapter on the stability of materials in service. The remainder of the discussion of service behavior is included with earlier sections on properties of metallic, polymeric, and ceramic materials. This rearrangement provides a more logical and efficient presentatión.

Example problems and study problems have been reviewed, and those less pertinent have been deleted in favor of new ones.

All these changes have come about as a result of classroom development by the author and his associates.

Bearing in mind that a textbook such as this must meet the needs of a variety of schools, the author has tried to overcome one major problem which often confronts the instructor: a time limitation which makes it necessary for him to decide which topics he may delete. The author has indicated those topics, examples, and problems which may be assigned at the discretion of the instructor. Students who have not covered the optional material will not be placed under a handicap when they come to later required sections. *Those sections and subsections marked with a bullet (•) contain material which is not a prerequisite for later unmarked sections and problems.* (The subject matter may, however, pertain to later marked sections.) Thus instructors will be able to adjust their timetables as need arises. The marked sections contain (a) illustrations of engineering interest (such as p-n junctions), (b) certain new, or more advanced topics which were not in the first edition (e.g., the relationship between diffusion coefficients and temperature), and (c) topics included in the first edition, but not mandatory in a time-limited course (e.g., graphitization processes).

A book such as this cannot be a one-man project. Although it is impossible to give individual thanks to all the helpful faculty colleagues and to the innumerable students who have contributed in their way to this book, the author wishes to express gratitude to them at this time, as well as to those colleagues in other institutions who have taken time to offer their comments, suggestions, and corrections to the first edition. In the revision of the text, attention has been given to each of their suggestions. Specific thanks are due Professor W. C. Bigelow of the University of Michigan and Professor Morris Cohen of the Massachusetts Institute of Technology, who have worked closely with the author. Also the help of Miss Dolores Gillies in Ann Arbor, and the Addison-Wesley personnel in Reading, is acknowledged with gratitude.

Ann Arbor
February 1964   L. H. V. V.

contents

_____

• Topic is optional with the instructor.

ix

1

engineering requirements of materials

1-1 Introduction. Every engineer—mechanical, civil, electrical, or other—is vitally concerned with the materials available to him. Whether his product is a bridge, a computer, a space vehicle, or an automobile, he must have an intimate knowledge of the properties and behavioral characteristics of the materials he proposes to use. Consider, for a moment, the variety of materials used in the manufacture of an automobile: iron, steel, glass, plastics, rubber—to name a few. And for steel alone there are as many as 2000 varieties or modifications. On what basis is the selection of the material for a particular part to be made?

In making his choice, the engineer must take into account such properties as strength, electrical and/or thermal conductivity, density, and others. Further, he must consider the behavior of the material during processing and use, where formability, machinability, electrical stability, chemical durability, and radiation behavior are important, as well as cost and availability. For example (Fig. 1–1), the steel for a drive pinion must machine easily in production, but must then be toughened enough to withstand hard usage. Fenders must be made of a metal that is easily shaped, but which will resist deformation by impact. Electrical wiring must be able to withstand extremes of temperature, and semiconductors must have constant amperage/voltage characteristics over long periods of time.

Many improved engineering designs depend on the development of completely new materials. For example, the transistor could not have been built with the materials available a decade ago; the development of the solar battery required a

Fig. 1–1. Finished drive pinion. This gear must be machinable during production, and then have its properties changed before use, to toughen it. (Courtesy of Climax Molybdenum Co.)

new kind of semiconductor; and although engineering designs for gas-turbine engines are far advanced, there still is a need for an inexpensive material that will resist high temperatures, for the turbine blades.

Since it is obviously impossible for the engineer to have detailed knowledge of the many thousands of materials already available, as well as to keep abreast of new developments, he must have a firm grasp of the underlying principles that govern the properties of *all* materials. We shall start by becoming acquainted with some engineering terms and measurements, and shall then consider (1) the structure of materials, and (2) how the properties of materials are affected under service conditions. Our study of structure will range from those features which are amenable to direct observation to those which are submicroscopic: from the gross component parts to the grains and crystals of which they are composed, and down to the atomic particles which determine the properties of the material. Our discussion of in-service conditions will include the effects of mechanical loading, temperature, electric and magnetic fields, chemical surroundings, and the currently emphasized exposure to radiation.

1–2 Mechanical properties. Probably the first characteristic of a material that comes to mind, particularly in connection with such large structures as bridges or buildings, is *strength*. Other mechanical characteristics are *elasticity, ductility, creep, hardness,* and *toughness*. Each of these is associated with the ability of the material to resist mechanical forces. But the engineer does not always want his materials to resist all deformation. A spring, for example, is intended to change its shape under load, although no permanent deformation should persist after the load is removed. On the other hand, the material used for the fender of an automobile must be permanently deformed in the shaping operation.

To provide a working basis for making comparisons between structural properties and the effects of in-service behavior on those properties, we shall first define some of the more commonly used engineering terms.

Stress is defined as force per unit area, and is expressed in pounds per square inch (psi). Stress is calculated by simply dividing the force by the area on which it operates.

Example 1–1

Which part has the greater stress: (a) an aluminum bar of 0.97 in. × 1.21 in. cross section, under a load of 16,750 lb, or (b) a steel bar whose cross-sectional diameter is 0.505 in., under a 10,800-lb load?

Answer: Units: $\dfrac{\text{pounds}}{\text{(in)(in)}} = \text{psi.}$

Calculation: (a) $\dfrac{16,750}{(0.97)(1.21)} = 14,300$ psi; (b) $\dfrac{10,800}{(\pi/4)(0.505)^2} = 54,000$ psi.

Strain is the deformation of a material. The engineer commonly expresses strain in one of two ways: (1) the number of inches of deformation per inch of original length, or (2) the deformation length as a percent of the original length. Strain may be *elastic* or *plastic*.

Example 1-2

A 2-in. gage length is marked on a copper rod. The rod is strained so that the gage marks are 2.27 in. apart. Calculate the strain.

Answer: Units: $\dfrac{(\text{in} - \text{in})}{\text{in}} = \dfrac{\text{in}}{\text{in}} = \dfrac{\text{percent}}{100}.$

Calculation: $\dfrac{2.27 - 2.00}{2.00} = 0.135 \text{ in/in} = 13.5\%.$

Elastic strain is reversible strain; it disappears after the stress is removed. The elastic strain is nearly proportional to the amount of applied stress (Fig. 1-2).

The *modulus of elasticity* (Young's modulus) is the ratio between the stress applied and the elastic strain that results. It is related to *rigidity*. The modulus of elasticity resulting from tension or compression is expressed in psi. The value for this modulus is primarily determined by the composition of the material (Appendix E), and is only indirectly related to other mechanical properties

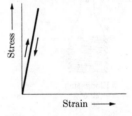

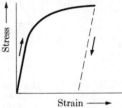

Fig. 1-2. Elastic stress-strain relationships. Elastic strain is proportional to amount of stress.

Fig. 1-3. Plastic stress-strain relationships. Plastic strain, which follows initial elastic strain, is not reversible. The elastic strain continues to increase during plastic deformation, but is reversible. (Compare with Fig. 1-2.)

Example 1-3

If the average modulus of elasticity of the steel used is 29,500,000 psi, how much will a wire 0.1 in. in diameter and 10 ft long be elongated when it supports a load of 1000 lb?

Answer: Modulus of elasticity $= \dfrac{\text{stress}}{\text{strain}}.$ (1-1)

Units: $\text{psi} = \dfrac{\text{lb/in}^2}{\text{in/in}}.$

Calculation: $29,500,000 = \dfrac{1000/(\pi/4)(0.1)^2}{\text{strain}}.$

Strain $= 0.0043 \text{ in/in}.$

Units: $(\text{in/in})(\text{in}) = (\text{in}).$

Elongation $= (0.0043)(120) = 0.52 \text{ in.}$

Plastic strain is the strain permanently given to a material by stresses which exceed the elastic limit (Fig. 1-3). Plastic strain is the result of a permanent displacement of the atoms inside the material, and therefore differs from elastic strain, where the same atomic neighbors are retained.

Ductility is the amount of plastic deformation at the breaking point. Thus its value may be expressed as *elongation* and in the same units as strain. A common (but not universal) gage length for measuring elongation is 2 in. As shown in Fig. 1–4, the gage length becomes important because plastic deformation is usually localized.

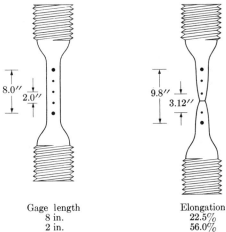

Gage length	Elongation
8 in.	22.5%
2 in.	56.0%

Fig. 1–4. Elongation versus gage length. Since final deformation is localized, an elongation value is meaningless unless the gage length is indicated.

A second measure of ductility is *reduction in area* at the point of fracture. Highly ductile materials are greatly reduced in cross section before breaking. This index is always expressed in percent and is calculated as follows:

$$\text{Reduction of area} = \frac{\text{original area} - \text{final area}}{\text{original area}}. \tag{1-2}$$

Stress-strain relationships. It is now possible to be more specific about the effect of stress on strain. Figure 1–5 shows the relationship for several different types of materials, each of which has a range of elastic or proportional strain.

The nonductile material in part (a) of the figure will not deform plastically before breaking. A ductile material has an *elastic limit* (or *proportional limit*) beyond which yield or plastic deformation occurs. The ability of a material to resist plastic deformation is called the *yield strength,* and is computed by dividing the force initiating the yield by the cross-sectional area. In materials such as some of the softer steels, the yield strength is marked by a definite *yield point* (Fig. 1–5b). In other materials, where the proportional limit is less obvious, it is common to define the yield load as that force required to give 0.2% (or some other specified value) plastic offset (Fig. 1–5c).

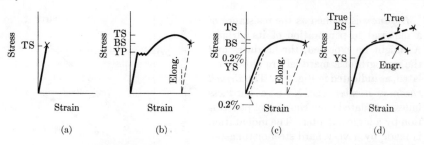

FIG. 1-5. Stress-strain diagrams. (a) Nonductile material with no plastic deformation (example: cast iron). (b) Ductile material with yield point (example: low-carbon steel). (c) Ductile material without marked yield point (example: aluminum). (d) True stress-strain curve versus engineering stress-strain curve. BS = breaking strength, TS = tensile strength, YS = yield strength, Elong. = elongation, × = rupture, YP = yield point.

The *tensile strength* of a material is calculated by dividing the maximum load by the original cross-sectional area. This strength, like all other strengths, is expressed in the same units as stress, psi. Note particularly that tensile strength is based on the original cross-sectional area. This is an important distinction, inasmuch as a ductile material will have its cross-sectional area somewhat reduced under maximum load. Although the *true*, or *physical*, stress in the material is based on actual area (Fig. 1-5d), the *engineering stress* is more important to the engineer, who must, of course, make his designs on the basis of initial dimensions.

Because the cross-sectional area of a ductile material may be reduced before it breaks, the *breaking strength* may be less than the *tensile strength*. Expressions for both are, by definition, based on original area (Fig. 1-5c).

• **Example 1-4**

A copper wire has an engineering breaking strength of 43,000 psi and a reduction of area of 77%. Calculate (a) the true tensile strength, and (b) the true strain ϵ_{tr} at the point of fracture. (The instantaneous strain $d\epsilon$ is equal to dl/l.)

Answer:

(a)
$$\frac{F}{A_0} = 43,000 \text{ psi}, \quad F = 43,000 \ A_0,$$

$$\frac{F}{A_{tr}} = \frac{F}{(1 - 0.77)A_0} = \frac{43,000}{0.23} = 187,000 \text{ psi}.$$

(b) Since
$$d\epsilon \equiv \frac{dl}{l}, \quad \epsilon_{tr} = \int_{l_0}^{l_f} \frac{dl}{l} = \ln \frac{l_f}{l_0}.$$

Also
$$A_0 l_0 = A_f l_f,$$

$$\epsilon_{t_1} = \ln \frac{A_0}{A_f} = \ln \frac{A_0}{0.23 \ A_0} = 1.47 \text{ or } 147\%.$$

• Examples preceded by a bullet may be assigned at the discretion of the instructor. (*See* preface.)

Hardness is defined as the resistance of a material to penetration of its surface. As might be expected, the hardness and the strength of a material are closely related, as indicated in Fig. 1-6. The *Brinell hardness number* (BHN) is a hardness index calculated from the area of penetration by a large indenter. The indentation is made by a very hard steel or tungsten carbide ball under a standardized load. The *Rockwell hardness* (R), another of several common indexes of hardness used by engineers, is related to BHN (Appendix C) but is measured by the depth of penetration by a small standardized indenter. Several different Rockwell scales for materials of different hardness ranges have been established by selecting various indenter shapes and loads.

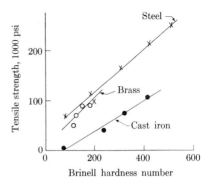

FIG. 1-6. Tensile strength versus Brinell Hardness Number (BHN). Examples: Steels, brasses, and cast irons.

Toughness is a measure of the *energy* required to break a material. This is in contrast to *strength*, which is a measure of the *stress* required to deform or break a material. Energy, the product of force times distance, is expressed in foot-pounds; it is closely related to the area under the stress-strain curve. A ductile material with the same strength as a nonductile material will require more energy for breaking and be tougher (Fig. 1-7). Standardized *Charpy* or *Izod* tests are used to measure toughness. They differ only in the shape of the test piece and in the method of applying the energy.

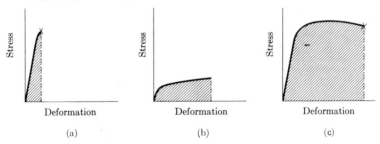

FIG. 1-7. Toughness is a measure of the energy required to break a material. Therefore it is depicted by the area under the stress-strain curve. Part (c) represents the toughest behavior of the three examples.

1-3 Thermal properties. The distinction between temperature and heat is an important one. Temperature is a level of thermal activity, whereas heat is thermal energy.

Although engineers commonly use the fahrenheit temperature scale, they should be "bilingual" in this respect and be able to make direct comparisons with the celsius (centigrade) scale. Calculations are more easily made with the celsius scale, and an increasing number of industrial processes are being set up on this basis. A direct conversion can be made from one scale to the other by means of the following relationships:

$$°F = 1.8(°C) + 32°, \tag{1-3}$$

$$°C = \tfrac{5}{9}[(°F) - 32°]. \tag{1-4}$$

For any selected chemical component of a material, the *melting point* and the *boiling point* are significant temperature levels because they are transition points between different structural arrangements of the atoms within the material.

Heat is expressed in Btu's in English units, and as calories in metric units. One Btu is the energy required to increase the temperature of one pound of water 1°F at its greatest density (39°F). Thus, the units for *heat capacity* are Btu/lb·°F, or in the metric system cal/gm·°C. The *specific heat* of a material is defined as the ratio of the heat capacity of the material to that of water.

Various heats of transformation are of importance in materials. The better known of these are the *heat of fusion* and the *heat of vaporization*, which are the heats required to produce melting and gasification, respectively. Each involves a change within the material from one atomic or molecular structure to another. We shall learn later that there are various structural changes possible within solids, and that these changes also require a change in heat or thermal energy content of the material.

Thermal expansion is self-descriptive and is commonly expressed with a coefficient of in./in.·°F (or cm/cm·°C). We usually assume that the coefficient of thermal expansion does not vary with temperature. For reasons we shall present later, it should be noted that the coefficient of thermal expansion is temperature sensitive and usually increases as the temperature is raised (Fig. 1-8). Discon-

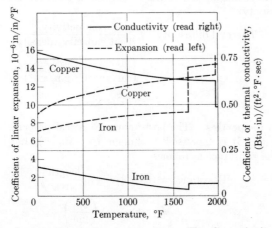

FIG. 1-8. Thermal properties versus temperature. The discontinuity for copper at 1985°F (1085°C) is a result of melting. Iron has a discontinuity because there is a rearrangement of the atoms at 1670°F (910°C). See Chapter 3.

tinuous volume changes occur with changes of state because there is a change in the arrangement of the atoms and molecules within the material. Here, as with mechanical deformation, a contrast may be made between those responses of the material wherein the same neighbors are retained for any particular atom, and those wherein the atoms or molecules are rearranged. This contrast will continue to appear in later discussions.

Heat transfer through solids most commonly occurs by *thermal conductivity*, whose coefficients are expressed in units such as (Btu·in.)/(°F·hr·ft²), or (cal·cm)/ (°C·sec·cm²). It should be noted that the units for thermal conductivity are *not* (Btu/in./°F/hr/ft²). The preceding coefficient of thermal conductivity is also temperature sensitive. However, unlike the coefficient of thermal expansion, this coefficient decreases as the temperature is raised above room temperature. (The reasons for this behavior will be discussed later.) The changes of atomic packing, which accompany melting and other atomic rearrangements arising from temperature variations, produce discontinuities in the thermal-conductivity values (Fig. 1–8).

The engineer is commonly interested in the unsteady state of thermal transfer, as well as the steady state. In the unsteady state, thermal transfer produces a temperature change, and thus decreases the thermal gradient. Under such conditions, thermal diffusivity h is important:

$$h = k/c_p\rho, \tag{1-5}$$

where k is the thermal conductivity, c_p is the heat capacity, and ρ is the density. A material with high heat requirements per unit volume $c_p\rho$ has a low thermal diffusivity, simply because more calories (or Btu's) must be added to or removed from the material in order to change the temperature. The units applicable to thermal diffusivity, indicated below, will provide a basis for later considerations of atomic diffusivity.

$$\text{Thermal diffusivity} = \frac{\text{conductivity}}{\text{(heat capacity)(density)}}$$

$$= \frac{(\text{cal·cm})/(°\text{C·sec·cm}^2)}{(\text{cal/gm·°C})(\text{gm/cm}^3)}$$

$$= \text{cm}^2/\text{sec}. \tag{1-6}$$

1–4 Electrical properties. The best-known electrical property of a material is that of resistivity. It is expressed in ohm·cm (or ohm·in.), and is related to the common units of resistance as follows:

$$\text{Resistance} = (\text{resistivity}) \left(\frac{\text{length}}{\text{area}}\right)$$

$$= (\text{ohm·cm}) \left(\frac{\text{cm}}{\text{cm}^2}\right)$$

$$= (\text{ohm·in}) \left(\frac{\text{in}}{\text{in}^2}\right). \tag{1-7}$$

Example 1-5

Copper has a resistivity of 1.7×10^{-6} ohm·cm. What is the resistance of a wire which is 0.022 in. in diameter and 96 ft long?

Answer: Units: $\text{Resistance} = \left(\dfrac{\text{ohm·cm}}{2.54 \text{ cm/in}} \right) \left(\dfrac{(12 \text{ in/ft})(\text{ft})}{\text{in}^2} \right).$

Calculation: $\text{Resistance} = \left(\dfrac{1.7 \times 10^{-6}}{2.54} \right) \left(\dfrac{(12)(96)}{(\pi/4)(0.022)^2} \right) = 2.0 \text{ ohms.}$

Electrical conductivity is the reciprocal of electrical resistivity. It is expressed in mho/cm (mho $=$ ohm^{-1}). The relationship of conductivity to the number of carriers, the charge per carrier, and the mobility will be discussed in further detail in Chapter 5, as will the relationship between electrical conductivity and (1) temperature and (2) strain.

In contrast to electrical conductors which transfer electrical charges, many materials of engineering importance are used as *dielectrics* or nonconductors. If the dielectric material is used' solely as an insulator to prevent charge transfer, it is necessary to consider its *dielectric strength*. This property is usually expressed in volts per mil (1000 mils $=$ 1 in.); however, let us note that the insulating ability of a material does not always increase in direct proportion to its thickness. Many other factors, such as surface area, porosity, and defects influence the insulating characteristics of a material.

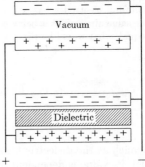

FIG. 1-9. The relative dielectric constant can be discussed in terms of the amount of electricity which may be stored in a capacitor. The relative dielectric constant equals the quantity of electricity stored across an insulating material divided by the quantity stored across a vacuum.

Dielectric properties of importance also include the *dielectric constant*, which is best explained in terms of a capacitor, a device for storing electrical charge. A capacitor is composed of a negative and a positive electrode, between which there is either a vacuum or an insulating material. The negative electrode stores charge, and charge is removed from the positive electrode (Fig. 1-9). The amount of charge which is stored is dependent on, among other things, the dielectric material between the plates. These dielectrics will not transport electric charges, but they are not inert insulators because an externally applied field can displace the electronic and ionic charges from their normal position in the internal structure of the material. This behavior can be compared to elastic strain in mechanical loading, as discussed earlier, inasmuch as the charges return to their normal position when the electric field is removed. (See Chapter 5 for further detail.)

The charge Q (expressed as coulombs, or amp·sec) which is held by a capacitor is proportional to the voltage V through a capacitance C expressed in farads:

$$Q = CV. \qquad (1\text{-}8)$$

The capacitance is further dependent on the relative dielectric constant κ' and the geometry of the capacitor. For a parallel-plate capacitor:

$$C = \frac{\kappa' A}{(4.452)(10^6)d}, \qquad (1\text{-}9)$$

where C is in microfarads, A is the area in square inches, and d is the distance between the plates. The conversion factor, 4.452, is chosen such that the relative dielectric constant κ' is dimensionless and equal to 1.0 when there is a vacuum between the plates. The value of κ' for the various materials which might be used as a dielectric in this position depends on the amount of charge displacement which occurs as a result of the electric field of the plate. A combination of Eqs. (1–8) and (1–9) would indicate that the quantity of electrical charge stored in a capacitor varies with the relative dielectric constant (Fig. 1–9).

Example 1–6

A capacitor designed to use wax-paper spacers (dielectric constant $\kappa' = 1.75$) between aluminum-foil electrodes has a capacitance of 0.013 farad. A plastic film ($\kappa' = 2.10$) with the same dimensions is being considered as a substitute for the paper. Other factors being equal, what would be the new capacitance of the capacitor?

Answer:

$$\frac{A}{(4.452)(10^6)d} = \left(\frac{C}{\kappa'}\right)_{\text{paper}} = \left(\frac{C}{\kappa'}\right)_{\text{plastic}},$$

$$C_{\text{plastic}} = \frac{(0.013)(2.10)}{1.75} = 0.0156 \text{ farad.}$$

Inasmuch as the dielectric constant arises from charge displacement within the material, its value is dependent on both temperature and frequency, as well as on the structure of the material. These factors will receive attention in subsequent chapters.

1–5 Chemical properties. Almost all materials used by engineers are subject to chemical deterioration. For some materials chemical *solution* is important. In other cases the effect of direct *oxidation* of a metal or of an organic material such as rubber is of major concern. In addition, the ability of a material to resist chemical *corrosion* due to environment is of primary importance. The attention we give our automobiles is an obvious example of our concern with the extent of chemical corrosion. Since corrosion is frequently irregular in attack, it is difficult to measure. The most common unit of corrosion is inches of surface lost per year.

1-6 Optical properties. Although optical properties of engineering importance include index of refraction, absorptivity, and emissivity, only the first of these will be discussed here, because the other two are somewhat specialized. The index of refraction n is the ratio of the velocity of light in a vacuum, c, to the velocity of light within a material, V_m:

$$n = \frac{c}{V_m}. \qquad (1\text{--}10)$$

The index may also be expressed in terms of the angle of incidence i and the angle of refraction r,

$$n = \frac{\sin i}{\sin r}. \qquad (1\text{--}11)$$

1-7 Cost. Although cost is certainly not a *property* of a material, it frequently is the governing factor in the selection of a material for an engineering component or structure. Cost is commonly figured in value per pound or per part, but a more significant figure is cost per unit of useful life. It is often advantageous to pay more per pound, or more per part, if by so doing we can increase the life and decrease maintenance and replacement costs.

1-8 Measurement of engineering properties. *Qualitative information.* Schematic diagrams which show the effect of one variable on a dependent property are indispensable aids in translating complicated empirical relationships into qualitative terms. Figure 1–10, for example, illustrates the change in the strength of concrete in relation to the amount of water added. Concrete, of course, is strongest when a minimum amount of water is used, although there must be sufficient water to make the concrete workable.

Other variables may be shown schematically by the use of additional parameters. Figure 1–11 adds the parameter of time, t, to the relationship previously given in Fig. 1–10. Figure 1–11 tells us that (1) for any given addition of water to cement, the strength increases as the period of time increases, (2) for any given period of time, the strength is less if excess water was used, and (3) a given strength may be attained in less time if less water is used.

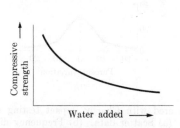

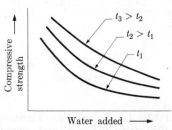

FIG. 1–10. Schematic representation of two variables. Strength of concrete versus water content. The water content is the independent variable.

FIG. 1–11. Schematic representation of three variables. Strength of concrete as related to time t and water content.

Schematic representations help the engineer to determine in advance what variables can be controlled to obtain the desired result. With such information he can anticipate possible modifications of his materials in production or in service. *Quantitative data.* It is often important to secure quantitative data concerning the properties of materials. Thus, from Fig. 1–12, the design engineer observes that concrete may have a compressive strength of 4500 psi if six gallons of water are used with each sack of portland cement. However, to make the information complete, the parameter of time as well as data on particle size and temperature should be included, since each of these influences the quantitative relationships.

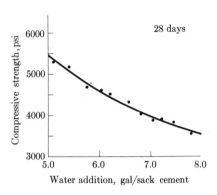

FIG. 1–12. Quantitative values. Strength of concrete versus water content (ASTM Testing Standards No. C 39–49).

Another factor, equally important in the presentation of many quantitative data, is the variance* that may be encountered in the testing. Figure 1–13 shows the range of values obtained in the impact testing of fifty samples of steel at 70°F. There is a rather large variance in the data, although the samples and testing procedures were identical, so far as could be determined. The variation in impact values can arise from several sources: (1) undetected differences within the steel which was sampled, (2) differences in the preparation of the samples, (3) differences in the testing procedure. The large variations shown here would necessitate additional testing to establish an average impact value.

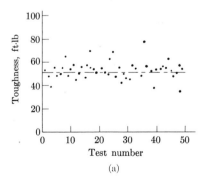

(a)

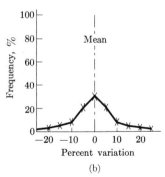

(b)

FIG. 1–13. Large variance. Variations encountered with Charpy impact testing of SAE 1040 steel (70°F). All tests were identical. (a) Scatter data. (b) Frequency distribution.

---

* Variance is a statistical measure of probable variation and is equal to the square of the standard deviation.

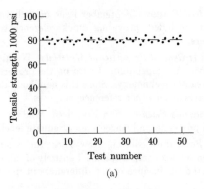
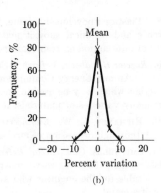

(a)   (b)

FIG. 1–14. Small variance. Variations encountered with tensile testing of SAE 1040 steel (70°F). All tests were identical. (a) Scatter data. (b) Frequency distribution.

Although the variance is not always as marked as in the example of Fig. 1–13 (see Fig. 1–14), the engineer must anticipate the kind of variations to be expected, since frequently he cannot directly test the materials he plans to use. Furthermore, allowances must be made for the additional variances encountered in service. One of the more significant examples of this added service effect was observed in the early British Comets, where no allowance was made for the metal fatigue encountered in pressurizing and depressurizing the cabins of these airplanes at high altitudes.

References for Further Reading

Properties of Materials

1–1. Appendix E. *Properties of Selected Engineering Materials.*

1–2. BRADY, G. S., *Materials Handbook.* New York: McGraw-Hill, 1951. This book has one or two paragraphs describing each of a thousand or more types of materials.

1–3. *Ceramic Data Book.* Chicago: Industrial Publications, Inc., published annually. Contains data on the properties of the more common ceramic materials, including specific data in the following divisions: refractories, structural clay products, enamels, glass, whiteware, and electrical ceramics.

1–4. *Corrosion in Action.* New York: International Nickel Co., 1955. An introduction to the principles of corrosion; excellently illustrated.

1–5. KINNEY, G. F., *Engineering Properties and Applications of Plastics.* New York: John Wiley & Sons, 1957. The first chapters consider the main categories of plastics. Subsequently, their mechanical, thermal, optical, and electrical properties are considered.

1–6. MARIN, J., *Mechanical Behavior of Engineering Materials.* Englewood Cliffs, N.J.: Prentice-Hall, 1962. Gives a continuum approach to mechanical properties; advanced undergraduate level.

1–7. *Metals Handbook,* Volume I. Cleveland: American Society for Metals, 1961. This basic reference book for all metallurgists is essentially an encyclopedia of metals.

1-8. "Plastics Encyclopedia Issue," *Modern Plastics*. September issue of each year. Reference and technical subject matter are included, providing quick reference to a variety of information on resins and polymers.

1-9. *Reactor Handbook, Volume 3, Section 1: General Properties of Materials*. Washington, D.C.: Atomic Energy Commission, 1955. A compendium of data on the properties of materials which may be used in nuclear-reactor technology. Since this handbook thus covers many varieties of materials, it also serves for other reference purposes.

1-10. RICHARDS, C. W., *Engineering Materials Science*. San Francisco: Wadsworth, 1961. A thorough discussion of mechanical properties; advanced undergraduate level.

1-11. SMITHELLS, C. J., *Metal Reference Book*, third edition. New York: Interscience Publishers, Inc., 1961. A two-volume reference book composed almost entirely of tabular data; suitable for the engineer who knows the significance of the differences in the behavior of a metal.

1-12. WOLDMAN, N. F., *Engineering Alloys*. Cleveland: American Society for Metals, 1954. Over 19,000 alloys are listed, with their properties, compositions, and typical applications.

Materials Testing

1-13. *ASTM Standards*. Philadelphia: American Society for Testing Materials, 1961 (with frequent revisions). This is a multivolume set of standards accepted by a wide cross section of American industry. Testing specifications are outlined in detail.

1-14. BORNEMANN, A., and R. S. WILLIAMS, *Metals Technology*. Cleveland: American Society for Metals, 1954. Includes laboratory exercises, along with the description of test equipment for the more common tests. For the beginning student.

Materials Applications (General)

1-15. *Materials in Design Engineering*. New York: Reinhold; published monthly. A trade magazine, with articles on all varieties of materials which have engineering importance, written at the technical level of the competent engineer.

1-16. *Ceramic Industry*. One of several trade magazines covering the ceramic materials.

1-17. *Metal Progress*. One of several trade magazines covering metallic materials.

1-18. *Modern Plastics*. One of several trade magazines covering plastic materials.

Problems

1-1. (a) A bar 0.5 in. in diameter supports a load of 15,000 lb. What is the stress placed on the bar? (b) If the bar of part (a) has a modulus of elasticity of 30,000,000 psi, how many inches per inch would the bar be strained if a 15,000-lb load were applied?
Answer: (a) 76,000 psi (b) 0.0025 in/in

1-2. The bar in Problem 1-1 supports a maximum load of 26,000 lb without permanent deformation. What is its _____ strength?

1-3. The bar of Problem 1-1 breaks with a load of 25,000 lb. Its final diameter is 0.31 in. (a) What is its true breaking strength? (b) What is its engineering breaking strength? • (c) What is the true strain at fracture?
Answer: (a) 331,000 psi (b) 127,000 psi (c) 96%

1-4. An aluminum bar 0.505 in. in diameter has 2-in. gage marks. The following data are obtained:

Load, lb	Gage length, in.
2000	2.0020
4000	2.0039
6000	2.0061
8000	2.193

(a) Draw a stress-strain curve. (b) What is the bar's modulus of elasticity?

1-5. A copper alloy has a modulus of elasticity of 16,000,000 psi, a yield strength of 48,000 psi, and a tensile strength of 51,000 psi. (a) How much stress would be required to stretch a 10.0-ft bar of this alloy 0.06 in.? (b) What size round bar would be required to support a load of 5000 lb without permanent deformation?

Answer: (a) 8000 psi (b) 0.364 in. in diameter

1-6. A steel bar $\frac{1}{4}$ in. $\times$ $\frac{1}{2}$ in. in cross section is 10.00 ft long and supports a maximum longitudinal load of 16,700 lb without permanent deformation. (a) What is its elastic limit? (b) Determine the length of the bar under this load, given that the modulus of elasticity for steel is 30,000,000 psi.

1-7. Aluminum (6151 alloy) has a modulus of elasticity of 10^7 psi and a yield strength of 40,000 psi. (a) How much load can be supported by a 0.108-in. wire of this alloy without permanent deformation? (b) If a load of 97 lb is supported by a 100-ft wire of this size, what is the total elongation?

Answer: (a) 367 lb (b) 1.27 in. elongation

1-8. Monel metal (70 Ni–30 Cu) has a modulus of elasticity of 26×10^6 psi and a yield strength of 65,000 psi. (a) How much load could be supported by a rod 0.715 in. in diameter without permanent deformation? (b) If a maximum total elongation of 0.1 in. is permissible in a 7-ft bar, how large a load could be applied to this 0.715-in. rod?

1-9. A 0.25-in. diameter 1020 steel bar 6 ft long supports a weight of 1000 lb. What is the difference in elongation if the bar is changed to a 70–30 Monel? (See Problem 1-8.)

Answer: 0.007 in./6 ft

1-10. The following data were obtained from a standard 0.505-in. test specimen of a metal bar:

Load, lb	Strain, in/in
4,000	0.005
7,900	0.010
10,300	0.015
11,600	0.02
12,600	0.03
13,200	0.04
13,000	0.06
11,000	0.08
10,800	Broke (diameter = 0.21 in.)

Supply the following information: (a) Tensile strength, (b) 0.2% offset yield strength, (c) ductility, (d) breaking stresses (true and engineering).

1-11. A load of 1000 lb hanging from a steel wire 8 ft long, of cross-sectional area 0.025 in², was found to stretch the wire elastically 0.12 in. Compute (a) the stress, (b) the strain, and (c) the value of Young's modulus.

Answer: (a) 40,000 psi (b) 0.00125 in/in (c) 32×10^6 psi

1-12. A rule-of-thumb calculation states that the tensile strength of steel is 500 times its Brinell hardness. (a) What percentage error arises from the use of this rule for the six steels shown in Fig. 1–6? (b) for the five cast irons?

1-13. (a) What is the maximum permissible conductivity in a 1-in. wall if the hot and cold sides are at 1000°F and 425°F, respectively, and if no more than 100 Btu/ft²/hr are to be transmitted? (b) 1 Btu·in/ft²·hr·°F equals how many cal·cm/cm²·sec·°C?

Answer: (a) 0.174 Btu·in/ft²·hr·°F (b) 0.000344 cal·cm/cm²·sec·°C

1-14. A wall is 5 in. thick and has a thermal conductivity of 1.44 Btu·in/°F·hr·ft². (a) What is the rate of heat loss through the wall in Btu's if the inside is at 80°F and the outside is at 20°F? (b) What is the average temperature gradient in the wall in metric units?

1-15. The average coefficient of thermal expansion of a steel rod is 7.5×10^{-6} in/in/°F. (a) How much temperature change is required to provide the same linear change as a stress of 90,000 psi? (b) What volume change does this temperature change produce?

Answer: (a) 400°F (b) 0.9 v/o

1-16. Calcite (limestone) has an average linear coefficient of expansion of 6.4×10^{-6} in/in/°F between 70°F and 400°F and 7.5×10^{-6} in/in/°F between 70°F and 1000°F. (a) What is the average coefficient of expansion between 400°F and 1000°F? (b) The true volume was 1.000 in³ at 400°F. What is the true volume at 70°F?

1-17. The heat capacity C_p of iron is $3.04 + 7.58 \times 10^{-3}T + 0.60 \times 10^5 T^{-2}$ cal/mol·°K, where T is temperature in °K. (a) What is the thermal diffusivity of iron at 20°C? (b) at 500°C? [*Note:* Use data from Fig. 1–8.]

Answer: (a) 0.23 cm²/sec (b) 0.12 cm²/sec

1-18. The resistivity of an aluminum alloy is 2.8×10^{-6} ohm·cm. What would be the resistance of an aluminum wire 40 in. long and 0.01 cm² in cross section?

1-19. (a) If a pure copper wire (resistivity = 1.7×10^{-6} ohm·cm) 0.04 in. in diameter is used for an electrical circuit carrying 10 amp, how many watts of heat will be lost per foot? (b) How many more watts would be lost if the copper wire were replaced by a brass wire of the same size (resistivity = 3.2×10^{-6} ohm·cm)?

Answer: (a) 0.64 watt (b) 0.56 watt

1-20. A copper wire has a diameter of 0.011 in. Copper has a resistivity of 1.7×10^{-6} ohm·cm. How many feet of wire would be required to give a resistance of 3.0 ohms?

1-21. Research in plastics has yielded a new type of insulator. The dielectric strength is calculated to be 950 volts/mil at a frequency of 60 cycles. How thick must a layer of this plastic be to withstand breakdown if the wire is to carry 18,500 volts and a safety factor of 15% is required?

Answer: 0.0224 in.

1-22. The dielectric constant of a glass ribbon is 5.1. Would a capacitor using such a glass ribbon 0.01 in. thick have greater or less capacitance than another similar capacitor using a 5-mil plastic with a dielectric constant of 2.1?

2

atomic bonding

THE STRUCTURE OF ATOMS

2-1 Introduction. At one time the atom was believed to be the ultimate unit in the subdivision of matter. However, subsequently it became known that the atom is composed of still smaller units. It is now possible to subdivide atoms and to explore their internal structure.

No attempt will be made here to consider all of the subatomic relationships. However, it is necessary to consider the general structure of the atom in order to develop a concept of the factors which govern the properties of materials. For example, when a material is stressed, the attractive forces between the atoms resist the stress and keep the materials from deforming and pulling apart. Electrical conductivity arises from the mobility of electrons associated with the "parent" atoms. Oxidation of metals is caused by the diffusion of metal atoms or of the oxygen atoms through the surface scale to form the oxide product. These and other phenomena are best explained by considering a model of an atom.

2-2 Neutrons, protons, and electrons. The atom contains a *nucleus* and surrounding *electrons*. The nucleus is composed of *protons* and *neutrons*. The electrons are charged particles with 1/1836 the mass of a neutron. The charge of the electron is taken to be negative. Since electrons are components of all atoms, their electrical charge is frequently regarded as unity. In physical units, this charge is actually equal to 1.6×10^{-19} amp·sec (coulomb) per electron.

We know that a proton carries a charge that is equal but opposite to that of an electron. For example, hydrogen, the simplest of all atoms, is composed of a proton and an electron, and is electrically neutral. The fact that a neutron is electrically neutral leads to the suggestion that it is a more intimate combination of a proton and an electron. This conclusion is sufficient for our purposes, since it has been shown that the following reaction may occur with an appropriate exchange of energy:

$$n \rightleftarrows p^+ + e^-. \tag{2-1}$$

2-3 Atomic weight and atomic number. On a simplified basis, an atom of any element may be considered to be a combination of protons and neutrons in a nucleus surrounded by electrons. Since an electron weighs only about 0.0005 as much as a neutron or proton, the weight of an atom is nearly proportional to the total weight of protons and neutrons in its nucleus. This weight of an element is called the *atomic weight*. Atomic weights range from 1.008 for hydrogen, which has only one proton, to nearly 250 for some of the unstable transuranium elements

17

IA	IIA	IIIB	IVB	VB	VIB	VIIB	VIII	VIII	VIII	IB	IIB	IIIA	IVA	VA	VIA	VIIA	0
1 H 1.00797																1 H 1.0079	2 He 4.0026
3 Li 6.939	4 Be 9.012											5 B 10.811	6 C 12.011	7 N 14.007	8 O 15.9994	9 F 18.998	10 Ne 20.183
11 Na 22.990	12 Mg 24.312											13 Al 26.98	14 Si 28.086	15 P 30.97	16 S 32.064	17 Cl 35.453	18 Ar 39.95
19 K 39.102	20 Ca 40.08	21 Sc 44.96	22 Ti 47.90	23 V 50.94	24 Cr 52.00	25 Mn 54.94	26 Fe 55.85	27 Co 58.93	28 Ni 58.71	29 Cu 63.54	30 Zn 65.37	31 Ga 69.72	32 Ge 72.59	33 As 74.92	34 Se 78.96	35 Br 79.91	36 Kr 83.80
37 Rb 85.47	38 Sr 87.62	39 Y 88.91	40 Zr 91.22	41 Nb 92.91	42 Mo 95.94	43 Tc 99	44 Ru 101.07	45 Rh 102.91	46 Pd 106.4	47 Ag 107.87	48 Cd 112.40	49 In 114.82	50 Sn 118.69	51 Sb 121.75	52 Te 127.60	53 I 126.90	54 Xe 131.30
55 Cs 132.90	56 Ba 137.34	57–71 La series*	72 Hf 178.49	73 Ta 180.95	74 W 183.85	75 Re 186.2	76 Os 190.2	77 Ir 192.2	78 Pt 195.1	79 Au 196.97	80 Hg 200.59	81 Tl 204.37	82 Pb 207.19	83 Bi 208.98	84 Po 210	85 At 210	86 Rn 222
87 Fr 223	88 Ra 226	89– Ac series†															

58 Ce 140.12	59 Pr 140.91	60 Nd 144.24	61 Pm 147	62 Sm 150.35	63 Eu 151.96	64 Gd 157.25	65 Tb 158.92	66 Dy 162.50	67 Ho 164.93	68 Er 167.26	69 Tm 168.93	70 Yb 173.04	71 Lu 174.97
90 Th 232.04	91 Pa 231	92 U 238.03	93 Np 237	94 Pu 239	95 Am 241	96 Cm 242	97 Bk 249	98 Cf 252	99 Es 254	100 Fm 253	101 Md	102 No	103 Lw

←————— Metals —————→ ←————— Nonmetals —————→

FIG. 2–1. Periodic table of elements. The atomic number and the atomic weight (carbon = 12.000) are shown for each element.

(Fig. 2–1 and Appendix D). Atomic weight is expressed in grams per *gram-atom*. One gram-atom always contains 6.02×10^{23} atoms (Avogadro's number). Thus,

$$\text{Weight of atom} = \frac{\text{atomic weight}}{6.02 \times 10^{23}} \qquad (2\text{–}2)$$

expressed in

$$\frac{\text{gm}}{\text{atom}} = \frac{\text{gm/gram-atom}}{\text{atoms/gram-atom}}.$$

Surprisingly, except for density and specific heat, the factor of atomic weight exerts relatively little influence on the engineering properties outlined in the preceding chapter. The number of electrons which surround the nucleus of a neutral atom is more significant. This number, called the *atomic number*, is equal to the number of protons within the nucleus. Each element is unique with respect to the number of its electrons and protons. Appendix D lists the elements from hydrogen, with an atomic number of one, to uranium (92), and beyond. It is the electrons, particularly the outermost ones, which affect most of the properties of engineering interest: they determine the chemical properties; they establish the nature of the interatomic bonding, and therefore the mechanical and strength characteristics; they control the size of the atom and affect the electrical conductivity of materials; and they influence the optical characteristics. Consequently, we shall pay considerable attention to the distribution and energy levels of the electrons around the nucleus of the atom.

• **2–4 Quantum numbers.**   There is a pattern among the elements which was recognized long ago and gave rise to the periodic table (Fig. 2–1). This table is very useful to the chemist, because elements from the same group have similar chemical behaviors. This periodicity also has significance in connection with the electrical, magnetic, and mechanical properties of materials. The periodic table is arranged according to the way additional electrons occur in elements of increasing atomic number.

The electrons surrounding the nucleus of the atom do not all have the same energy level; therefore it is convenient to divide the electrons into shells, or groups with different energy characteristics. The first or lowest-energy *quantum shell* contains a maximum of two electrons. The second shell contains a maximum of 8; the third, 18; and the fourth, 32. Thus the maximum number of electrons in a given shell is $2n^2$, where n is called the principal quantum number of the shell.

Although the above electron-shell concept is a convenient one, and will be used frequently in succeeding sections, it is oversimplified because it implies that all electrons within a shell are equivalent. Actually they are not equivalent, and a more complete treatment is necessary if we are to understand the properties of materials. Such a treatment is possible without rigorous explanation and may be approached through what is called the *Pauli exclusion principle:* viz., only two

---

• Sections preceded by a bullet may be assigned at the discretion of the instructor. (*See* preface.)

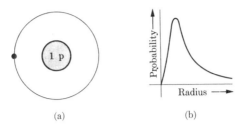

(a)   (b)

FIG. 2-2. Hydrogen. (a) Simplified sketch showing one proton in the nucleus and an electron in the first quantum group. (b) Radial probability of electron location. Although the electron-to-proton distance is not fixed, there is a certain distance which has a higher probability of occurrence. Except for their opposite magnetic moments, the two electrons of helium have energies and probable locations similar to those of the one electron of hydrogen.

interacting electrons can have the same orbital quantum numbers, and even those two are not fully identical because they exhibit inverted magnetic behaviors, or "spins." This principle states that there are specific rules governing the energy level and probable location of the electrons which surround an atom. For example, the single electron of a hydrogen atom is normally at the lowest possible energy level, with the result that the most probable position of the electron is that indicated in Fig. 2-2.

The two electrons of a helium atom fill the first quantum shell. Therefore, this element is very stable and does not combine with other elements. Furthermore, considerable energy is required to remove one of the electrons from helium.

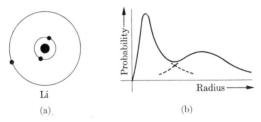

Li
(a)   (b)

FIG. 2-3. Lithium. (a) This simplified sketch shows how a second quantum group is started because the first one has its maximum of two electrons. (b) The radial probability for electron location.

Lithium has an atomic number of three. Its third electron must go into the second quantum shell, with a probable location as shown in Fig. 2-3. Next in order are beryllium, boron, carbon, nitrogen, oxygen, fluorine, and neon, each of which adds one more electron to the second quantum shell. However, as we noted earlier, only *two* electrons can have the same energy characteristics, and therefore the same location probability. Additional location or distribution probabilities therefore arise, and subshells are established. Figure 2-4 shows the distribution

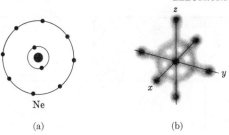

Ne

(a)   (b)

Fig. 2–4. Neon. Only the valence electrons are indicated. (a) In this simplified sketch, the second quantum shell is filled. (b) The distribution probability is spherical for only two of the eight valence electrons. The remaining three pairs of electrons are in quantum subshells which have a high probability of being located along the three axes. This is a very stable electron arrangement.

probabilities for the eight valence electrons of neon. (The two electrons of the first quantum shell are subvalent.) This distribution of eight electrons around an atom, whenever it occurs, is very stable.

• **2–5 Electronic notation.** Experimental verification of electronic groupings and subgroupings was initially obtained through spectrometric studies, from which it was concluded that a quantum of energy is required to move an electron from one energy level to a next-higher energy level. Conversely, a quantum of energy (called a *photon*) is released when an electron drops from a higher into a lower level. The energy E of the photon may be calculated directly from the photon wavelength λ through the equation,

$$E = \frac{hc}{\lambda} = h\nu, \qquad (2\text{–}3)$$

where h is Planck's constant and c is the velocity of light. The wave frequency is c/λ or ν.

Spectrographic notation was incorporated into the discussions of these early spectrometric experiments. Thus, since the sharpest spectral lines arise from the electrons which drop into the position of lowest energy within a given quantum shell, the notation s has been used for the electrons of each shell which have the lowest energy levels. Consequently $1s^2$ indicates that two electrons (of opposite magnetic spins) are located in the low-energy position of the first quantum shell (i.e., the K-shell). Likewise, $2s^2$ indicates that two electrons are located in the lowest-energy position of the second quantum shell (the L-shell). Two is the maximum number of electrons that can exist in the s-subshell.

Each succeeding shell has two or more subshells which are designated p, d, and f. The maximum number of electrons in these subshells is 6, 10, and 14, respectively. Let us take, for example, neon, which has its L-shell, or second quantum shell, completely filled. It has the electron notation of $1s^2 2s^2 2p^6$, which indicates that two electrons are in the first shell and eight electrons in the second shell (with two in its lower subshell and six in the next-highest subshell). The extension of the notation scheme indicated above may be obtained from Table 2–1.

• **TABLE 2–1**

ELECTRON QUANTUM NUMBERS*

Element		K (n = 1)	L (n = 2)		M (n = 3)			N (n = 4)				O (n = 5)				P (n = 6)			Q (n = 7)
Symbol	Number	1s	2s	2p	3s	3p	3d	4s	4p	4d	4f	5s	5p	5d	5f	6s	6p	6d	7s
H	1	1																	
He	2	2																	
Li	3	2	1																
Be	4	2	2																
B	5	2	2	1															
C	6	2	2	2															
N	7	2	2	3															
O	8	2	2	4															
F	9	2	2	5															
Ne	10	2	2	6															
Na	11	2	2	6	1														
Mg	12	2	2	6	2														
Al	13	2	2	6	2	1													
Si	14	2	2	6	2	2													
P	15	2	2	6	2	3													
S	16	2	2	6	2	4													
Cl	17	2	2	6	2	5													
Ar	18	2	2	6	2	6													
K	19	2	2	6	2	6		1											
Ca	20	2	2	6	2	6		2											
Sc	21	2	2	6	2	6	1	2											

Ti	22	2	2	6	2	6	2	2			
V	23	2	2	6	2	6	3	2			
Cr	24	2	2	6	2	6	5	1			
Mn	25	2	2	6	2	6	5	2			
Fe	26	2	2	6	2	6	6	2			
Co	27	2	2	6	2	6	7	2			
Ni	28	2	2	6	2	6	8	2			
Cu	29	2	2	6	2	6	10	1			
Zn	30	2	2	6	2	6	10	2			
Ga	31	2	2	6	2	6	10	2	1		
Ge	32	2	2	6	2	6	10	2	2		
As	33	2	2	6	2	6	10	2	3		
Se	34	2	2	6	2	6	10	2	4		
Br	35	2	2	6	2	6	10	2	5		
Kr	36	2	2	6	2	6	10	2	6		
Rb	37	2	2	6	2	6	10	2	6		1
Sr	38	2	2	6	2	6	10	2	6		2
Y	39	2	2	6	2	6	10	2	6	1	2
Zr	40	2	2	6	2	6	10	2	6	2	2
Nb	41	2	2	6	2	6	10	2	6	4	1
Mo	42	2	2	6	2	6	10	2	6	5	1
Tc	43	2	2	6	2	6	10	2	6	6	1
Ru	44	2	2	6	2	6	10	2	6	7	1
Rh	45	2	2	6	2	6	10	2	6	8	1
Pd	46	2	2	6	2	6	10	2	6	10	

(continued)

• TABLE 2–1 (continued)

ELECTRON QUANTUM NUMBERS*

Element Symbol	Number	K (n = 1) 1s	L (n = 2) 2s	2p	M (n = 3) 3s	3p	3d	N (n = 4) 4s	4p	4d	4f	O (n = 5) 5s	5p	5d	5f	P (n = 6) 6s	6p	6d	Q (n = 7) 7s
Ag	47	2	2	6	2	6	10	2	6	10		1							
Cd	48	2	2	6	2	6	10	2	6	10		2							
In	49	2	2	6	2	6	10	2	6	10		2	1						
Sn	50	2	2	6	2	6	10	2	6	10		2	2						
Sb	51	2	2	6	2	6	10	2	6	10		2	3						
Te	52	2	2	6	2	6	10	2	6	10		2	4						
I	53	2	2	6	2	6	10	2	6	10		2	5						
Xe	54	2	2	6	2	6	10	2	6	10		2	6						
Cs	55	2	2	6	2	6	10	2	6	10		2	6			1			
Ba	56	2	2	6	2	6	10	2	6	10		2	6			2			
La	57	2	2	6	2	6	10	2	6	10		2	6	1		2			
Ce	58	2	2	6	2	6	10	2	6	10	2	2	6			2			
Pr	59	2	2	6	2	6	10	2	6	10	3	2	6			2			
Nd	60	2	2	6	2	6	10	2	6	10	4	2	6			2			
Pm	61	2	2	6	2	6	10	2	6	10	5	2	6			2			
Sm	62	2	2	6	2	6	10	2	6	10	6	2	6			2			
Eu	63	2	2	6	2	6	10	2	6	10	7	2	6			2			
Gd	64	2	2	6	2	6	10	2	6	10	7	2	6	1		2			
Tb	65	2	2	6	2	6	10	2	6	10	8	2	6	1		2			
Dy	66	2	2	6	2	6	10	2	6	10	10	2	6			2			
Ho	67	2	2	6	2	6	10	2	6	10	11	2	6			2			
Er	68	2	2	6	2	6	10	2	6	10	12	2	6			2			
Tm	69	2	2	6	2	6	10	2	6	10	13	2	6			2			
Yb	70	2	2	6	2	6	10	2	6	10	14	2	6			2			
Lu	71	2	2	6	2	6	10	2	6	10	14	2	6	1		2			

Z		1s	2s	2p	3s	3p	3d	4s	4p	4d	4f	5s	5p	5d	5f	6s	6p	6d	7s
72	Hf	2	2	6	2	6	10	2	6	10	14	2	6	2		2			
73	Ta	2	2	6	2	6	10	2	6	10	14	2	6	3		2			
74	W	2	2	6	2	6	10	2	6	10	14	2	6	4		2			
75	Re	2	2	6	2	6	10	2	6	10	14	2	6	5		2			
76	Os	2	2	6	2	6	10	2	6	10	14	2	6	6		2			
77	Ir	2	2	6	2	6	10	2	6	10	14	2	6	7		2			
78	Pt	2	2	6	2	6	10	2	6	10	14	2	6	8		2			
79	Au	2	2	6	2	6	10	2	6	10	14	2	6	10		1			
80	Hg	2	2	6	2	6	10	2	6	10	14	2	6	10		2			
81	Tl	2	2	6	2	6	10	2	6	10	14	2	6	10		2	1		
82	Pb	2	2	6	2	6	10	2	6	10	14	2	6	10		2	2		
83	Bi	2	2	6	2	6	10	2	6	10	14	2	6	10		2	3		
84	Po	2	2	6	2	6	10	2	6	10	14	2	6	10		2	4		
85	At	2	2	6	2	6	10	2	6	10	14	2	6	10		2	5		
86	Rn	2	2	6	2	6	10	2	6	10	14	2	6	10		2	6		
87	Fr	2	2	6	2	6	10	2	6	10	14	2	6	10		2	6		1
88	Ra	2	2	6	2	6	10	2	6	10	14	2	6	10		2	6		2
89	Ac	2	2	6	2	6	10	2	6	10	14	2	6	10		2	6	1	2
90	Th	2	2	6	2	6	10	2	6	10	14	2	6	10		2	6	2	2
91	Pa	2	2	6	2	6	10	2	6	10	14	2	6	10	2	2	6	1	2
92	U	2	2	6	2	6	10	2	6	10	14	2	6	10	3	2	6	1	2
93	Np	2	2	6	2	6	10	2	6	10	14	2	6	10	5	2	6		2
94	Pu	2	2	6	2	6	10	2	6	10	14	2	6	10	6	2	6		2
95	Am	2	2	6	2	6	10	2	6	10	14	2	6	10	7	2	6		2
96	Cm	2	2	6	2	6	10	2	6	10	14	2	6	10	7	2	6	1	2

• **Example 2–1**

Iron has 26 protons. Two electrons go into the $4s$ subshell before the $3d$ subshell is filled. Show the electronic notation for a single iron atom, and for ferrous and ferric iron ions.

Answer:

$$Fe = 1s^2 2s^2 2p^6 3s^2 3p^6 3d^6 4s^2, \tag{2-4}$$

$$Fe^{2+} = 1s^2 2s^2 2p^6 3s^2 3p^6 3d^6, \tag{2-5}$$

$$Fe^{3+} = 1s^2 2s^2 2p^6 3s^2 3p^6 3d^5. \tag{2-6}$$

The sequential progression of levels becomes apparent when we examine Table 2–1. It should be emphasized that there is an overlap in the energy levels of succeeding subshells, and also of succeeding quantum shells. Because of this overlap, quantum groups with larger numbers may receive electrons in their low-energy levels before the preceding shells or subshells are filled, because electrons, like all matter, are most stable when they possess the least energy. Thus there are groups of transition elements, such as the scandium-to-nickel series of Table 2–1, in which the outer or valence subshell is partially filled before a full quota of ten electrons is present in the $3d$-subshell. The same situation occurs in the $4d$-subshell of the yttrium-to-palladium series. Furthermore, it is apparent that in the whole series of rare-earth elements there is successive addition of electrons to the $4f$-subshell in spite of the fact that there are eight or more electrons in the fifth or O-shell. Finally, the addition of $5f$ electrons starts a second rare-earth series which includes uranium and neighboring elements.

INTERATOMIC ATTRACTIONS

2–6 Introduction. Since most of the materials used by engineers are solids or liquids, it is desirable to understand the attractions that hold the atoms together. The importance of these attractions may be illustrated with a piece of copper wire, of which each gram contains $(6.02 \times 10^{23})/63.54$ atoms. Each pound contains 454 times this number of atoms. Under normal conditions the forces of attraction which bond the atoms together are strong. If this were not true, they would easily separate, the metal would deform under small loads, and atomic vibrations associated with thermal energy would gasify the atoms at low temperatures. As in the case of this wire, the engineering properties of any material depend on the interatomic forces which are present.

Interatomic attractions are caused by the electronic structure of atoms. The noble (inert or chemically inactive) gases, such as He, Ne, A, etc., have only limited attractions to other atoms because they have a very stable arrangement of eight electrons (2 for He) in their outer, or valence, electron shell, and at the same time have no net charge as a result of an unbalanced number of protons and electrons. Most other elements, unlike the noble gases, must achieve the highly stable configuration of having eight electrons available for their outer electron shells through one of the following procedures: (1) receiving extra electrons, (2) releasing electrons, or (3) sharing electrons. The first two of these processes produce ions with a net negative or positive charge and thus provide the ions with coulombic attractions to other ions of unlike charge. The third process obviously requires an intimate association between atoms in order for the sharing of electrons to be operative. Where applicable, the above three processes produce strong or primary bonds. Energies approximating 100 kcal/mole (i.e., $100,000$ cal/6.02×10^{23} bonds) are required to rupture these bonds. Other weaker or secondary bonds (less than 10 kcal/mole) are also always present, but gain importance when they are the only forces present.

2–7 Ionic bonds. The interatomic bond that is easiest to describe is the ionic bond, which results from the mutual attraction of positive and negative charges. Atoms of elements such as sodium and calcium, with one and two electrons in their valence shells, respectively, easily release these outer electrons and become positively charged ions. Likewise, chlorine and oxygen atoms readily add to their outer shells until they have eight electrons by accepting one or two electrons and thus becoming negatively charged ions. Since there is always a *coulombic attraction* between negatively and positively charged materials, a bond is developed between neighboring ions of unlike charges (Fig. 2–5).

Our first inclination is to expect that the sodium and chlorine ions would join up as pairs, but a moment's reflection throws doubt on this possibility. If this were to happen, there would be strong attractive forces within the paired ions, but negligible attraction between different pairs. As a result solid NaCl could not exist as we know it.

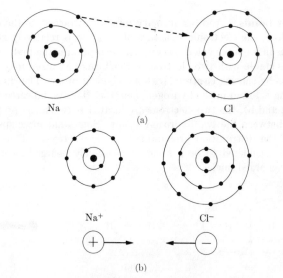

Fig. 2–5. Ionization. Electron transfer in NaCl formation produces stable outer shells. The resulting positive and negative ions are mutually attracted, by coulombic forces, to form an ionic bond.

Actually, a negative charge possesses an attraction for *all* positively charged particles and a positive charge for *all* negatively charged particles. Consequently, sodium ions surround themselves with negative chlorine ions, and chlorine ions surround themselves with positive sodium ions, the attraction being equal in all directions (Fig. 2–6). The major requirement in an ionically bonded material is that the number of positive charges equal the number of negative charges. Thus, sodium chloride has a composition of NaCl. Magnesium chloride has a composition of $MgCl_2$, because the magnesium atom can supply two electrons from its valence shell but a chlorine atom can accept only one.

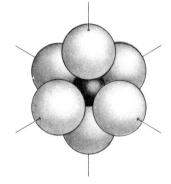

FIG. 2–6. Three-dimensional structure of sodium chloride. The positive sodium ion has equal attraction for all six neighboring negative chlorine ions. (Compare with Fig. 3–10.)

2-8 Covalent bonds.   Another primary force of attraction is the *covalent* bond. As stated before, the electronic structure of an atom is relatively stable if it has eight electrons in its outer valence shell. (An exception is the first, or *K*-quantum shell, which is stable with two electrons.) Sometimes an atom may acquire these eight electrons by sharing electrons with an adjacent atom. The simplest example of such sharing is found in the hydrogen molecule, H_2. As indicated schematically in Fig. 2–7 (a and b), the two electrons are located between the protons and thus form a bond between the two hydrogen atoms. Somewhat more specifically, Fig. 2–7(c) shows the distribution probability for the electrons. Thus the covalent bond may be considered to be a bond of negatively charged electrons between the positively charged nuclei.

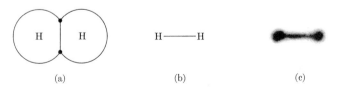

FIG. 2–7. Covalent bond of hydrogen. Parts (a) and (b) are simplified presentations. Part (c) shows distribution probability for the two electrons which form the covalent bond in a hydrogen molecule.

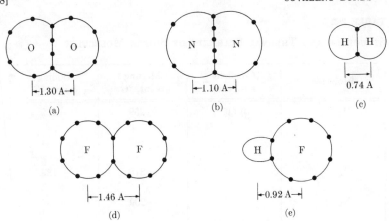

Fig. 2–8. Diatomic molecules. The schematic arrangement of the electrons in the outer shell is shown: (a) O_2, (b) N_2, (c) H_2, (d) F_2, (e) HF. Note (1) that a closer bond is produced as more electrons are shared, and (2) the imbalance in the HF.

Other diatomic molecules are shown schematically in Fig. 2–8. Note that the covalently bonded atoms need not be alike; for instance, HF. Also, the interatomic distance is reduced when more than one pair of electrons is shared.

Polyatomic combinations are also common. Methane (Fig. 2–9) is an example. Here the carbon atom is surrounded by four hydrogen atoms according to the relation

$$4H^{\cdot} + {\overset{\cdot\cdot}{C}}{\cdot} \rightarrow \begin{matrix} & H & \\ & \overset{\cdot\cdot}{} & \\ H & : C & : H. \\ & \overset{\cdot\cdot}{} & \\ & H & \end{matrix} \qquad (2\text{--}7)$$

Although Fig. 2–9(b) shows a "hard-ball" model with a definite surface around the atoms, the reader should realize that the atom surfaces are not precise (cf. Fig. 2–7b).

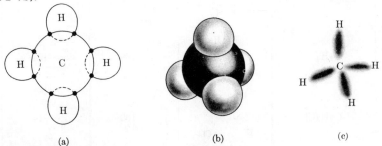

Fig. 2–9. Models of methane, CH_4. (a) Two-dimensional representation. (b) Three-dimensional hard-ball model. (c) Bonds of covalent electrons.

TABLE 2-2

STRUCTURE AND THERMAL STABILITY OF SIMPLE MOLECULES

Molecule	Covalent structure	Melting point, °C	Boiling point, °C
H_2	H : H	−259	−252
Cl_2	: C̈l : C̈l :	−102	−34
O_2	: Ö : O :	−218	−183
N_2	: N : N :	−209	−195
CH_4	H H : C̈ : H H	−183	−161
CF_4	: F : : F̈ : C̈ : F̈ : : F :	−185	−128
CCl_4	: Cl : : C̈l : C : C̈l : : Cl :	−23	76
NH_3	H : N̈ : H H	−78	−33
C_2H_6	H H H : C̈ : C̈ : H H H	−172	−88
C_2H_4	H H C̈ : C̈ H H	−169	−104
C_2H_3Cl	H H C : C H : Cl :	−160	−14

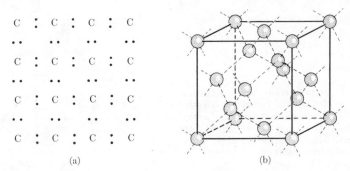

FIG. 2–10. Diamond structure. The strength of the covalent bonds is what accounts for the great hardness of diamond. (a) Two-dimensional representation. (b) Three-dimensional representation.

That covalent bonds provide strong attractive forces between atoms is evidenced in diamond, which is the hardest material found in nature, and which is entirely carbon. Each carbon atom has four electrons in its outer shell, which it shares with four adjacent atoms, to form a three-dimensional lattice entirely bonded by covalent pairs (Fig. 2–10). The strength of the covalent bond in carbon is demonstrated not only by the great hardness of diamond, but by the extremely high temperature (>6000°F) to which it can be heated before its structure is disrupted by thermal energy.

Even though covalent bonds are strong, not all materials with covalent bonds have high melting and boiling points, or great strength. Methane, for instance, has several covalent bonds (Fig. 2–9a), but the resulting molecule has very little attraction for adjacent molecules because the electronic requirements in the outer shells have already been met. Thus the methane molecule, like the noble gas atoms of helium, neon, and argon, acts almost independently of other molecules. Consequently methane does not condense until its temperature drops to −161°C (−258°F). Table 2–2 shows the melting and boiling temperatures of other covalently bonded molecules, each with strong intramolecular attractions but weak intermolecular attractions.

2–9 Metallic bonds. In addition to ionic and covalent bonds, a third type of primary interatomic force, the *metallic bond*, is capable of holding atoms together. Unfortunately, a model for metallic bonding is not as simple to construct as those for ionic (Fig. 2–5) and covalent bonding (Fig. 2–8). However, a simplified concept is sufficient for our purpose. If there are only a few valence (outer-shell) electrons within an atom, they may be removed relatively easily, while the balance of the electrons are held firmly to the nucleus. This, in effect, forms a structure of positive ions and "free" electrons (Fig. 2–11). The positive ion "cores" consist of the nucleus and the nonvalence electrons. Because the valence electrons are free to move about within the metal structure, they form what is frequently described as an electron "cloud" or "gas." As shown in Fig. 2–11, the positive ions

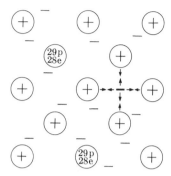

Fig. 2–11. Metallic bond. A schematic representation of unattached electrons (electron "cloud") in a structure of positive "cores." The metallic bond may be considered to be an attraction between the positive "cores" and the negative, unattached electrons (example: copper).

and the negative electron "cloud" provide attractive forces which bond the metal atoms together.

Although this description is greatly simplified, it does provide a useful explanation for many of the properties of metals. For example, the crystalline array of atoms in a solid metal (see Section 3–11) helps to determine the metal's mechanical properties. The free electrons give the metal its characteristically high electrical conductivity, since they are free to move in an electric field. The high thermal conductivity of metals is also associated with the mobility of the valence electrons, which can transfer thermal energy from a high to a low temperature level. A fourth effect of metallic bonding is that the free electrons in the metal absorb light energy, so that all metals are opaque to transmitted light.

2–10 Combinations of primary bonds. Although we have treated the three primary interatomic attraction forces separately, many materials can be bonded in more than one manner. For example, the valence electrons of HCl might be distributed in either of the two configurations shown in Fig. 2–12. As shown in Fig. 2–13, H_2 has three alternatives for the distribution of its valence electrons, since there are two ionic bonding arrangements and one covalent arrangement between any pair of hydrogen atoms. Experiment has shown that each of these three modifications actually exists in an H_2 molecule. Although the electrons are free to resonate among the three arrangements, in hydrogen they are usually distributed covalently. As a result, two hydrogen atoms act like a diatomic molecule.

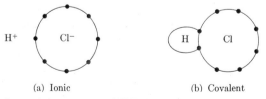

(a) Ionic   (b) Covalent

Fig. 2–12. Two alternative structures of HCl (simplified). The choice depends on the environment. For example, (a) predominates in a liquid solution, (b) predominates in a gas.

(a)   (b)   (c)

Fig. 2–13. Alternative bondings in hydrogen. The shaded areas show the distribution probability of the two electrons in each of the three bonding arrangements. Parts (a) and (c) are essentially equivalent and ionic; (b) is covalent. The most usual form is the covalent one, which is the form of hydrogen gas. However, (a) and (c) may exist briefly.

It is also possible to find more than one type of primary bond existing in a material. Calcium sulfate ($CaSO_4$) is an example, best illustrated by the reaction

$$
Ca + \ \overset{\cdot\cdot}{\underset{\cdot\cdot}{.\ O}}\!:\!\overset{\cdot\cdot}{\underset{\cdot\cdot}{O\!:\!S\!:\!O}}\!\cdot\ \rightarrow\ Ca^{2+} + \ \overset{\cdot\cdot}{\underset{\cdot\cdot}{\cdot O}}\!:\!\overset{\cdot\cdot}{\underset{\cdot\cdot}{O\!:\!S\!:\!O}}\!\cdot\! \tag{2–8}
$$

The SO_4 group is two electrons short of supplying a full outer shell to each of the five atoms, but calcium has two electrons which are easily removed and transferred to the SO_4. The result is a Ca^{2+} ion with attraction for an SO_4^{2-} ion. In turn, in the sulfate ion the sulfur and oxygen atoms are held together covalently.

2–11 Van der Waals forces. The three types of bonds considered above are all relatively strong primary bonds which hold atoms together. Weaker, secondary bonds, which also supply interatomic attraction, are grouped here as *van der Waals forces*, although there are actually several different mechanisms involved. Were it not for the fact that sometimes they are the only forces which operate, van der Waals bonding might be overlooked.

In a noble gas like helium, the outer shell, with its two electrons, is complete, and other noble gases, such as neon and argon, have a full complement of eight electrons in their outer shells. In these stable situations none of the primary bonds can be effective, since covalent, ionic, and metallic bonds all require adjustments in the valence electrons. As a result, atoms of these noble gases have little attraction for one another, and with rare exceptions they remain monatomic at ordinary temperatures. Only at extremely low temperatures, when thermal vibrations have been greatly reduced, do these gases condense (Table 2–3). It is this condensation that makes it evident that there are weak interatomic attractions which pull the atoms together.

Similar evidence for these weak attractions is found in the substances listed in Table 2–2. As pointed out earlier, these gases have satisfied their valence-shell requirements by covalent bonding within the molecule. The condensation of these simple molecules occurs only when thermal vibrations are sufficiently reduced in energy to permit the weak van der Waals forces to become operative.

TABLE 2-3

MELTING AND BOILING TEMPERATURES OF NOBLE GASES

Gas	Melting temperature, °C	Boiling temperature, °C
He	−272.2	−268.9
Ne	−248.7	−245.9
A	−189.2	−185.7
Kr	−157.0	−152.9
Xe	−112.0	−107.1
Ra	− 71.0	− 61.8

Molecular polarization. Most van der Waals forces of attraction arise from *electrical dipoles*, which are illustrated most simply in a molecule such as hydrogen fluoride (Fig. 2–14a). There are two electrons available to the *K*-shell of the hydrogen and eight electrons available to the outer *L*-shell of the fluorine. However, within the molecule there is an electrical imbalance, because the shared electrons surround the positive charges in the nucleus of the fluorine atom more completely than they surround the nucleus of the hydrogen atom. Consequently, the *center of positive charge* and the *center of negative charge* do not coincide, and an electrical dipole is produced (Fig. 2–14b).

An electrical dipole is formed in any asymmetric molecule, thus providing a mechanism for molecular bonding. Figure 2–14(c) illustrates polar attractions between adjacent molecules. The molecular polarization of HF is so marked that it possesses one of the highest boiling points of diatomic molecules (19.4°C). Polyatomic molecules can develop even more extreme polarization characteristics because there are additional opportunities for internal electrical imbalance.

Dispersion effects. In all symmetric molecules and in all noble gas atoms, a momentary polarization occurs as a result of the random movement of the elec-

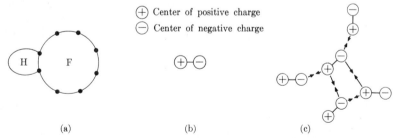

(a)   (b)   (c)

FIG. 2–14. Polarization. (a) An electrical imbalance called polarization occurs in asymmetrical molecules such as HF. (b) This imbalance produces an electrical dipole with one end (+) and the other (−). (c) The resulting dipoles provide a mechanism for secondary forces of attraction between molecules. The positive end of one dipole is attracted to the negative end of another.

TABLE 2-4

BOILING TEMPERATURES VERSUS MOLECULAR WEIGHTS

Gas	Molecular weight, gm	Boiling temperature, °C
H_2	2.016	−252
N_2	28.016	−195
O_2	32.0000	−183
Cl_2	70.91	− 34
CH_4	16.04	−161
CF_4	88.01	−128
CCl_4	153.83	+ 76
He	4.003	−268.9
Ne	20.18	−245.9
A	39.94	−185.7

trons (Fig. 2–15). This random, fluctuating polarization has been called the *dispersion effect*. The resulting interatomic attractions are weak but real, as evidenced by the fact that symmetric molecules and monatomic gases do condense at sufficiently low temperatures (Table 2–4).

Hydrogen bridge. A third type of weak bonding is the hydrogen bridge. Its existence provides the attraction between H_2O molecules, and is responsible for the high boiling temperature and heat of vaporization of water. The hydrogen bridge is actually a special case of molecular polarization. The small hydrogen nucleus, which is a proton, is attracted to the unshared electrons in a neighboring H_2O molecule to provide a bond between the two molecules (Fig. 2–16).

The hydrogen bridge is not limited to water and ice; it may be found in other molecules, such as those of ammonia (NH_3).

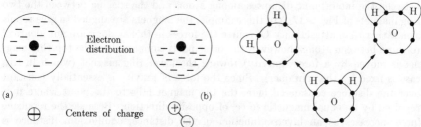

(a)

(b)

FIG. 2–15. Electronic polarization (dispersion effects). An *electrical dipole* is momentarily established in an atom with only weak attraction for adjacent atoms. (a) Uniform electron distribution. (b) Momentary polarized distribution.

FIG. 2–16. Hydrogen bridge. The hydrogen bridge arises from the attraction of the exposed hydrogen nucleus in one molecule to unshared electrons of the oxygen (or nitrogen) of adjacent molecules.

ATOMIC COORDINATION

2-12 Introduction.   Although in the case of diatomic molecules there is bonding and coordination of only two atoms, most materials involve a coordination of many atoms into an integrated structure. Two main factors, interatomic distances and spatial arrangements, are of importance. Let us therefore consider them in some detail.

2-13 Interatomic distances.   The forces of attraction between atoms, which we considered in the preceding sections, pull the atoms together; but what keeps the atoms from being drawn still closer together? It should be apparent from the preceding figures and discussion that there is much vacant "space" in the volume surrounding the nucleus of an atom. The existence of this space is evidenced by the fact that neutrons can move through the fuel and the other materials of a nuclear reactor, traveling through many atoms before they are finally stopped (Fig. 12–41).

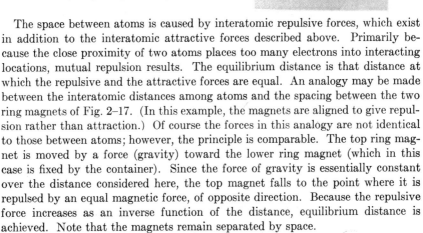

FIG. 2–17. Balance of forces (ceramic ring magnets). Downward force on upper ring is caused by gravity. Upward force is caused by magnetic repulsion. Space remains between the two magnets at the equilibrium position. (Of course the forces in this analogy are not identical to those between atoms; however, the principle is comparable.)

The space between atoms is caused by interatomic repulsive forces, which exist in addition to the interatomic attractive forces described above. Primarily because the close proximity of two atoms places too many electrons into interacting locations, mutual repulsion results. The equilibrium distance is that distance at which the repulsive and the attractive forces are equal. An analogy may be made between the interatomic distances among atoms and the spacing between the two ring magnets of Fig. 2–17. (In this example, the magnets are aligned to give repulsion rather than attraction.) Of course the forces in this analogy are not identical to those between atoms; however, the principle is comparable. The top ring magnet is moved by a force (gravity) toward the lower ring magnet (which in this case is fixed by the container). Since the force of gravity is essentially constant over the distance considered here, the top magnet falls to the point where it is repulsed by an equal magnetic force, of opposite direction. Because the repulsive force increases as an inverse function of the distance, equilibrium distance is achieved. Note that the magnets remain separated by space.

Coulombic forces. The ionic bond will be used to illustrate the balance between attractive and repulsive forces in materials. The force F_C developed between two point charges is

$$F_C = -\frac{(Z_1 e)(Z_2 e)}{a_{1-2}^2}.$$ (2-9)

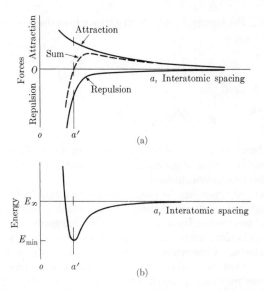

FIG. 2–18. Interatomic distances. (a) The equilibrium spacing o–a' is the distance at which the attractive forces equal the repulsive forces. (b) The lowest potential energy occurs when o–a' is the interatomic distance.

In this equation, a_{1-2} is the distance between the two points, Z_1 and Z_2 are the number of charges at each point and may be either positive or negative. The electronic charge e is 1.6×10^{-19} coulomb, as indicated in Section 2–2. (*See* Appendix A for other standard constants.) The above equation is simplified when we consider two unlike monovalent ions:

$$F_C = + \frac{e^2}{a^2}. \qquad (2\text{–}10)$$

Electronic repulsive forces. The repelling force F_R between the electronic fields of two atoms is also an inverse function of distance, but to a higher power:

$$F_R = - \frac{nb}{a^{n+1}}. \qquad (2\text{–}11)$$

Both b and n are constants, with n equal to approximately 9 in ionic solids. Thus the repulsive forces become significant at a much shorter range than the attractive forces. The attractive and repulsive forces are shown in Fig. 2–18(a), together with their *sum*.

Bonding energy. The sum of the above two forces provides the basis for bonding energy and equilibrium interatomic distances (Fig. 2–18). Since energy is the product of force and distance,

$$E = \int (F_C + F_R)\, da. \qquad \bullet \ (2\text{–}12)$$

In relation to E_∞, the energy at infinite distance where there is no interaction, the energy at distance a is

$$E = \int_\infty^a \left[\frac{(-Z_1 Z_2)e^2}{a^2} - \frac{nb}{a^{n+1}} \right] da \qquad \bullet \text{ (2-13)}$$

and

$$E = \frac{(Z_1 Z_2)e^2}{a} + \frac{b}{a^n}. \qquad (2\text{-}14)$$

This curve is shown in Fig. 2–18(b). At the point where $F_C = -F_R$, dE/da is equal to zero, and the value of the energy is the lowest. Therefore, the distance a' is the equilibrium interatomic distance.

Energies of several types may be used to move the atoms from their equilibrium distance. At high temperatures, thermal energy, which produces atomic motions, may be sufficient to separate the atoms completely and gasify the material. Strong electrical and mechanical forces can also pull the atoms apart, to deform or even fracture the material. Conversely, a solid or liquid resists compression because the compressive forces must overcome greater and greater repulsive forces. In this respect atoms may be compared with hard rubber balls; although it is possible to compress them to smaller dimensions, it becomes extremely difficult.

2–14 Atomic and ionic radii. The equilibrium distance between the centers of two neighboring atoms may be considered to be the sum of their radii (Fig. 2–19). In metallic iron, for example, the mean distance between the centers of the atoms is 2.482 A (angstrom units*) at room temperature. Since both atoms are the same, the radius of the iron atom is 1.241 A.

Several factors can change this distance. The first is temperature. Any increase in energy above the minimum point shown in Fig. 2–18(b) will increase the mean distance because of the asymmetric shape of the energy trough. This increase in the mean spacing between atoms accounts for the thermal expansion of materials.

Ionic valence also influences interatomic spacing (Appendix D). The ferrous iron ion (Fe^{2+}) has a radius of 0.83 A, which is smaller than that of the metallic iron atom. Since the two outer valence electrons have been removed (Fig. 2–20), the remaining 24 electrons are pulled in closer to the nucleus, which still maintains a positive charge of 26. A further reduction in interatomic spacing is observed when another electron is removed to produce the ferric ion (Fe^{3+}). The radius of this ion is 0.67 A, or only about one-half that of metallic iron.

A negative ion is larger than its corresponding atom. Since there are more electrons surrounding the nucleus than there are protons in the nucleus, the added electrons are not as closely attracted to the nucleus as were the original electrons.

---

* 1 angstrom unit $= 10^{-8}$ cm, or 10^{-7} mm, or 10^{-4} micron. The radii used in this book are from the 1961 ASM *Metals Handbook*.

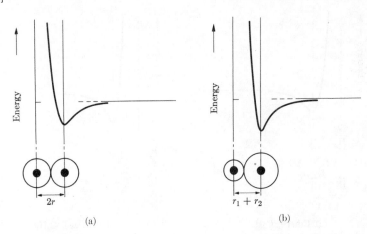

(a)

(b)

Fig. 2–19. Bond lengths. The distance of minimum energy between two adjacent atoms is the bond length. It is equal to the sum of the two radii. (a) In a pure metal, all atoms have the same radius. (b) In an ionic solid, the radii are different.

A third factor affecting the size of the atom or ion is the number of adjacent atoms. An iron atom has a radius of 1.241 A when it is in contact with 8 adjacent iron atoms, which is the normal arrangement at room temperature. If the atoms are rearranged to place this one iron atom in contact with 12 other iron atoms, the radius of each atom is increased slightly, to 1.269 A. With more adjacent atoms, there is more electronic repulsion from neighboring atoms, and consequently the interatomic distances are increased.

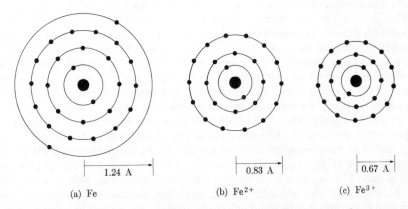

1.24 A

0.83 A

0.67 A

(a) Fe

(b) Fe^{2+}

(c) Fe^{3+}

Fig. 2–20. Atom and ion sizes. (a) Both iron atoms and iron ions have the same number of protons (26). (b) If two electrons are removed, the remaining 24 electrons and adjacent negative ions are pulled closer to the 26-proton nucleus. (c) A ferric ion has its 23 electrons still closer to the nucleus.

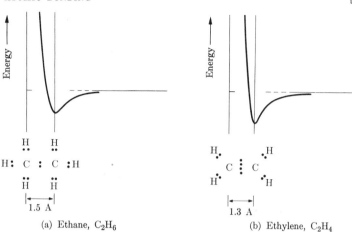

(a) Ethane, C_2H_6 (b) Ethylene, C_2H_4

FIG. 2–21. Molecular bond lengths. The interatomic distance between the carbon atoms is reduced when more electrons must be shared covalently. In addition, the energy necessary for separation is increased.

The final effect on interatomic spacing which will be considered here is related to the covalent bonds. Figure 2–21 compares the interatomic distances between the carbon atoms in ethane and in ethylene. In the latter molecule four electrons are shared by the two carbon atoms, but in the ethane molecule only two electrons are shared. The center-to-center distances for the two carbon atoms is reduced and the energy troughs become deeper as their valence structures become more strongly bonded.

2–15 Coordination number. So far we have discussed diatomic combinations which involve only two atoms. However, since most engineering materials have coordinated groups of many atoms, attention must be given to polyatomic groups. Therefore, when we are analyzing the bonding of atoms within materials, we speak of a *coordination number*. The coordination number, CN, simply refers to the number of first neighbors which an atom has. Thus, in Fig. 2–9, the coordination number for carbon is four. In contrast, the hydrogens have only one immediate neighbor, so that their coordination numbers are only one.

Two factors control the coordination number of an atom. The first is covalency. Specifically, the number of covalent bonds around an atom is dependent on the number of its valence electrons. Thus the halides, which are in Group VII of the periodic table (Fig. 2–1), form only one bond and thus have a coordination number of one. The members of the oxygen family in Group VI are held in a molecule with two bonds, and normally have a maximum coordination number of two. (Of course, oxygen may be coordinated with only one other atom through a double bond.) The nitrogen elements have a maximum coordination number of three since they are in Group V. Finally, carbon and silicon, in Group IV, have four bonds with other atoms, and a maximum coordination number of four (Fig. 2–10b).

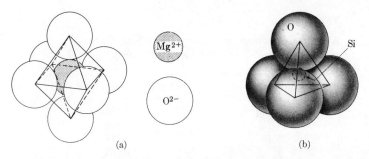

FIG. 2–22. Coordination numbers. (a) A maximum of six oxygen ions (O^{2-}) can surround each magnesium ion (Mg^{2+}). (b) The coordination number of Si^{4+} among O^{2-} is only four because the ion-size ratio is less than 0.414 (Table 2–5).

The second factor affecting the coordination number is atomic packing. Since energy is given off as atoms or ions are brought closer together (until their equilibrium distance is reached), a material becomes more stable if atoms are closely packed and the average interatomic distances are reduced. Consider a magnesium ion, Mg^{2+}, with a radius of 0.78 A. It would be possible to locate as many as six oxygen ions, O^{2-}, with radii of 1.32 A, around each cation (Fig. 2–22a). In this case, the size ratio is 0.78/1.32 or 0.59. The size ratio is smaller for Si^{4+} and O^{2-} ions, 0.39/1.32 or 0.3 (Table 2–5). Thus it is impossible in silica, SiO_2, for a silicon ion to have a higher coordination number among oxygen ions than four, for if it did, the negative oxygen ions would repel each other and the Si-to-O distances

TABLE 2–5

SELECTED ATOMIC AND IONIC RADII
(See Appendix D for additional values)

Element	Metallic atoms		Ions			Covalent bonds	
	CN*	Radius, A	Valence	CN	Radius, A	Bonds	Distance/2, A
Carbon			4$^+$	6	0.25	1	0.77
						2	0.66
						3	0.60
Oxygen			2$^-$	6	1.32	2	0.65
Sodium	8	1.857	1$^+$	6	0.98		
Magnesium	12	1.594	2$^+$	6	0.78		
Silicon			4$^+$	4	0.39†	4	1.17
Chlorine			1$^-$	6	1.81	1	0.99
Iron	8	1.241	2$^+$	6	0.83		
	12	1.27	3$^+$	6	0.67		
Copper	12	1.278	1$^+$	6	0.96		

* Coordination number.
† Radius = 0.41 when CN = 6.

TABLE 2–6

ATOMIC COORDINATION VERSUS IONIC SIZE RATIO
(See Examples 2–2 and 2–3 for calculations)

Coordination number	Minimum ratio of ionic radii
3-fold	0.155
4	0.225
6	0.414
8	0.732
12	1.0

would be greater than the equilibrium spacing of 1.71 A. In a pure metal where all the atoms are the same size, the coordination number can be at most 12.

Geometric rules governing the coordination number are summarized in Table 2–6. Since ions must be distorted if more than the indicated number of large ions surround a small ion, the minimum ratios of Table 2–6 are rather definite. Generally the coordination number increases if the minimum ratio for the next-larger coordination number is exceeded. Thus we seldom find Mg^{2+} ions among O^{2-} with CN of four, because the size ratio is 0.59. A reduction of the coordination number to four would reduce the packing efficiency and thereby increase the energy contained by the material.

Apparent exceptions to the above rules occur with the stereo-specific requirements of covalent bonding. For example, in diamond (Fig. 2–10), carbon maintains a CN of four even though all atoms are identical in size, and Table 2–6 indicates that 12 neighbors might be possible, because only four pairs of electrons can be shared.

In general, the coordination numbers of metals and ionic solids are governed by their packing efficiency, and the coordination numbers of covalent solids by the limits of their electron sharing.

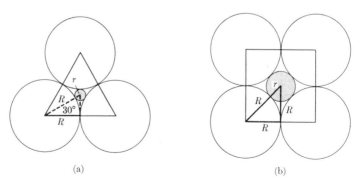

(a)   (b)

FIG. 2–23.   Coordination calculations.   (a) Three-fold coordination.   (b) Six-fold coordination.   [Compare with examples and Fig. 2–22(a).]

Example 2–2

Show the significance of 0.155 as the minimum ratio for a coordination number of three (Table 2–6).

Answer: The minimum ratio of sizes possible to permit a coordination number of three is shown in Fig. 2–23(a). In this relationship,

$$\cos 30° = \frac{R}{R + r} = 0.866,$$

$$\frac{r}{R} = \frac{1 - 0.866}{0.866} = 0.155.$$

Example 2–3

Show the significance of 0.414 as the minimum ratio for a coordination number of six.

Answer: The minimum ratio of sizes possible to permit a coordination number of six is shown in Fig. 2–23(b). In this relationship,

$$(R + 2r + R)^2 = (2R)^2 + (2R)^2$$

or

$$2r + 2R = \sqrt{2}\,(2R),$$

$$r = \sqrt{2}\,R - R,$$

and

$$\frac{r}{R} = 1.414 - 1 = 0.414.$$

SUMMARY

2–16 Generalizations regarding properties.   Several of the engineering properties of Chapter 1 may be related *qualitatively* to the atomic bonding characteristics described in this chapter.

(1) Density is controlled by atomic weight, atomic radius, and coordination number. The latter is a significant factor because it controls the packing factor.

(2) Melting and boiling temperatures can be correlated with the depth of the energy trough shown in Fig. 2–18. Atoms have minimum energy (at the bottom of the trough) at a temperature of absolute zero. Increased temperatures raise the energy until the atoms are able to separate themselves one from another.

(3) Strength is also correlatable with the height of the total force or sum curve of Fig. 2–18(a). That force, when related to the cross-sectional area, gives the stress required to separate atoms. (As we shall see in Section 6–5, materials can deform through a process other than direct separation of the atoms. However, the amount of stress required to deform them is still governed by the interatomic forces.) Also, since larger interatomic forces of attraction imply deeper energy troughs, we observe that materials with high melting points are often the harder materials: e.g., diamond, Al_2O_3, TiC, etc. In contrast, in materials with weaker bonds there is a correlation between softness and low melting point: e.g., lead, plastics, ice, and grease. Apparent exceptions to these generalizations can arise when more than one type of bond is present, as in graphite and clay.

(4) The modulus of elasticity can be calculated from the slope of the sum curve of Fig. 2–18(a) because at the equilibrium distance, where the net force is zero, dF/da relates stress to strain. As long as the strain or change in interatomic distance is a fraction of a percent, the modulus of elasticity remains essentially constant. Extreme compression or extreme tension respectively raise or lower the modulus of elasticity.

(5) Thermal expansions of materials with comparable atomic packing factors vary inversely with their melting temperatures. This indirect relationship exists because the higher-melting-point materials have deeper and therefore more symmetrical energy troughs. Thus their mean interatomic distances increase less with a given change in thermal energy. Examples of several metals include: Hg, melting temperature equals $-39°C$, coefficient of linear expansion equals 40×10^{-6}cm/cm·°C; Pb, 327°C, 29×10^{-6}cm/cm·°C; Al, 660°C, 25×10^{-6}cm/cm·°C; Cu, 1083°C, 17×10^{-6}cm/cm·°C; Fe, 1539°C, 12×10^{-6}cm/cm·°C; W, 3410°C, 4.2×10^{-6}cm/cm·°C.

(6) Electrical conductivity is very dependent on the nature of the atomic bonds. Both ionically and covalently bonded materials are extremely poor conductors, because electrons are not free to leave their host atoms. On the other hand, the free electrons of metals easily move along a potential gradient. Semiconductors will be considered in Chapter 5; however, we can note here that their conductivity is controlled by the freedom of movement of their electrons.

(7) Thermal conductivity is high in materials with metallic bonds, because free electrons are very efficient carriers of thermal as well as electrical energy.

(8) The influence of the structure of atoms on chemical properties has not been elaborated on here, since the chemical differences between elements depend primarily on the number of valence electrons. Furthermore, all chemical reactions involve the formation and the disruption of bonds. So far as engineering materials are concerned, the *corrosion* reaction (Chapter 12) is probably the most significant chemical reaction. In corrosion, the separation of a metallic ion from the metal proper involves the removal of valence electrons from the outer shell of the atom.

In subsequent chapters, we shall develop the principles which control the properties of engineering materials by utilizing the concepts of atomic structure.

2–17 Types of materials. Most engineering materials may be categorized into one of three types: *metals, plastics,* or *ceramics.* We consider metals to be composed of elements which readily give up electrons to provide a metallic bond and electrical conductivity. Nonmetallic elements which share electrons comprise the organic materials constituting plastics; thus covalent bonds are prevalent. Ceramic materials contain compounds of metallic and nonmetallic elements, such as MgO, $BaTiO_3$, SiO_2, SiC, glasses, etc. Such compounds contain both ionic and covalent bonds.

Although we have indicated three main categories of materials, it must be recognized that the three categories are not sharply delineated. Rather, we find some materials (e.g., the silicones) whose nature is intermediate between ceramics and plastics; likewise, materials such as GaAs (a semiconductor) could be classified either as a metal or a ceramic. Finally, graphite is an atypical material which has certain features in common with all three categories. Even though these gradations do exist, it will be to our advantage to separate categories among the three types when we study specific materials (Chapters 7, 8, and 9).

References for Further Reading

2–1. ADDISON, W. E., *Structural Principles in Inorganic Compounds.* New York: John Wiley & Sons, 1961. Paperback. Chapter 1 has a nonmathematical presentation of electronic theory of the atom and chemical bonding. Recommended for the undergraduate who wants more information on bonding than is given in this text.

2–2. COTTRELL, A. H., *Theoretical Structural Metallurgy.* New York: St. Martin's Press, 1955. Chapter 1 gives supplemental reading on the structure of the atom, for the instructor or advanced undergraduate.

2–3. GOLDMAN, J. E., "Structure of Atoms and Atomic Aggregates," *The Science of Engineering Materials.* New York: John Wiley & Sons, 1957. A physical presentation which includes empirical relationships. For the instructor.

2–4. HUME-ROTHERY, W., *Atomic Theory for Students in Metallurgy.* London: Institute of Metals, 1955. Written for the metallurgy student.

2–5. PAULING, L., *General Chemistry,* second edition. San Francisco: Freeman, 1958. Chapter 5 describes periodic-table relationships. Introductory.

2–6. PAULING, L., *The Nature of the Chemical Bond.* Ithaca, N. Y.: Cornell University Press, 1948. An advanced text describing the characteristics of the bonding forces in solids.

2–7. SCARLETT, A. J., and J. GÓMEZ-IBANEZ, *General College Chemistry.* New York: Henry Holt, 1954. Part III considers the structure of matter and the chemical bond, at the college-freshman level. Recommended as another presentation of the subject matter covered in Chapter 2 of this book.

2–8. SCHMIDT, A. X., and C. A. MARLIES, *Principles of High Polymer Theory and Practice.* New York: McGraw-Hill, 1948. Pages 20–36 discuss types of atomic bonds. Recommended for students who have a special interest in polymers (i.e., plastics).

2–9. SIENKO, M. J., and R. A. PLANE, *Chemistry,* second edition. New York: McGraw-Hill, 1961. Chapter 4 introduces chemical bonds. This book is highly recommended as a chemistry basis for a materials course.

2–10. SORUM, C. H., *Fundamentals of General Chemistry.* Englewood Cliffs: N. J.: Prentice-Hall, 1955. Chapter 7 discusses the atomic structure at the college-freshman level. Recommended as another presentation of the subject matter presented in Chapter 2 of this book.

2–11. WULFF, J., *et al., Structures and Properties of Materials.* Cambridge, Mass.: M.I.T. Press, 1963. Multilithed. Chapters 2 and 3 introduce the structure of the atom and bonding. The approach is more rigorous than in this text.

Problems

2-1. (a) What is the weight of an aluminum atom? (b) The density of aluminum is 2.70 gm/cm^3; how many atoms per cm^3?

Answer: (a) 4.48×10^{-23} gm/atom   (b) 6.02×10^{22} atom/cm^3

2-2. (a) How many iron atoms are there per gram? (b) What is the volume of a grain of metal containing 10^{20} iron atoms?

2-3. (a) Al$_2$O$_3$ has a density of 3.8 gm/cm^3. How many atoms are present per cm^3? (b) Per gram?

Answer: (a) 1.12×10^{23} atoms/cm^3 (b) 2.95×10^{22} atoms/gm

2-4. A cubic volume of MgO which is 4.20 angstroms along each edge contains 4 Mg^{2+} ions and 4 O^{2-} ions. What is the density of MgO?

• 2-5. Give the notation for the electronic structure of (a) zirconium atoms, (b) Zr^{4+} ions.

Answer: (a) $1s^2 2s^2 2p^6 3s^2 3p^6 3d^{10} 4s^2 4p^6 4d^2 5s^2$ (b) $1s^2 2s^2 2p^6 3s^2 3p^6 3d^{10} 4s^2 4p^6$

• 2-6. Indicate the number of $3d$ electrons in each of the following: (a) V^{3+}; (b) V^{5+}; (c) Cr^{3+}; (d) Fe^{3+}; (e) Fe^{2+}; (f) Mn^{2+}; (g) Mn^{4+}; (h) Ni^{2+}; (i) Co^{2+}; (j) Cu$^+$; (k) Cu^{2+}.

• 2-7. It takes approximately 10^{-19} cal to break the covalent bond between carbon and nitrogen. What wavelength would be required of a photon to supply this energy? (*See* Appendix A for constants.)

Answer: 4750 A

• 2-8. An electron absorbs the energy from a photon of ultraviolet light ($\lambda = 2768$ A). How many ev are absorbed?

2-9. A divalent positive ion and a divalent negative ion are at an equilibrium distance when their centers are 2.45 A apart. If $n = 9$ in Eq. (2-11), what is the value of b in the same equation?

Answer: $+1.33 \times 10^{-80}$ erg·cm^9

2-10. (a) Plot the net, or sum, of forces between the two ions of Problem 2-9 from 2 A to 20 A. • (b) Plot the energy of separation over the same distances.

2-11. Show the origin of 0.732 in Table 2-6.

Answer: $2(r + R) = \sqrt{3}(2R)$

2-12. Show the origin of 0.225 in Table 2-6. [*Hint:* Height of a tetrahedron is (0.817) (edge), and the center of the tetrahedron is 25% of the height.]

2-13. (a) What is the radius of the smallest cation that can have a 6-fold coordination with O^{2-} ions? (b) 8-fold coordination?

Answer: (a) 0.545 A   (b) 0.965 A

2-14. (a) From Appendix D, cite three divalent cations which can have CN = 6 with S^{2-} but not CN = 8. (b) Cite two divalent ions which can have CN = 8 with F$^-$.

2-15. Silicon tetrafluoride (SiF$_4$) has a rather stable molecule with a relatively low melting temperature ($-107°$F). Account for these facts by predicting the nature of its bonds. (Use a sketch if necessary.)

2-16. Sulfur dichloride has a molecular weight of 103 and a boiling point of 59°C. Draw a diagram showing the valence electron structure of this compound.

• Problems preceded by a bullet are based, in part, on optional sections.

2-17. Sketch the valence-shell electron structure of a ClO_4^- ion.

2-18. Sketch the valence-shell electron structure of an SO_4^{2-} ion.

2-19. Sketch the valence-shell electron structure of a PO_4^{3-} ion.

2-20. Sketch the valence-shell electron structure of an SiO_4^{4-} ion.

2-21. (a) Sketch the valence-shell electron structure of formaldehyde (CH_2O). (b) Show the centers of positive and negative charges.

2-22. Show the centers of positive and negative charges in (a) CCl_4, (b) $C_2H_2Cl_2$, (c) CH_3Cl.

3

atomic arrangements

MOLECULAR STRUCTURES

3-1 Introduction. The properties of materials depend on the arrangement of their atoms. Such arrangements may be classified as (1) *molecular* structures, i.e., groupings of atoms, (2) *crystal* structures, i.e., a repetitious pattern of atoms, and (3) *amorphous* structures, i.e., structures without specific form. We shall first consider molecular structures.

A *molecule* may be defined as a limited number of atoms which are strongly bonded together but whose bonds with other, similar groups of atoms are relatively weak. These groups of atoms, which possess no net charge, act as a unit because the *intra*molecular attractions are strong, primary bonds, whereas the *inter*molecular bonds result from weaker, van der Waals forces.

The more common examples of molecules include compounds such as H_2O, CO_2, CCl_4, O_2, N_2, and HNO_3. Within each of these molecules, the atoms are held together by strong attractive forces that usually have covalent bonds, although ionic bonds are not uncommon. Unlike the forces that hold atoms together, the bonds between molecules are weak and consequently each molecule is free to act more or less independently. These observations are borne out by the following facts: (1) Each of these molecular compounds has a low melting and a low boiling temperature compared with other materials. (2) The molecular solids are soft because the molecules can slide past each other with small stress applications. (3) The molecules remain intact in the liquid and gaseous forms.

The molecules listed above are comparatively small; other molecules have large numbers of atoms. For example, pentatriacontane (shown in Fig. 3-1c) has over 100 atoms, and some molecules contain as many as several thousand. Whether the molecule is small like CH_4, or much larger than that shown in Fig. 3-1(c), the distinction between the strong intramolecular and the weaker intermolecular bonds still holds.

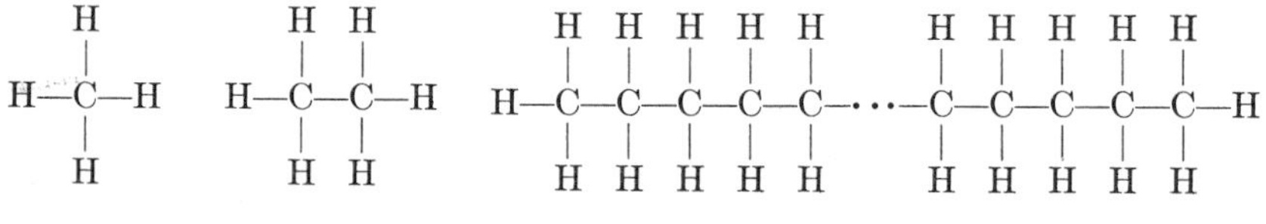

(a) Methane   (b) Ethane   (c) Pentatriacontane (i.e.. 35-ane)

FIG. 3-1. Examples of molecules. Molecules are discrete groups of atoms. Primary bonds hold the atoms together within the molecule. Weaker, secondary forces attract molecules to each other.

48

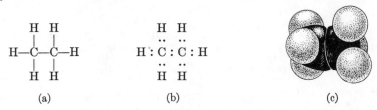

FIG. 3-2. Ethane. The (a) conventional and (b) electron pair representations of ethane are shown in two dimensions. A covalent bond always consists of two shared electrons. (c) Three-dimensional representation.

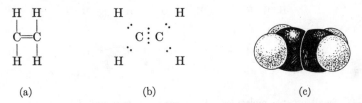

FIG. 3-3. Ethylene. The (a) conventional and (b) electron pair representations of ethylene are shown in two dimensions. (c) Three-dimensional representation. The double bond between the two carbons is shorter and less flexible than a single bond.

In Fig. 3-1(a) the bonds are shown in the conventional manner. Each bond is made by a pair of covalent electrons. Recall from Section 2-8 that shared electrons must form a completed orbital within a shell. Thus in each example in Figs. 3-2 and 3-3 the sketches are identical except for notation. The elements commonly encountered in molecules are the nonmetals and hydrogen. Carbon is the most important nonmetallic element; in addition, oxygen, nitrogen, silicon, sulphur, and the halides may also be present.

3-2 Number of bonds. In the discussion of the coordination number in Section 2-15, it was pointed out that the number of covalent bonds around an atom depended on the number of electrons in the outer, or valence quantum shell. Except for hydrogen and helium, the general rule for the number of bonds, N, is

$$N = 8 - G, \tag{3-1}$$

where G is the Group Number of the atom within the periodic table (Fig. 2-1). The elements more commonly encountered in molecules have the following number of bonds: H, F, Cl (one each); O, S (two each); N (three); and C and Si (four each). Figure 3-4 shows several molecules which illustrate these relationships.

3-3 Bond lengths and energies. The strength of the bonds between atoms in a molecule is, of course, dependent on the kinds of atoms and the number of bonds. Table 3-1 is a compilation of bond lengths and energies for those atom couples most frequently encountered in molecular structures. The energy is expressed in

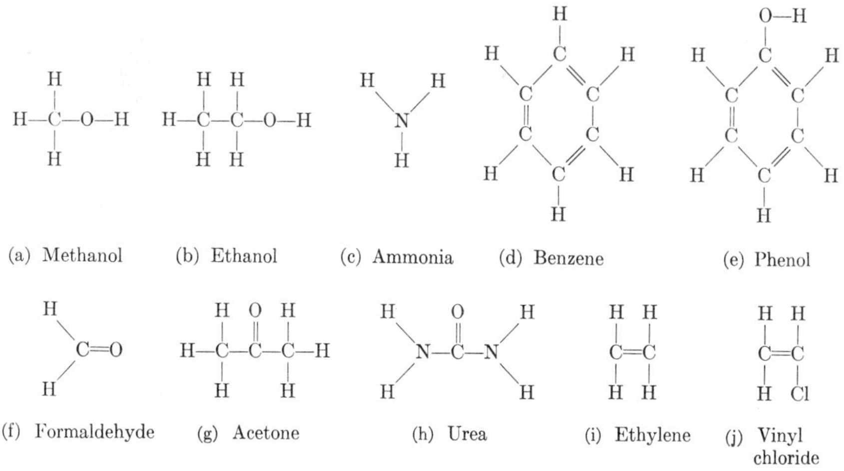

FIG. 3-4. Small organic molecules. Each carbon is surrounded by four bonds, each nitrogen by three, each oxygen by two, and each hydrogen and chlorine by one.

TABLE 3-1

BOND LENGTHS AND ENERGIES*

Bond	Bond length, A (approx.)†	Bond energy, kcal/gm-mole (approx.)†
C—C	1.5	83
C=C	1.3	146
C≡C	1.2	185
C—H	1.1	99
C—Cl	1.8	81
C—N	1.5	73
C—O	1.5	86
C=O	1.2	179
N—H	1.0	93
O—H	1.0	111
O—Si	1.8	90
Cl—Cl	2.0	58
H—H	0.74	100

* Adapted from Billmeyer, F. W., Jr., *Textbook of Polymer Science.* New York: Interscience, 1962, page 16.

† These values vary somewhat with various adjacent bonds.

kilocalories per gram-mole. For example, 83,000 calories of energy are required to break 6.02×10^{23} C—C bonds, or $83,000/(6.02 \times 10^{23})$ calories per bond.

Double and triple bonds are shorter in length and require more energy for breakage. Also, since distortions may be encountered by highly polarized adjacent units (see Section 2–11), there will be some variation in the energies and lengths of these bonds.

3–4 Bond angles. The molecules sketched in Fig. 3–4 are shown in only two dimensions. However, most triatomic or larger molecules have more than one or two dimensions, and this means that *bond angles* are encountered across intervening atoms. In the liquid and gaseous water molecule, for example, the bond angle across the oxygen atom is 105°. In the paraffin chains, the carbon-carbon-carbon bond angle is 109°. Figure 3–5 shows typical arrangements.

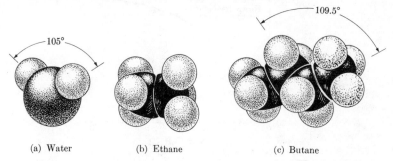

(a) Water   (b) Ethane   (c) Butane

Fig. 3–5. Three-dimensional sketches of molecules. Note the bond angles.

3–5 Isomers. In molecules of the same composition, more than one atomic arrangement is usually possible. This is illustrated in Fig. 3–6 for propyl and isopropyl alcohol. Variations in the structure of molecules with the same composition are called *isomers*. Differences in structure affect the properties of molecules because of the resulting change in molecular polarization (Section 2–11). For example, the melting and boiling temperatures for propyl alcohol are −127°C and 97.2°C, respectively, whereas for isopropyl alcohol the corresponding temperatures are −89°C and 82.3°C.

$$
\begin{array}{ccc}
\text{H} & \text{H} & \text{H} \\
| & | & | \\
\text{H—C—C—C—O—H} \\
| & | & | \\
\text{H} & \text{H} & \text{H}
\end{array}
\qquad\qquad
\begin{array}{ccc}
 & \text{H} & \\
 & | & \\
\text{H} & \text{O} & \text{H} \\
| & | & | \\
\text{H—C—C—C—H} \\
| & | & | \\
\text{H} & \text{H} & \text{H}
\end{array}
$$

(a)   (b)

Fig. 3–6. Isomers of propanol. (a) Normal propyl alcohol. (b) Isopropyl alcohol. The molecules have the same composition but different structures. Consequently, the properties are different. Compare with polymorphism of crystalline materials (Section 3–18).

3–6 Saturated hydrocarbons. A knowledge of the simple hydrocarbons is fundamental to the understanding of molecules. The smallest hydrocarbon is methane, CH_4, which is shown in Fig. 3–1. Starting with this smallest unit, more and more carbon and hydrogen atoms can be added to produce larger and larger molecules. Theoretically this process can be carried on indefinitely. These molecules, whose general formula is C_nH_{2n+2}, are called the *paraffins*. In the paraffin series, all bonds are single pairs of covalent electrons. Consequently, each carbon within the chain is surrounded by a full complement of four neighboring atoms. Since there is no way for additional atoms to be added to the chain, these molecules are considered to be *saturated*.

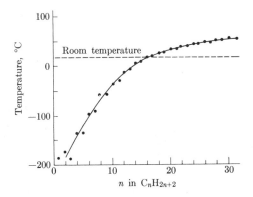

FIG. 3–7. Melting temperatures versus molecule size (paraffin series of hydrocarbons).

Molecules of this type possess strong *intra*molecular covalent bonds and weaker *inter*molecular van der Waals bonds (Section 3–1); hence the molecules act individually and have only weak attractions for one another. This is indicated through their relatively low melting points. However, as shown by the melting points in Fig. 3–7, not all the molecules in this series have equally weak intermolecular attractions. The approximate melting points for saturated hydrocarbons may be expressed by the following empirical equation:

$$\frac{1}{T_m} = 2.395 \times 10^{-3} + \frac{17.1 \times 10^{-3}}{n}, \qquad (3–2)$$

where T_m is the absolute melting temperature (°K) for a molecule with n carbon atoms.

Large molecules have relatively greater van der Waals (cohesive) attractions because there are more locations along the edges of the molecules for the dispersion effects or induced dipoles (Section 2–11); consequently, proportionately more energy must be supplied to a large than to a small molecule to remove it from the field of attraction of an adjacent molecule. The contrast between paraffin and fuels supports the validity of this conclusion for the hydrocarbon series.

Paraffin contains $30\pm$ carbon atoms per molecule and is relatively rigid at room temperature, whereas hydrocarbon fuels, whose molecules contain fewer than 15 carbon atoms, are liquids or gases. The plastic *polyethylene* is essentially a hydrocarbon with several hundred carbons. Its melting temperature is even higher than that of paraffin wax, although less than 145°C (293°F), because the melting temperature of C_nH_{2n+2} approaches this level asymptotically [Eq. (3–2)].

3–7 Unsaturated hydrocarbons. In the paraffin series there is one electron pair between each hydrogen and its adjacent carbon, and one electron pair between sequential carbons. As discussed previously, it is also possible for a molecule like ethylene to have two electron pairs, or covalent bonds, holding the adjacent carbon atoms together. Unlike ethane, *ethylene* and other double-bonded linear molecules are not saturated with the maximum number of hydrogens (Fig. 3–3). In general, any molecule with multiple carbon-to-carbon bonds is considered to be *unsaturated*. These unsaturated molecules serve a major purpose in *polymerization* of small molecules into a single large molecule, as illustrated in Fig. 3–8.

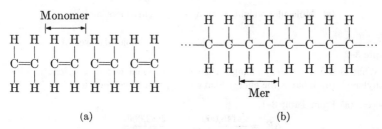

FIG. 3–8. Addition polymerization of ethylene. (a) Monomers of ethylene. (b) Polymer containing many C_2H_4 mers, or units. The original double bond of the ethylene monomer is broken to form two single bonds and thus connect adjacent mers.

3–8 Polymeric molecules. A polymer (literally, *many units*) is a large molecule which is made up of many small repeating units or mers. Most of the materials which we call plastics are made up of polymers. Therefore, we shall, in Chapter 7, discuss these macro-molecules in some detail. However, here it is important to note only two things about polymers: First, if we know the structure of the repeating mers, we are able to describe the structure of the large molecules. Second, most polymers originate as a combination of monomers (literally, *single units*).

Example 3–1

Vinyl chloride, C_2H_3Cl, is a molecule with a structure similar to ethylene, except that one of the four hydrogens is replaced with chlorine. (a) Show the change in bonds which results from the polymerization of vinyl chloride to polyvinyl chloride. (b) What is the weight of each mer in grams? (c) What is the molecular weight if there are 250 mers per polymer?

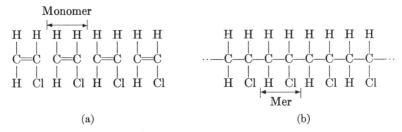

Fig. 3-9. Addition polymerization of vinyl chloride (see Example 3-2). As in the case of polyethylene, double bonds are broken to form two single bonds.

Answer: (a) See Fig. 3-9.

(b) $$\text{Weight/mer} = \frac{\text{gm/mer weight}}{\text{mers/mer weight}}$$

$$= \frac{(2)(12) + (3)(1) + 35.5}{6.02 \times 10^{23}}$$

$$= 1.04 \times 10^{-22} \text{ gm/mer.}$$

(c) Molecular weight $= (\text{gm/mer weight})(\text{mers/mole})$
$$= (62.5)(250)$$
$$= 1.56 \times 10^{4} \text{ gm/molecular weight}$$

Example 3-2

(a) What is the net energy change when an additional mer of ethylene is added to polyethylene? (b) What is the energy change per gram of polyethylene?

Answer: (a) From Table 3-1,

$$\Delta E = \frac{146,000}{6.02 \times 10^{23}} - \frac{2(83,000)}{6.02 \times 10^{23}}$$

$$= -3.32 \times 10^{-20} \text{ cal/mer.}$$

Since ΔE is negative, energy is released.

(b) $$\text{Cal/gm} = \frac{\text{cal/mer}}{\text{gm/mer}}$$

$$= \frac{-3.32 \times 10^{-20}}{[(2)(12) + (4)(1)]/6.02 \times 10^{23}}$$

$$= -715 \text{ cal/gm.}$$

CRYSTAL STRUCTURE

3-9 Crystallinity. A molecule has a structural regularity because covalent bonds maintain a specific number and orientation of neighbors for each atom. Thus, a repetition may exist along the length of a linear polymer (Fig. 3-8). The majority of engineering materials have atom arrangements which also have repeating patterns in three dimensions. Such structures are called *crystals.*

The repeating three-dimensional pattern in crystals is due to atomic coordination (Section 2-15) within the material; in addition, the pattern sometimes controls

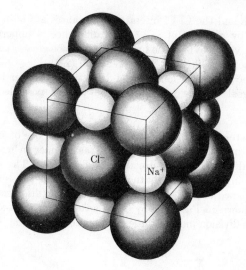

Fig. 3–10. Crystal structure. The cubic faces of table salt
are the crystal faces of the NaCl structure. MgO has the
same structure.

the external shape of the crystal. The six-pointed outline of snowflakes is probably
the most familiar example of this. The planar surfaces of gems, quartz (SiO_2)
crystals, and even ordinary table salt (NaCl) are all external manifestations of
internal crystalline arrangements. In each case the internal atomic arrangement
persists even though the external surfaces are altered. For example, the internal
structure of a quartz crystal is not altered when the surfaces of the crystal are
abraded to produce round silica sand. Likewise, there is a hexagonal arrangement
of water molecules in chunks of crushed ice as well as in snowflakes.

Let us use sodium chloride as an illustration of the role of atom packing on
crystallinity. The ion-size ratio of Na^+ and Cl^- is 0.98/1.81, or 0.54. Recall from
Table 2–6 that this ratio favors a coordination number of six. This was shown in
Fig. 2–22 for Mg^{2+} and O^{2-}, but would also be applicable for Na^+ and Cl^- The
first-neighbor arrangement of Fig. 2–22 shows only part of the structure; a more
complete pattern is shown in Fig. 3–10, in which we may note the following features.

(1) Each Na^+ and each Cl^- ion has six neighbors (if the pattern is extended
further into three dimensions).

(2) There are equal numbers of Na^+ ions and Cl^- ions (if the pattern is
continued).

(3) A small cube is established with planar faces and an edge of length ($2r +
2R$), where r and R are the radii of the Na^+ and Cl^- ions, respectively.

(4) The pattern in a small cube, called the *unit cell*, is identical to the pattern
of all other cubes of NaCl. Thus if we know the structure of the repeating unit
cells, we are able to describe the structure of the crystal. (Cf. mers in Section 3–8.)

(5) The Na-Na and the Cl-Cl interatomic distances are both greater than the Na-Cl distances by a factor of $\sqrt{2}$. This difference is important because the coulombic attractive forces between unlike ions must be greater than the coulombic repulsive forces between like ions [Eqs. (2–9) and (2–10)].

Each of the above observations will be discussed at further length. However, our immediate goal will be to consider the various possible types of crystal structures.

3–10 Crystal systems.   Atomic packing may take on one of seven main crystal patterns. These are closely associated with the manner in which space can be divided into equal volumes by intersecting plane surfaces. The simplest and most regular of these involves three mutually perpendicular sets of equally spaced, parallel planes aligned to give a series of cubes. We can also describe this division in the manner shown in Fig. 3–11 by equal spacings on right-angle axes. Other methods of space division include those combinations shown in Table 3–2.

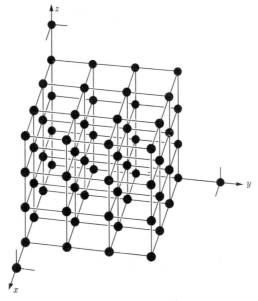

Fig. 3–11. Cubic cells. Space is divided by three sets of equally spaced parallel planes. The x, y, and z reference axes are mutually perpendicular. Each point of intersection is equivalent.

These seven *systems* include all the possible geometries of division of space by continuous plane surfaces. Most of the crystals we shall encounter in this book fall into the cubic system. Examples include most of the common metals (except zinc and magnesium, which are hexagonal), and some of the simpler ceramic compounds such as MgO, TiC, and $BaTiO_3$.

TABLE 3-2

GEOMETRY OF CRYSTAL SYSTEMS

System	Axes	Axial angles
Cubic	$a_1 = a_2 = a_3$	All angles = 90°
Tetragonal	$a_1 = a_2 \neq c$	All angles = 90°
Orthorhombic	$a \neq b \neq c$	All angles = 90°
Monoclinic	$a \neq b \neq c$	2 angles = 90°; 1 angle $\neq$ 90°
Triclinic	$a \neq b \neq c$	All angles different; none equal 90°
Hexagonal	$a_1 = a_2 = a_3 \neq c$	Angles = 90° and 120°
Rhombohedral	$a_1 = a_2 = a_3$	All angles equal, but not 90°

3-11 Cubic crystals. Atoms may be packed in a cubic pattern with three different types of repetition: simple cubic (sc), body-centered cubic (bcc), and face-centered cubic (fcc). Each will be considered in turn by paying attention to pure metals which have only one kind of atom. The slightly more complex structures which contain two types of atoms will be handled more completely in later chapters.

Simple cubic. This structure, which is shown in Fig. 3–12, is hypothetical for pure metals but provides us with a good starting point. In addition to the three axial dimensions, a, being equal, and the axes at right angles, there are equivalent positions in each cell. For example, the center of this cell has surroundings identical to the center of the next, and to all unit cells in this crystal. Likewise, the lower right corner (or any other specific position) of all unit cells is identical. To describe one unit cell is to describe the whole crystal.

The structure shown in Fig. 3–12 would contain one metal atom per unit cell. (Only one octant of each of the eight atoms shown lies within the unit cell). Herein is the reason why metals do not crystallize in the simple cubic structure. If the

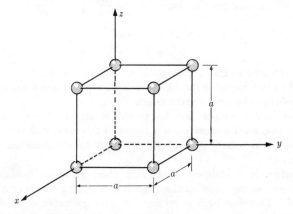

FIG. 3–12. Simple cubic structure. The corners of the unit cells are at like positions in the crystal. $a = a = a$. Axes are at right angles.

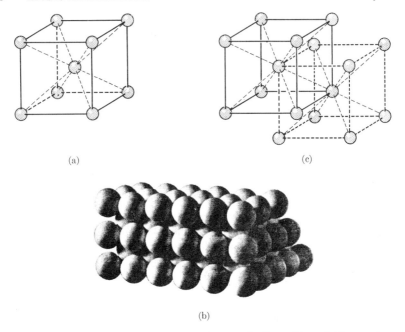

(a)   (c)

(b)

FIG. 3–13. Body-centered cubic structure of a metal. Parts (a) and (c) are schematic views showing the location of atom centers. (b) Model made from hard balls. (Bruce Rogers, *The Nature of Metals*. Cleveland: American Society for Metals, 1951.)

metal atoms are considered to be "hard balls" of radius r, only 52% of the space would be occupied:

$$\text{Atomic packing factor} = \frac{\text{volume of atoms}}{\text{volume of unit cell}} \qquad (3\text{–}3)$$

$$= \frac{4\pi r^3/3}{(2r)^3} = 0.52.$$

Other metallic structures give higher packing factors. (A simple cubic structure will be described in Chapter 8 for compounds in which a small cation is located at the center of the cube among eight anions.)

Body-centered cubic structures. Iron has a cubic structure. At room temperature, the unit cell of iron has an atom at each corner of the cube, and another atom at the body center of the cube (Fig. 3–13a). Such a crystal structure has been named *body-centered cubic.*

Each iron atom in a body-centered cubic (bcc) structure is surrounded by eight adjacent iron atoms, whether the atom is located at a corner or at the center of the unit cell. Therefore each atom has the same geometric environment (Fig. 3–13c). There are two atoms per unit cell in a bcc structure. One atom is at the center of the cube, and eight octants are located at the eight corners (Fig. 3–14).

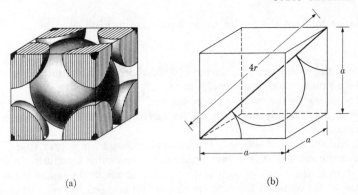

(a)   (b)

FIG. 3–14. Body-centered cubic unit cell. In a metal the bcc structure has two atoms per unit cell and an atomic packing factor of 0.68. The lattice constant a is related to the atomic radius as shown by Eq. (3–4).

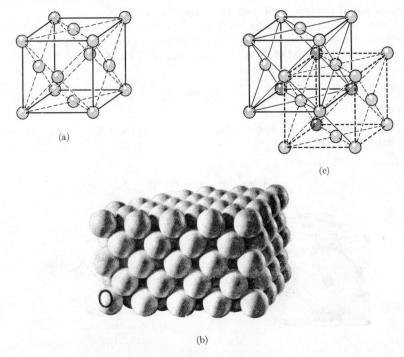

(a)

(c)

(b)

FIG. 3–15. Face-centered cubic structure of a metal. Parts (a) and (c) are schematic views showing location of atom centers. (b) Model made from hard balls. (Bruce Rogers, *The Nature of Metals.* Cleveland: American Society for Metals, 1951.)

The lattice constant a is related to the atomic radius r by

$$a_{\text{bcc}} = 4r/\sqrt{3}.\qquad(3\text{–}4)$$

Therefore the atomic packing factor is 0.68, which is significantly greater than that for a simple cubic structure of a metal.

Although iron is the most common material with a body-centered cubic structure, it is not the only one. Chromium and tungsten also have body-centered cubic arrangements.

Face-centered cubic structures. The atom arrangement in copper (Fig. 3–15) is not quite the same as that in iron, although it has a cubic structure. In addition to an atom at the corner of each unit cell, there is one at the center of each face, but none at the center of the cube. Such a lattice is called *face-centered cubic.*

Face-centered cubic (fcc) structures are somewhat more common among metals than are body-centered cubic structures. Aluminum, copper, lead, silver, and nickel possess this atomic arrangement. Face-centered cubic structures are also found in compounds as revealed in Fig. 3–10, where the Cl^- ions at the cube corners and at the face centers are all equivalent.

A metal with an fcc structure has four times as many atoms as it has unit cells. The eight corner octants contribute a total of one atom, and the six face-centered atoms contribute a total of three atoms per unit cell (Fig. 3–16). The lattice constant a is related to the atomic radius r by

$$a_{\text{fcc}} = 4r/\sqrt{2}.\qquad(3\text{–}5)$$

Example 3–3

Calculate (a) the atomic packing factor of an fcc metal (Fig. 3–16); (b) the ionic packing factor of fcc NaCl (Fig. 3–10).

Answer: (a) Equation (3–3),

$$\text{PF} = \frac{4(4\pi r^3/3)}{a^3} = \frac{16\pi r^3(2\sqrt{2})}{(3)(64r^3)} = 0.74.$$

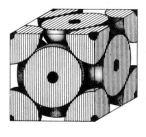

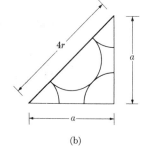

(a)   (b)

Fig. 3–16. Face-centered cubic unit cell. In a metal the fcc structure has four atoms per unit cell and an atomic packing factor of 0.74. The lattice constant a is related to the atomic radius as shown by Eq. (3–5).

(b) Equation (3–3) and Fig. 3–10,

$$\text{PF} = \frac{4(4\pi r^3/3) + 4(4\pi R^3/3)}{(2r + 2R)^3} = \frac{16\pi(0.98^3 + 1.81^3)}{3(8)(0.98 + 1.81)^3} = 0.67.$$

It is apparent from Example 3–3(a) that the packing factor is independent of atom size, if only one size is present. In contrast, the relative sizes do affect the packing factor when more than one type of atom is present. The face-centered cubic structure has the highest packing factor (0.74) that is possible for a pure metal, and thus this structure is called a *cubic close-packed* structure. As we might expect, many metals have this structure, although we shall see in a moment that a hexagonal close-packed structure also has a packing factor of 0.74. The coordination number in an fcc metal is 12, which accounts for the high packing factor. (This may be contrasted to the CN of 8 and the PF of 0.68 of a bcc metal.)

3–12 Hexagonal crystals. The structures of Figs. 3–17(a) and 3–17(b) are two representations of *simple hexagonal* unit cells. These cells have no internal positions which are equivalent to the corner positions. Although the volume of the cell is three times as great in Fig. 3–17(a) as in Fig. 3–17(b), there are three times as many atoms (3 versus 1); therefore the number of atoms per unit volume remains the same.

Metals do not crystallize in the simple hexagonal pattern because the packing factor is too low. However, we shall find compounds containing more than one type of atom with this pattern of equivalent positions.

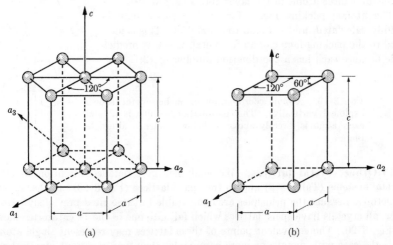

FIG. 3–17. Simple hexagonal unit cells. (a) Hexagonal representation. (b) Rhombic representation. The two are equivalent with $a \neq c$, a basal angle of 120°, and vertical angle of 90°.

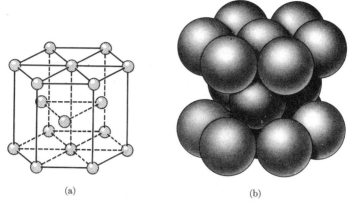

(a)   (b)

FIG. 3–18. Hexagonal close-packed structure. (a) Schematic view showing the location of atom centers. (b) Model made from hard balls.

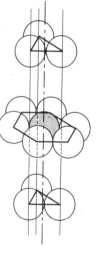

Hexagonal close-packed structures. The specific hexagonal structure formed by magnesium is shown in Fig. 3–18. Such a structure, which is more dense than that represented by Fig. 3–17, is called a *hexagonal close-packed* (hcp) structure. It is characterized by the fact that each atom in one layer is located directly above or below interstices among three atoms in the adjacent layers. Consequently, each atom touches three atoms in the layer below its plane, six atoms in its own plane, and three atoms in the layer above (Fig. 3–19).

The atomic packing factor for an hcp metal may be readily calculated, and is found to equal 0.74. This is identical to the packing factor of an fcc metal, which is predictable because each has a coordination number of 12.

FIG. 3–19. Atomic coordination in an hcp metal (shown exploded vertically). The coordination number is 12, and each atom is directly above or below atoms in alternate planes.

3–13 Other crystal lattices. We shall not give detailed attention to other crystal systems (Table 3–2) and to the space lattices (Fig. 3–20) of other crystal structures, because the principles are comparable to those cited previously. However, all crystals have space lattices which fall into one of the 14 categories shown in Fig. 3–20. The equivalent points of these lattices may represent single atoms, as is the case with metals, or more commonly, they may represent identical and repeating sites among several atoms. For example, the fcc lattice establishes the equivalent locations of all the ions, and not just the Cl$^-$ ions in NaCl (Fig. 3–10).

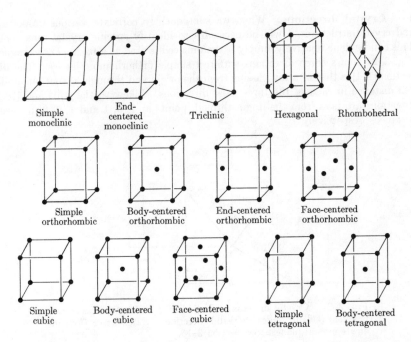

FIG. 3–20. Space lattices. These 14 *Bravais lattices* continue in three dimensions. Each indicated point has identical surroundings. Compare with Table 3–2.

Example 3–4

Copper has an fcc structure and an atom radius of 1.278 A. Calculate its density and check this value with the density listed in Appendix D.

Answer: Equation (3–5),

$$a = \frac{4}{\sqrt{2}} \ (1.278 \text{ A}) \ = \ 3.61 \text{ A}.$$

Figure 3–16,

$$\text{atoms/unit cell} \ = \ \frac{8}{8} + \frac{6}{2} \ = \ 4,$$

$$\text{density} \ = \ \frac{\text{weight/unit cell}}{\text{volume/unit cell}} \qquad (3\text{–}6a)$$

$$= \ \frac{(\text{atoms/unit cell})(\text{gm/atom})}{(\text{lattice constant})^3}. \qquad (3\text{–}6b)$$

$$\text{Density} \ = \ \frac{4[63.5/(0.602 \times 10^{24})]}{(3.61)^3 \times 10^{-24}} \ = \ 8.98 \text{ gm/cm}^3.$$

The experimental value listed in Appendix D is 8.96 gm/cm³.

3–14 Crystal directions. When we subsequently correlate various properties and crystal structures it will be necessary to identify specific crystal directions. This can be done relatively simply if the unit cell is used as a basis. For example, Fig. 3–21 shows three directions within a simple orthorhombic lattice. The direction [111] is that of a ray passing from the origin and through a point one unit-cell distance in each of the three axial directions. Likewise, the [101] and [100] directions are rays from the origin through points at 1, 0, 1 and 1, 0, 0 unit-cell distances, respectively.

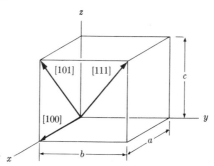

FIG. 3–21. Crystal directions. Established custom utilizes square brackets [hkl] to indicate crystal directions. Parentheses (hkl) indicate crystal planes. See Section 3–15.

The following features are to be noted:

(1) Unit-cell intercepts, and not actual distances, are used. In the orthorhombic lattice of Fig. 3–21, $a \neq b \neq c$.

(2) Crystal axes are used as base directions.

(3) A [222] direction is identical to a [111] direction. Therefore the lowest combination of integers is used.

(4) Directions such as [112] may also be identified. (This direction is a ray from the origin through the center of the top face.)

Example 3–5

(a) What is the linear density of atoms along the [110] direction of copper? (b) What is the repetition spacing (Burgers vector) of atoms in the [211] direction?

Answer: (a) Linear density = atoms/cm   (3–7)

$$= \frac{2}{\sqrt{2}\,a} = \frac{2}{(4)(1.278 \times 10^{-8})} = 3.9 \times 10^7 \text{ atoms/cm.}$$

(b) From Fig. 3–15(a),

$$\text{repetition spacing} = \sqrt{a^2 + (a/2)^2 + (a/2)^2}$$
$$= \sqrt{6}\,(a/2) = 2\sqrt{3}\,(1.278) = 4.43 \text{ A.}$$

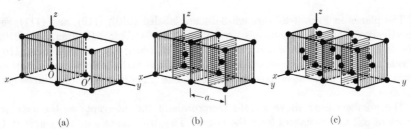

FIG. 3–22. (010) planes in cubic structures. (a) Simple cubic. (b) Bcc. (c) Fcc. [Note that the (020) planes included for bcc and fcc are equivalent to (010) planes.]

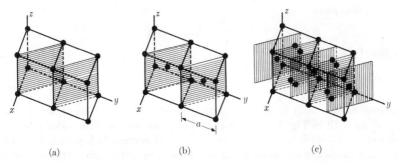

FIG. 3–23. (110) planes in cubic structures. (a) Simple cubic. (b) Bcc. (c) Fcc. [The (220) planes included for fcc are equivalent to (110) planes.]

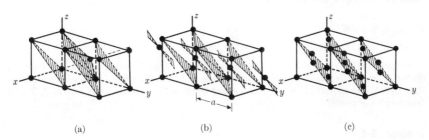

FIG. 3–24. ($\bar{1}$11) planes in cubic structures. (a) Simple cubic. (b) Bcc. (c) Fcc. Negative intercepts are indicated by bars above the index. [The ($\bar{2}$22) planes included for bcc are equivalent to ($\bar{1}$11) planes.]

3–15 Crystal planes. A crystal contains planes of atoms, and these planes influence the properties and behavior of crystals. Thus it will be advantageous to identify the various atomic planes that exist in a crystal.

The lattice planes most readily visualized are those which outline the unit cell, but there are many other planes. The most important planes in cubic crystals are shown in Figs. 3–22, 3–23, and 3–24.

The planes in Figs. 3–22 through 3–24 are labeled (010), (110), and ($\bar{1}$11), respectively. These *(hkl)* symbols are called *Miller indices*. In brief, the (010) planes are parallel to the *x* and *z* crystal axes that orient the unit cell. The (110) planes are parallel to the *z* crystal axis, but cut the *x*- and *y*- axes at unit distances from the origin or point of axis intersection. The ($\bar{1}$11) planes cut the three crystal axes.

The numbers used above are the reciprocals of the intercepts on the axes, in terms of cell unit distances from the origin. The (010) plane cuts the *y*-axis at 1, the *x*- and *z*-axes at ∞:

$$\frac{1}{\infty}, \ \frac{1}{1}, \ \frac{1}{\infty} = (010).$$

For the (110) plane:

$$\frac{1}{1}, \ \frac{1}{1}, \ \frac{1}{\infty} = (110).$$

For the ($\bar{1}$11) plane:

$$\frac{-1}{1}, \ \frac{1}{1}, \ \frac{1}{1} = (\bar{1}11).$$

Inasmuch as the point of origin is arbitrarily chosen, i.e., it could as well have been at point O' in Fig. 3–22(a) as at O, the plane with a (010) index is equally arbitrary. Thus (010) is a symbol for all planes of atoms which are parallel to the plane that meets the definition given in the previous paragraph. This generalization of the indices is completely logical, inasmuch as all these parallel planes are geometrically similar. Miller indices may also be negative, and the minus sign is then shown above the digit, e.g., ($\bar{1}1\bar{1}$).

Example 3–6

Sketch the (112) plane in a simple cubic unit cell.

Answer: (112) is the reciprocal of 1, 1, $\frac{1}{2}$. Thus *a*, *b*, and *c* equal 1, 1, and $\frac{1}{2}$ unit-cell distances, respectively. This plane is sketched in Fig. 3–25. Since parallel planes have the same Miller indices, a second plane could be drawn to intercept the axes at 2, 2, and 1 unit-cell distances.

Example 3–7

Sketch a (111) plane through a unit cell of a simple tetragonal crystal having a *c/a* ratio of 0.62.

Answer: Figure 3–26 shows this plane. The (111) plane cuts the three axes at unit distances. However, the unit distance along the *z*-axis is shorter than the unit distances on the *x*- and *y*-axes.

Planar densities. When we are considering plastic deformation, we need to know the density of atoms on a crystal plane. The following example shows how we may calculate this by means of the relationship:

$$\text{Planar density} = \text{atoms/unit area.} \tag{3–8}$$

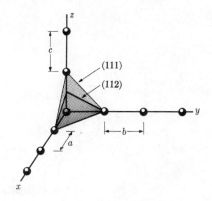

FIG. 3–25. Miller indices. The (112) plane cuts the three axes at 1, 1, and $\frac{1}{2}$ unit distances.

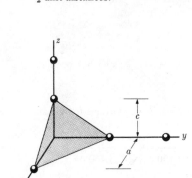

FIG. 3–26. Noncubic intercepts (tetragonal structure). The (111) plane cuts the three axes of any crystal at equal unit distances. However, since c may not equal a, the actual intercepting distances are different.

$$\frac{c}{a} = 0.62$$

Example 3–8

How many atoms per mm^2 are there on the (100) and (111) planes of lead (fcc)?

Answer:

$$\text{Pb radius} = 1.750, \quad \text{(from Appendix D)}$$

$$a_{\text{Pb}} = \frac{4r}{\sqrt{2}} = \frac{4(1.750)}{1.414} = 4.95 \text{ A.}$$

Figure 3–27 shows that the (100) plane contains two atoms per unit-cell face.

$$(100): \text{ atoms/mm}^2 = \frac{2 \text{ atoms}}{(4.95 \times 10^{-7} \text{ mm})^2}$$

$$= 8.2 \times 10^{12} \text{ atoms/mm}^2.$$

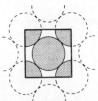

FIG. 3–27. (100) atom concentration (fcc). A (100) plane in an fcc structure has two atoms per a^2.

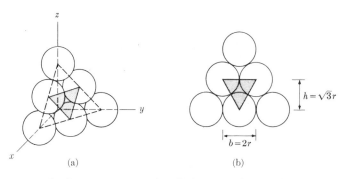

FIG. 3-28. (111) atom concentration (fcc). A (111) plane has one-half atom per $\sqrt{3}r^2$.

Figure 3-28(b) shows that the (111) plane contains ($\frac{3}{6} = \frac{1}{2}$) atoms for the triangular area shown.

$$(111):\quad \text{atoms/A}^2 = \frac{\frac{1}{2}}{\frac{1}{2}bh} = \frac{\frac{1}{2}}{\frac{1}{2}(2)(1.750\,\text{A})(\sqrt{3})(1.750\,\text{A})}$$
$$= 0.095\,\text{atoms/A}^2$$
$$= 9.5 \times 10^{12}\,\text{atoms/mm}^2.$$

• *Interplanar spacings.* Figure 3-29 reveals the distances between (111) planes, d_{111}, as being one-third of the body diagonal of the unit cell. Likewise, Fig. 3-30 shows the values of d_{110} and d_{220}.* In the cubic system, the distance between planes is

$$d_{hkl} = \frac{a}{\sqrt{h^2 + k^2 + l^2}}, \tag{3-9}$$

where a is the lattice constant and h, k, and l are the indices of the planes. The interplanar spacings for noncubic crystals may be expressed in an equation similar to Eq. (3-9), although slightly more complex.

By now it should be apparent why we use the reciprocal procedure for identifying crystal planes. These indices lend themselves to simplified calculations.

• **Example 3-9**

Compare the values of d_{200} and d_{111} in lead (fcc).

Answer: $a_{\text{Pb}} = 4.95\,\text{A}$ (from previous example).

Figure 3-30 indicates that there are two (200) interplanar distances per unit-cell dimension in an fcc structure.

$$d_{200} = \frac{4.95}{2}\,\text{A} = 2.475\,\text{A}.$$

---

* Miller indices are reduced to the lowest prime numbers; d_{hkl} spacings are not.

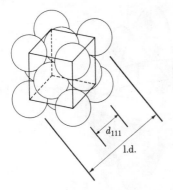

FIG. 3–29.   Interplanar spacings (fcc). There are three d_{111} interplanar spacings per long diagonal of a unit cell in an fcc structure.

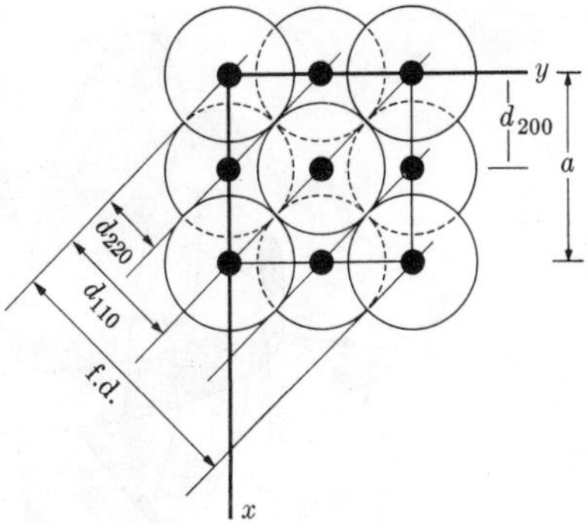

FIG. 3–30.   (110) interplanar spacings. There are four (220) interplanar spacings per face diagonal of the fcc cell. Since the three unit distances are identical in a cubic structure, there are five other comparable sets of planes. Show what they are.

Figure 3–29 indicates that there are three d_{111} interplanar spacings per body diagonal of an fcc unit cell. Since the body diagonal equals $\sqrt{3}a$,

$$d_{111} = \tfrac{1}{3}(\sqrt{3})(4.95 \text{ A}) = 2.86 \text{ A}.$$

This may also be calculated from Eq. (3–9):

$$d_{111} = \frac{4.95}{\sqrt{1^2 + 1^2 + 1^2}} = 2.86 \text{ A}.$$

• **3–16 X-ray analyses.**   Lattice structures are determined experimentally by *x-ray analyses*, which also reveal the crystal structure (Figs. 3–31 and 3-32). The atomic distances are then calculated by the relationships listed previously [Eqs. (3–4) and (3–5)].

When x-rays are directed at a crystalline material they are diffracted by the planes of atoms or ions within the crystal. The diffraction angle depends on the wavelength of the x-rays and the distance between adjacent planes. Consider the parallel planes of atoms in Fig. 3–33, from which a wave is diffracted. The waves may be "reflected" from an atom at H or H', and remain in phase at K. However, x-rays are not only reflected from the surface plane but also from subsurface planes. If these reflections are to remain in phase, the distance $MH''P$ must equal one or more integral wavelengths of the rays. Therefore, from geometry,

$$n\lambda = 2d \sin \theta, \qquad\qquad (3\text{–}10)$$

where λ is the wavelength, d is the interplanar spacing and θ is the angle of incidence. The value n is the number of waves which occur in the distance $MH''P$. The reflections are generally weaker when more than one extra wave is present.

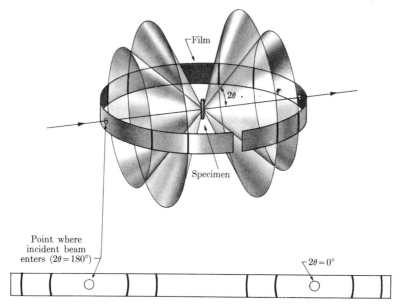

FIG. 3–31. The exposure of x-ray diffraction patterns. Angle 2θ is precisely fixed by the lattice spacing d and the wavelength λ as shown in Eq. (3–10). Every cone of reflection is recorded in two places on the strip of film. (B.D. Cullity, *Elements of X-ray Diffraction*. Reading, Mass.: Addison-Wesley, 1956.)

• **Example 3–10**

An x-ray diffraction analysis of a crystal is made with x-rays having a wavelength of 0.58 A. Reflections are observed at angles of (a) 6.45°, (b) 9.15°, and (c) 13.0°. What interplanar spacings are present in the crystal?

Answer:

$$n\lambda = 2d \sin \theta,$$

$$\frac{d}{n} = \frac{\lambda}{2 \sin \theta}$$

$$(a) \quad = \frac{0.58}{2(\sin 6.45°)} = 2.575 \text{ A},$$

$$(b) \quad = \frac{0.58}{2(\sin 9.15°)} = 1.82 \text{ A},$$

$$(c) \quad = \frac{0.58}{2(\sin 13.0°)} = 1.29 \text{ A}.$$

It will be noted that d/n in (a) is twice the value of d/n in (c); therefore angles 6.45° and 13.0° must represent different values of n for the same interplanar spacing. In this case n could equal 1 in (a) and 2 in (c) and d would be 2.58 A. We can assume that n equals one in (b), inasmuch as no other reflections are stated; therefore there is a second d of 1.82 A.

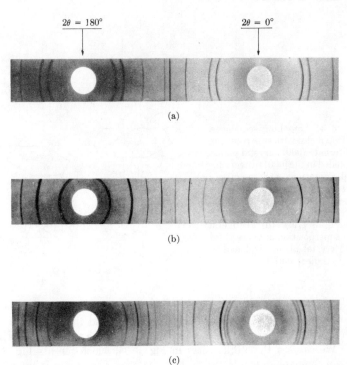

FIG. 3–32. X-ray diffraction patterns for (a) copper, fcc; (b) tungsten, bcc; and (c) zinc, hcp. The crystal structure and the lattice constants may be calculated from patterns such as these. See references for further reading. (B. D. Cullity, *Elements of X-ray Diffraction*. Reading, Mass.: Addison-Wesley, 1956.)

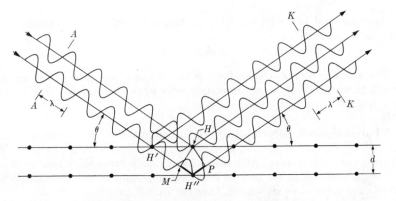

FIG. 3–33. X-ray diffraction.

FIG. 3–34. Stacking sequences. (a) Hcp metal with superposition of alternate (0001) crystal planes (exploded in the [0001] direction); (hkil) notations are sometimes used for hexagonal crystals, because four axes may be chosen. Three of these are in one plane. (Cf. Fig. 3–17a.) (b) Fcc metal with superposition of every third (111) crystal plane (exploded in the [111] direction).

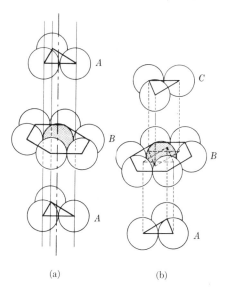

(a)   (b)

3–17 Stacking sequences. We noted in Sections 3–11 and 3–12 that fcc metals and hcp metals have the same packing factor (0.74) and the same coordination number (12). This means that we must look further for the real differences in their lattices. We can see these differences in Fig. 3–34, which repeats Fig. 3–19 so that we can compare an hcp lattice with an fcc one. The former is exploded in a vertical [0001] direction while the fcc lattice is exploded in the [111] direction. The atomic arrangement of the hcp metal in the (0001) plane is the same as that of the fcc metal in the (111) plane. However, in the hcp metal, alternate atom planes are in superposition to give a stacking sequence as follows:

$$\cdots\; A\;\; B\;\; A\;\; B\;\; A\;\; B\;\; A\;\; B\;\; A\;\; B \;\cdots. \tag{3–11}$$

On the other hand, in the fcc metal the stacking sequence is superpositioned every third plane to give:

$$\cdots\; A\;\; B\;\; C\;\; A\;\; B\;\; C\;\; A\;\; B\;\; C\;\; A \;\cdots. \tag{3–12}$$

Thus, although copper is fcc and zinc is hcp, the two form closely related structures, a factor that will become important later when we consider alloys such as brass, which contain both copper and zinc.

3–18 Polymorphism (allotropism). We recall from Section 3–5 that molecules may possess different structures, even though the composition is identical. We call these molecules *isomers.* An analogous situation, polymorphism, can be found in crystals, and in fact will become extremely important to us. *Polymorphs* are two or more types of crystals which have the same composition.

The prime example of polymorphism in metals will be iron, since our whole ability to heat-treat steel and modify its properties stems from the fact that, as iron is heated, it changes from the bcc to an fcc lattice. Furthermore, the change is reversible as iron cools. At room temperature bcc iron has a coordination number of 8, an atomic packing factor of 0.68, and an atomic radius of 1.241 A. Pure iron changes to fcc at 910°C, at which point its coordination number is 12, its atomic packing factor is 0.74, and its atomic radius is 1.292 A. [At 910°C (1670°F) the atomic radius of bcc iron, due to thermal expansion, is 1.258 A.]

Many other compositions have two or more polymorphic forms. In fact some, such as SiC, have as many as 20 crystalline modifications; however, this is unusual. Invariably, polymorphs have differences in density and other properties. In succeeding chapters we shall be interested in the property variations and in the time required to change from one crystal modification (phase) to another.

Example 3–11

Iron changes from bcc to fcc at 910°C. At this temperature the atomic radii of the iron atoms in the two structures are 1.258 A and 1.292 A, respectively. (a) What is the percent of volume change, v/o, as the structure changes? (b) Of linear change, l/o? [*Note:* As indicated in Section 2–14 and Table 2–5, the higher the coordination number the larger the radius.]

Answer: Basis: 4 iron atoms, or *two* unit cells of bcc iron, and *one* unit cell of fcc iron.

(a) In bcc, Eq. (3–4):

$$\text{Volume} = 2a^3$$
$$= 2\left[\frac{4(1.258)}{\sqrt{3}}\right]^3$$
$$= 49.1 \text{ A}^3.$$

In fcc, Eq. (3–5):

$$\text{Volume} = a^3$$
$$= \left[\frac{4(1.292)}{\sqrt{2}}\right]^3$$
$$= 48.7 \text{ A}^3;$$

$$\frac{48.7 - 49.1}{49.1} = -0.8 \text{ v/o change.}$$

(b)
$$(1 + \Delta L/L)^3 = 1 + \Delta V/V$$
$$\Delta L/L = \sqrt[3]{1 - 0.008} - 1$$
$$= -0.26 \text{ l/o change.}$$

Iron expands by thermal expansion until it reaches 910°C, where there is an abrupt shrinkage; further heating continues the expansion (Fig. 10–1a).

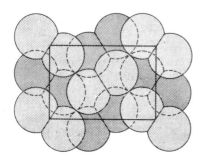

FIG. 3–35.   Molecular crystal (iodine). The molecule of I_2 acts as a unit in the repetitive crystal structure. This lattice is *simple orthorhombic* because $a \neq b \neq c$, and the face-centered positions are *not* identical to the corner positions. (The molecules are oriented differently.)

3–19 Molecular crystals.   Molecules, like atoms and ions, may form a crystalline pattern. However, there are three distinct differences: First, molecules are not spherical. Second, a molecule acts as a unit. Third, intermolecular attractions are weak van der Waals forces. Even so, packing efficiency is a controlling influence in molecular crystallization. Figure 3–35 shows a projection of the unit cell of a crystal of diatomic iodine molecules.

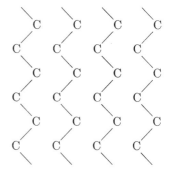

FIG. 3–36.   Polymer crystal (schematic). The adjacent molecules coordinate their positions with each other and so produce better packing and stronger van der Waals attractions. (The hydrogen atoms and other side radicals are not shown.)

Polymer crystals.   The greater complexity of the large polymer molecules interferes with the crystallization of polymers. Thus crystallization occurs less readily. However, under favorable conditions, polymers do crystallize, as shown schematically in Fig. 3–36. The resulting coordination increases the forces of attraction. For this reason we shall consider this subject in more detail in Chapter 7, where we shall give attention to the properties of organic materials.

NONCRYSTALLINE (AMORPHOUS) STRUCTURES

3–20 Introduction.   Let us here briefly consider those materials which do not have the long-range repetitive pattern of crystals. These amorphous (literally, "without form") materials include gases, liquids, and glasses. The first two are fluids, and are of major engineering importance as materials because they include not only many of our fuels, and the air necessary to combustion, but they also include water. Glass, the last of the three amorphous materials, has been called a rigid liquid; however, when we look at its structure we shall find that it is more than just a supercooled liquid.

3-21 Gases. There is no structure in a gas other than the structure within its individual molecules. Each atom or molecule is sufficiently far from other atoms or molecules to be essentially independent. The interactions caused by collisions are momentary and elastic.

Because the atoms or molecules are free to move independently, a gas which fills an available space exerts a pressure on its surroundings. The pressure P is dependent on the volume V, the temperature T, and the number of moles n, which are present. This is expressed by

$$PV = nRT. \tag{3-13}$$

Since 1 gm·mole $(6.02 \times 10^{23}$ molecules) of *any* gas occupies 22.4 liters at 0°C and 1 atmosphere pressure,* the value of the constant R in the above equation is 0.082 liter·atm/°K. Thus it is possible to calculate the density of a gas at selected temperatures and at relatively low pressures. We could also, if we wished, calculate an atomic packing factor for a gas, as we did for crystals; however, we would find that such a factor would be extremely low at pressures below 10 atm. At higher pressures, where the density and number of atoms is markedly higher, the gas does not strictly follow the ideal gas law given in Eq. (3-13).

Example 3-12

(a) Calculate the density of ethane at 20°C and 740 mm Hg pressure. (b) How many cubic angstroms are there per molecule?

Answer: On the basis of 1 gm·mole, or 30 gm,

$$\text{(a)} \qquad V = \frac{RT}{P} = \frac{(0.082)(293)}{(740/760)} = 24.5\, l = 24{,}500\text{ cm}^3;$$

$$\rho = \frac{30}{24{,}500} = 0.00122\text{ gm/cm}^3.$$

$$\text{(b)} \qquad \frac{24{,}500\text{ cm}^3}{0.602 \times 10^{24}\text{ molecules}} = 41{,}000\text{ Å}^3/\text{molecule}.$$

Other properties of a gas, such as its viscosity and its dielectric constant, depend on the number and size of molecules present; both properties increase as the pressure is increased.

3-22 Liquids. Liquids, like gases, are fluid and do not have a crystalline pattern of long-range order. However, here the similarity between gases and liquids stops. We find that the structure of liquids has much in common with the structure of crystals; their densities, and therefore their packing factors, are within a few percent of each other. A liquid is slightly less dense than a crystal; however, this cannot be considered a general rule because there are a number of materials, such as water, which expand on freezing.

---

* In British units, one lb·mole of any gas occupies 378 ft³ at 60°F and 1 atm.

Liquids have a short-range structure in which the interatomic distances between first neighbors are fairly uniform and are approximately the same as in crystals (Fig. 3–37). The average coordination number of most liquids is nearly equal to that of their comparable crystals. When we think about the above similarities, it is not surprising that a liquid is often considered to be a modification of a crystal, in which the thermal energy is sufficient to disrupt the long-range order of the crystal lattice. In order for this disruption to take place, the atoms (or molecules) must receive a specific increase of energy (heat of fusion); but once the disruption does occur, the atoms are free to move and cannot resist a shearing stress.

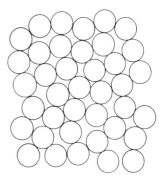

FIG. 3–37. Schematic structure of liquid metals. Interatomic distances are nearly uniform. There is no long-range order.

A crystal usually has a more efficient packing factor than a liquid, because energy is reduced as a liquid freezes, and shrinkage occurs. Exceptions occur in those materials which develop directional bonds within the crystal. For example, in ice, the H_2O molecules are so oriented that the hydrogen atoms serve as a bridge between adjacent molecules (Fig. 2–16); and in the absence of extra thermal energy, the oxygen atoms are repelled by one another. Thus ice does not have an efficient packing factor. The extra energy of fusion overcomes these special orientation patterns and permits the structure of ice to collapse into less volume. Of course, as further energy is introduced and the temperature is raised, thermal expansion again increases the volume (Fig. 12–34). In general, this expansion is a result of more "vacancies" or less efficient packing within the liquid structure.

3–23 Glasses. As indicated earlier, glasses are sometimes considered to be supercooled liquids, inasmuch as they are noncrystalline. However, only a few of the liquids which can be supercooled actually form glasses. Therefore, in order to make a distinction, we must look at the structure of glass more critically.

At high temperatures glasses form true liquids. The atoms have freedom to move around and respond to shear stresses. When a commercial glass at its liquid temperature is supercooled, there is thermal contraction caused by atomic rearrangements which produce more efficient packing of the atoms. This contraction

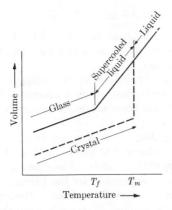

Fig. 3–38. Volume changes in glasses. When a liquid is supercooled below the melting temperature T_m, it contracts rapidly and continuously because the atoms develop more efficient packing arrangements. Below the glass transition, or fictive temperature T_f, no further rearrangement occurs, and the only further contraction is caused by reduced thermal vibrations.

(Fig. 3–38) is typical of all liquid glasses; however, with more extensive cooling, there is an abrupt change in the expansion coefficient of glasses. Below a certain temperature, called the *fictive temperature*, there is no further rearrangement of the atoms and the only contraction is a result of smaller thermal vibrations. This lower coefficient is comparable to the thermal coefficient in crystals where thermal vibrations are the only factor causing contraction.

The term *glass* applies to those materials which have the expansion characteristics of Fig. 3–38. Glasses may be either inorganic or organic, and are characterized by a short-range order (and an absence of long-range order). Figure 3–39(a) presents one of the simplest glasses (B_2O_3), in which each small boron atom fits among three larger oxygen atoms. Since boron has a valence of three and oxygen a valence of two, electrical balance is maintained if each oxygen atom is located between two boron atoms. As a result, a continuous structure of strongly bonded atoms is developed. Below the fictive temperature where the atoms are not readily rearranged, the fluid characteristics are lost and a noncrystalline solid exists. Such a solid has a significant resistance to shear stresses and therefore cannot be considered a true liquid.

 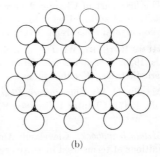

(a)   (b)

Fig. 3–39. Structure of B_2O_3. The glass (a) has short-range coordination order. The crystal (b) has long-range in addition to short-range order.

PHASES

3–24 Crystalline and amorphous phases. A phase has been defined as a *structurally homogeneous part of a material system.* This means that each phase of a material exhibits its own arrangement of atoms.

We have seen that a *crystalline phase* has a very definite atomic arrangement, with a long-range repetitious pattern that extends many atomic distances. The number of crystalline phases is immense because there are many permutations and combinations of atoms and groups of atoms.

Each *amorphous phase* has only a first-neighbor, or short-range, order. The contrast between crystalline and amorphous phases was shown in Fig. 3–39. Amorphous phases may be liquids or noncrystalline solids. Since amorphous phases have no long-range order, their atomic arrangements are less definite and permit greater compositional differences than do crystalline phases. However, this flexibility of atomic patterns reduces the number of possible amorphous phases that can coexist in a material. Some of the more common amorphous phases at room temperature are water, oil, mercury, bakelite, and glass.

Only one gaseous phase can exist in a given system. Because the atoms or molecules are far apart and randomly distributed in a gas, all kinds of vaporized materials may be mixed into one "structure."

References for Further Reading

3–1. ADDISON, W. E., *Structural Principles in Inorganic Compounds.* New York: John Wiley & Sons, 1961. Paperback. Nonmathematical presentation of crystalline compounds. For the undergraduate who wants more material on atom packing than is given in this text.

3–2. AZÁROFF, L. V., *Introduction to Solids.* New York: McGraw-Hill, 1960. Discusses crystals on the basis of atomic packing. Advanced undergraduate level.

3–3. BARRETT, C. S., *Structure of Metals.* New York: McGraw-Hill, 1952. Chapter 1 approaches materials from the viewpoint of the crystallographer. Crystals are systematized by their space groups. For the instructor or advanced student.

3–4. CULLITY, B. D., *Elements of X-ray Diffraction.* Reading, Mass.: Addison-Wesley, 1956. The first part of Chapter 2 pursues crystal structures slightly further than this book; easily read style. Useful to the advanced undergraduate student who wants to elaborate on crystal measurement techniques.

3–5. HUME-ROTHERY, W., *The Structure of Metals and Alloys.* London: The Institute of Metals, 1936. Chapter 2 considers the crystal structures of the elements on the basis of the periodic table. For the student.

3–6. MASON, C. W., *Introductory Physical Metallurgy.* Cleveland: American Society for Metals, 1947. Chapter 1 discusses the nature and formation of metal crystals. Introductory level.

3–7. *Metals Handbook.* Cleveland: American Society for Metals, 1948. Pages 16–19 give definitions of terms used in x-ray crystallography.

3–8. ROGERS, BRUCE A., *The Nature of Metals.* Ames, Iowa: Iowa State University Press; and Cleveland: American Society for Metals, 1951. Chapter 2 discusses how atoms are arranged in metals. Highly recommended as supplementary reading at the introductory level.

3–9. SINNOTT, M. J., *Solid State for Engineers.* New York: John Wiley & Sons, 1958. Chapter 2 presents crystals through the use of crystallographic laws. This chapter is on an introductory level.

3–10. WULFF, J., *et al.*, *Structures and Properties of Materials.* Cambridge, Mass.: M.I.T. Press, 1963. Multilithed. Chapters 4 and 5 present good sketches of atom packing and crystal structures.

Problems

(See Appendix D for crystal structures.)

3–1. Determine the molecular weight for each of the molecules of Fig. 3–4.
Answer: (a) 32 (b) 46 (c) 17 (d) 78 (e) 94 (f) 30 (g) 58 (h) 60 (i) 28 (j) 62.5

3–2. Sketch the structure of the various possible isomers for octane, C_8H_{18}.

3–3. Complete the following:

    (a) Methyl chloride (CH_3Cl) is to methane as _____ is to ethylene.

    (b) Vinyl alcohol (C_2H_3OH) is to ethylene as _____ is to ethane.

    (c) Styrene is to ethylene as phenol (C_6H_5OH) is to _____.

Answer: (a) vinyl chloride (b) ethanol (c) water

3–4. Complete the following:

    (a) Chloroprene ($CH_2:CH \cdot CCl:CH_2$) is to butadiene as _____ is to ethylene.

    (b) Ethylene glycol is to ethanol as _____ is to ethane.

    (c) Urea ($NH_2 \cdot CO \cdot NH_2$) is to acetone ($CH_3 \cdot CO \cdot CH_3$) as _____ is to methane.

3–5. What is the weight composition of chloroprene ($CH_2 : CH \cdot CCl : CH_2$)?
Answer: C = 54.3%; H = 5.65%; Cl = 40.1%

3–6. An organic compound contains 62.1 w/o carbon, 10.3 w/o hydrogen, and 27.6 w/o oxygen. Name a possible compound.

3–7. The average molecular weight of polyvinyl chloride molecules has been determined to be 9500 gm. How many mers does the average molecule contain?
Answer: 152 mers

3–8. Teflon is a polymer of tetrafluoroethylene (Appendix F). If there is an average of 742 mers per molecule, what is the average number of molecules per gm?

3–9. Show in tabular form the relationship between atom radii and unit-cell dimensions for face-centered, body-centered, and simple cubic metals:

	FCC	BCC	SC
Side of unit cell Face diagonal Body diagonal			

3–10. Lead is fcc and its atomic radius is 1.750×10^{-8} cm. What is the volume of its unit cell?

3–11. Silver is fcc and its atomic radius is 1.444 A. How large is the side of its unit cell?

Answer: 4.086 A

3–12. Gold is face-centered cubic. Its lattice constant is 4.078 A and its atomic weight is 197.0. (a) Calculate its density. (b) Check the value in a handbook.

3–13. Zinc has an hcp structure. The height of the unit cell is 4.94 A. The centers of the atoms in the base of the unit cell are 2.665 A apart. (a) How many atoms are there per hexagonal unit cell? (Show reasoning.) (b) What is the volume of the hexagonal unit cell? (c) Would the calculated density be greater or less than the true density of 7.135 gm/cm^3? (Justify your answer.)

Answer: (a) 6 (b) 9.1×10^{-23} cm^3 (c) 7.17 gm/cm^3. (This makes no allowance for imperfections.)

3–14. Sodium and chlorine weigh 22.990 and 35.453 gm per atomic weight, respectively. If the density is 2.165 gm/cm^3, calculate the dimensions of the unit cell of NaCl.

3–15. (a) What is the linear density of atoms along the [112] direction of iron? (b) of nickel?

Answer: (a) 1.42×10^7 atom/cm (b) 2.32×10^7 atom/cm

3–16. (a) How many atoms are there per square millimeter on a (100) plane of copper? (b) (110) plane? (c) (111) plane?

• 3–17. The lattice constant for a unit cell of aluminum is 4.049 A. (a) What is d_{220}? (b) d_{111}? (c) d_{200}?

Answer: (a) 1.431 A   (b) 2.338 A   (c) 2.025 A

• 3–18. Nickel is face-centered cubic with an atom radius of 1.245 A. (a) What is the d_{200} spacing? (b) the d_{220} spacing? (c) the d_{111} spacing?

• 3–19. The distance between (110) planes in a body-centered cubic structure is 2.03 A. (a) What is the size of the unit cell? (b) What is the radius of the atoms? (c) What might the metal be?

Answer: (a) 2.86 A   (b) 1.24 A   (c) bcc iron or Cr (not Ni)

• 3–20. A sodium chloride crystal is used to measure the wavelength of some x-rays. The diffraction angle is 5.2° for the d_{111} spacing of the chloride ions. What is the wavelength? (The lattice constant is 5.63 A.)

• 3–21. X-rays with a wavelength of 0.58 A are used for calculating d_{200} in nickel. The reflection angle is 9.5°. What is the size of the unit cell?

Answer: 3.52 A

3–22. MgO has the same structure as NaCl. Its density is 3.65 gm/cm^3. Use this data to calculate the length of the edge of the unit cell. (Do not use the radii of the ions, $Mg^{2+} = 0.78$ A or $O^{2-} = 1.32$ A, to arrive at your answer.)

3–23. Titanium has an hcp structure ($a = 2.956$ A, $c = 4.683$ A) below 880°C, and a bcc structure ($a = 3.32$ A) above this temperature. (a) Does titanium expand or contract as it is heated through 880°C? (b) Calculate the volume change in cm^3/gm.

Answer: (a) expands   (b) 0.007 cm^3/gm

3–24. Sodium has a bcc unit cell with $a = 4.29$ A. Show by an appropriate diagram (drawn approximately to scale) the arrangement of atoms in the crystal planes having Miller indices (110). • Calculate the spacing between these planes.

• Problems preceded by a bullet are based, in part, on optional sections.

3–25. The carbon atoms in diamond are arranged in cubic unit cells, with atoms at the ordinary face-centered positions and also at the following four positions (expressed in fractions of the a-, b-, and c-axes of the unit cell):

$$\tfrac{1}{4}, \tfrac{1}{4}, \tfrac{1}{4}, \quad \tfrac{3}{4}, \tfrac{3}{4}, \tfrac{1}{4}, \quad \tfrac{3}{4}, \tfrac{1}{4}, \tfrac{3}{4}, \quad \tfrac{1}{4}, \tfrac{3}{4}, \tfrac{3}{4}.$$

If the lattice parameter is 3.56 A, calculate the density of diamond.

Answer: 3.55 gm/cm^3

3–26. Assuming ions are spherical, (a) calculate the atomic packing factor of MgO; (b) of LiF. (They both have the structure shown in Fig. 3–10.)

3–27. Assuming atoms are spherical, calculate the atomic packing factor of diamond. (See Fig. 2–10b.)

Answer: 0.34

3–28. How many cubic angstroms are there per H_2O molecule (a) in ice? (b) in water at 4°C? (c) in water vapor at 100°C and 760 mm Hg pressure?

4

structural imperfections and atom movements

4–1 Introduction. The preceding chapter emphasized the regularity of atom arrangements within materials. For example, (1) one mer can show the structure of a whole polymer; (2) one unit cell shows the structure of the whole crystal; and (3) specific size ratios favor certain coordination numbers. These regularities simplify our analysis of materials because we are able to generalize from the individual unit. We are justified in doing this because most crystals and polymers have a structural repetition of the unit cells or the mers of which they are composed. However, there is a small fraction, sometimes less than one percent, which is not perfect. In this chapter, we shall look at these irregularities of structure quite closely, because the imperfections in materials often have a major influence on their properties.

Nonperfect materials are the result either of compositional variations or lattice imperfections, and these two topics will occupy most of this chapter. In addition, since the atoms of a crystal are not static (indeed they have mobility within a material), we shall discuss atom movements at the end of the chapter. These considerations—impurities, imperfections, and atom movements—enable us to anticipate properties more accurately than would be possible otherwise.

IMPURE PHASES

4–2 Solutions. Some metals used commercially for engineering purposes are pure. This is true of the copper utilized for electrical wiring, and the zinc coating on galvanized steel. Aluminum used for housewares contains only minor amounts of other elements; similarly, the Al_2O_3 phase in a spark-plug insulator is essentially pure Al_2O_3.

But in many cases, foreign elements are intentionally added to a material in order to enhance its properties. Brass is an example of copper which contains zinc. Likewise, a laser has Cr_2O_3 incorporated into the corundum (Al_2O_3) to produce a ruby. If such an addition becomes an integral part of the solid phase, the resulting phase is called a *solid solution*. Figure 4–1 shows a foreign atom which has become so much a part of the lattice that the crystal structure continues across the impurity.

4–3 Solid solutions in metals. Solid solutions form most readily when the solvent and solute atoms have similar sizes and electron structures. For example, brass is an alloy of copper and zinc. As individual metals these elements have atomic radii of 1.278 A and 1.332 A, respectively; they both have 28 subvalence

82

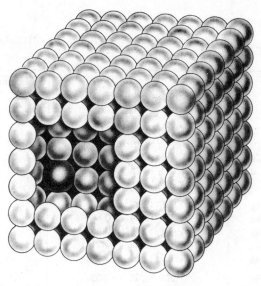

Fig. 4-1. Substituted atom. An atom can be replaced by another comparable atom. The impurity atom is considered to be a solute atom in a solid solvent. (Guy, A. G., *Elements of Physical Metallurgy*, Reading, Mass.: Addison-Wesley, 1959, p. 104.)

electrons and they each form crystal structures of their own with a coordination number of 12. Thus when zinc is added to copper it substitutes readily for the copper within the fcc lattice, until a maximum of nearly 40 percent of the copper atoms has been replaced. In this solid solution of copper and zinc, the distribution of zinc is entirely random (see Fig. 4-2).

Substitutional solid solutions. The solid solution described above is called a *substitutional* solid solution because the zinc atoms substitute for copper atoms in the crystal structure. This type of solid solution is quite common among various metal systems. The solution of copper and nickel to form *monel* is another example. In monel, any fraction of the atoms in the original copper structure may be replaced by nickel. Copper-nickel solid solutions may range from practically no

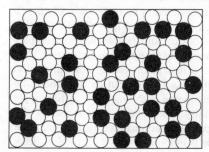

Fig. 4-2. Random substitutional solid solution (zinc in copper, i.e., brass). The crystal pattern is not altered. (Clyde Mason, *Introductory Physical Metallurgy.* Cleveland: American Society for Metals, 1947.)

TABLE 4–1

PERCENT SOLID SOLUTION VERSUS ATOMIC RADII OF METALS WITH SAME
STRUCTURE AS COPPER

Solute	Solvent	Size Ratio	Maximum solubility	
			w/o	a/o
Ni	Cu	$1.246/1.278 = 0.98$	100	100
Al	Cu	$1.431/1.278 = 1.12$	9	19
Ag	Cu	$1.444/1.278 = 1.14$	8	6
Pb	Cu	$1.750/1.278 = 1.37$	nil	nil
Ca	Cu	$1.965/1.278 = 1.54$	?	?
Ni	Ag	$1.246/1.444 = 0.86$	0.1	0.1
Cu	Ag	$1.278/1.444 = 0.88$	9	11
Al	Ag	$1.431/1.444 = 0.99$	6	20
Pb	Ag	$1.750/1.444 = 1.21$	5	3
Ca	Ag	$1.965/1.444 = 1.36$	nil	nil
Cu	Ni	$1.278/1.246 = 1.02$	100	100
Al	Ni	$1.431/1.246 = 1.14$	12	22
Ag	Ni	$1.444/1.246 = 1.16$	4	2
Pb	Ni	$1.750/1.246 = 1.40$	?	?
Ca	Ni	$1.965/1.246 = 1.58$	nil	nil
Ni	Al	$1.246/1.431 = 0.87$	0.05	0.03
Cu	Al	$1.278/1.431 = 0.90$	6	3
Ag	Al	$1.444/1.431 = 1.01$	48	19
Pb	Al	$1.750/1.431 = 1.22$	0.02	0.1
Ca	Al	$1.965/1.431 = 1.38$	nil	nil

nickel and almost 100 percent copper to almost 100 percent nickel and practically
no copper. All copper-nickel alloys are face-centered cubic.

On the other hand, there is a very definite limit to the amount of tin which may
replace copper to form *bronze*, and still maintain the face-centered cubic structure
of the copper. Tin in excess of the maximum amount of *solid solubility* must form
another phase. This *solubility limit* will be considered in more detail in Chapter 9.

If there is to be extensive replacement in a substitutional type of solid solution,
the atoms must be nearly the same size. Nickel and copper have a complete
range of solutions because their structures are the same and their radii are 1.246 A
and 1.278 A, respectively. As the difference in size increases, less substitution
can occur. Only 20 percent of copper atoms can be replaced by aluminum, because the latter has a radius of 1.431 A as compared with only 1.278 A for copper.
Table 4–1 shows the maximum solid solubility in copper of various metals with
the same fcc structure as copper. These data are summarized in Fig. 4–3. Extensive solid solubility rarely occurs if there is more than about 15 percent differ-

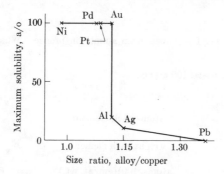

FIG. 4–3. Solid solubility versus atom size ratio (copper-base alloys with elements which are normally fcc).

ence in radius between the two kinds of atoms. There is further restriction on solubility when the two components have different structures or valences.

It should be noted from Table 4–1 that solubility is given in both *atomic percent* and *weight percent*. The limiting factor is the number of substituted atoms rather than the weight of the atoms which are substituted. However, engineers ordinarily express composition as weight percent. It is therefore necessary to know how to express weight percent in terms of atomic percent, and vice versa.*

Example 4–1

An alloy contains 80 w/o (weight percent) Al and 20 w/o Mg. What is the atomic percent (a/o) of each?

Answer: Calculation basis: 100 gm alloy.

Aluminum		Magnesium
80	gm of each element	20
$\dfrac{80}{26.98} (6.02 \times 10^{23})$	atoms of each element	$\dfrac{20}{24.3} (6.02 \times 10^{23})$
	$\left(\dfrac{\text{gm}}{\text{gm/at. wt.}}\right)\left(\dfrac{\text{atoms}}{\text{at. wt.}}\right)$	
$= (2.97)(6.02 \times 10^{23})$	atoms	$= (0.823)(6.02 \times 10^{23})$

Total atoms $= (2.97 + 0.823)(6.02 \times 10^{23})$.

$$Al = \frac{(2.97)(6.02 \times 10^{23})}{(3.793)(6.02 \times 10^{23})}$$

$$Mg = \frac{(0.823)(6.02 \times 10^{23})}{(3.793)(6.02 \times 10^{23})}$$

$$= 78.3 \text{ a/o Al}.$$

$$= 21.7 \text{ a/o Mg}.$$

---

* *Unless stated otherwise,* liquids and solids are expressed in weight percent and gases are expressed in volume or molecular percent.

Example 4–2

20 a/o Al is substituted for copper in an aluminum bronze. What weight percent is present?

Answer: Calculation basis: 100 atoms.

Copper		Aluminum
80	atoms each element	20
$\dfrac{80(63.54)}{6.02 \times 10^{23}}$	weight each element	$\dfrac{20(26.98)}{6.02 \times 10^{23}}$
	$\dfrac{(\text{atoms}/100)(\text{gm/at. wt.})}{\text{atoms/at. wt.}}$	
$= \dfrac{5090}{6.02 \times 10^{23}}$	$= \text{gm/100 atoms}$	$= \dfrac{540}{6.02 \times 10^{23}}$

$$\text{Total weight} = \frac{5090 + 540}{6.02 \times 10^{23}}.$$

$$\text{Cu} = \frac{5090/(6.02 \times 10^{23})}{5630/(6.02 \times 10^{23})} \qquad\qquad \text{Al} = 100 - 90.4$$

$$= 90.4 \text{ w/o Cu.} \qquad\qquad\qquad = 9.6 \text{ w/o Al.}$$

Ordered solid solutions. Figure 4–2 shows a *random substitution* of one atom for another in a crystal structure. In such a process, the chance of one element occupying any particular atomic site in the crystal is equal to the atomic percent of that element in the alloy. In this case, there is no order in the substitution of the two elements.

However, it is not unusual to find an *ordering* of the two types of atoms into a specific arrangement. Figure 4–4 shows an ordered structure in which each black "atom" is surrounded by white "atoms." Such ordering is more common at lower

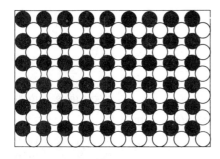

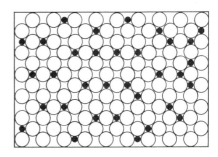

FIG. 4–4. Ordered substitutional solid solution. (Clyde Mason, *Introductory Physical Metallurgy.* Cleveland: American Society for Metals, 1947.)

FIG. 4–5. Interstitial solid solution (carbon in fcc iron). (Clyde Mason, *Introductory Physical Metallurgy.* Cleveland: American Society for Metals, 1947.)

temperatures, since greater thermal agitation tends to destroy the orderly arrangement.

Interstitial solid solutions. In another type of solid solution, illustrated in Fig. 4–5, a small atom may be located in the interstices between larger atoms. Carbon in iron is an example. At temperatures below about 1670°F, pure iron occurs as a body-centered cubic structure. Above 1670°F, there is a temperature range in which iron has a face-centered cubic structure. In the face-centered cubic lattice, a relatively large unoccupied "hole" exists in the center of the unit cell. Carbon, being an extremely small atom, can move into this hole to produce a solid solution of iron and carbon. When the iron has a body-centered cubic structure at lower temperatures, the interstices between the iron atoms become much smaller, and consequently the solubility of carbon in body-centered cubic iron is relatively small.

4–4 Solid solutions in ionic compounds. Substitutional solid solutions can occur in ionic phases as well as in metals in their solid form. In ionic phases, just as in the case of solid metals, atom or ion size is important. A simple example of an ionic solid solution is shown in Fig. 4–6. The structure is that of MgO (Fig. 3–10) in which the Mg^{2+} ions have been replaced by Fe^{2+} ions. Inasmuch as the radii of the two ions are 0.78 A and 0.83 A, complete substitution is possible. On the other hand, Ca^{2+} ions cannot be similarly substituted for Mg^{2+} because their radius of 1.06 A is comparatively large.*

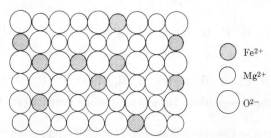

FIG. 4–6. Substitutional solid solution in a compound; Fe^{2+} is substituted for Mg^{2+} in the MgO structure.

An additional requirement, which is more stringent for solid solutions of ceramic compounds than for similar solid solutions of metals, is that the valence charges on the replaced ion and the new ion must be identical. For example, it would be difficult to replace the Mg^{2+} in MgO with an Li^+, although the two have identical radii, because there would be a net deficiency of charges. Such a substitution could be accomplished only if there were other compensating changes in charge. (See Section 8–5.)

---

* See Appendix D for ionic radii.

Compositional changes may also exist in nonstoichiometric compounds. These will be discussed in Section 4–7 under defect structures.

Example 4–3

Calculate the MgO/FeO weight ratio of the solid solution shown in Fig. 4–6.

Answer: Ion ratio (by count):

$$Mg^{2+}/Fe^{2+} = \tfrac{17}{10} = \text{mole ratio.}$$

$$\text{Weight MgO} = \frac{17(24.3 + 16.0)}{6.02 \times 10^{23}} = \frac{685}{AN}.$$

$$\text{Weight FeO} = \frac{10(55.8 + 16.0)}{6.02 \times 10^{23}} = \frac{718}{AN}.$$

$$\text{Weight ratio of MgO/FeO} = \tfrac{685}{718} = 0.96.$$

4–5 Copolymerization. The polymeric analog to solid solution is found in *copolymerization.* A polymer chain may contain more than one type of mer. Recall from Figs. 3–8 and 3–9 in Section 3–8 that ethylene and vinyl chloride have closely related structures; the only difference between them is that vinyl chloride has a chlorine atom in place of a hydrogen atom. Polymers may be made which incorporate monomers of both types to give mixed mers along the chain (Fig. 4–7).

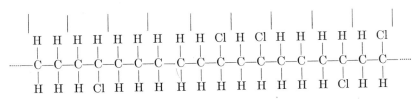

FIG. 4–7. Copolymerization. The polymer contains more than one type of mer.

We shall observe in Chapter 7 that copolymers have properties different from a polymer made from either of the contributing monomers.

CRYSTAL IMPERFECTIONS

4–6 Introduction. Lattice imperfections are found in most crystals. In some cases when missing atoms, displaced atoms, or extra atoms are involved, there may be *point defects.* The *line defect* involves the edge of an extra plane of atoms. Finally, imperfections may be *boundaries,* either between adjacent crystals or at the external surfaces of the crystal.

Such imperfections influence many of the characteristics of materials, such as mechanical strength, electrical properties, and chemical reactions, and we shall discuss these in subsequent chapters.

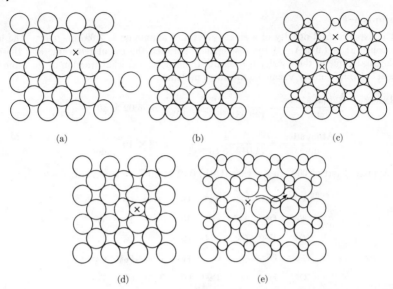

FIG. 4–8. Point defects. (a) Vacancies. (b) Di-vacancy (two missing atoms). (c) Schottky defect (ion pair vacancies). (d) Interstitialcy (compare with Fig. 4–5). (e) Frenkel defect (ion displacement).

4–7 Point defects. *Vacancies.* The simplest point defect is a vacancy, which simply involves a missing atom (Fig. 4–8a) within a metal. Such defects can be a result of imperfect packing during the original crystallization, or they may arise from thermal vibrations of the atoms at elevated temperatures (Section 4–12), because as thermal energy is increased there is an increased probability that individual atoms will jump out of their position of lowest energy. Vacancies may be single, as shown in Fig. 4–8(a), or two or more of them may condense into a di-vacancy (Fig. 4-8b) or a tri-vacancy.

Schottky imperfections are closely related to vacancies but are found in compounds which must maintain a charge balance (Fig. 4–8c). They involve vacancies of pairs of ions of opposite charges. Both vacancies and Schottky defects facilitate atomic diffusion (Section 4–11).

Interstitialcies. An extra atom may be lodged within a crystal structure, particularly if the atomic packing factor is low (Section 3–11). Such an imperfection produces atomic distortion (Fig. 4–8d) unless the interstitial atom is smaller than the rest of the atoms in the crystal (Fig. 4–5).

Frenkel defects. An ion displaced from the lattice into an interstitial site (Fig. 4–8e) is called a Frenkel defect. Close-packed structures have fewer interstitialcies and Frenkel defects than vacancies and Schottky defects, because additional energy is required to force the atoms into the new positions.

Example 4–4

The experimental density of a single crystal of aluminum is 2.697 gm/cm^3. The lattice constant is 4.049 A. If the discrepancy between the calculated value and the experimental value of the density is a result of vacancies, (a) what fraction of the atoms is absent? (b) how many vacancies are there per cm^3?

Answer: $\dfrac{\text{Actual atoms}}{\text{cm}^3} = \dfrac{2.697}{(26.98)/(6.02 \times 10^{23})} = 6.02 \times 10^{22} \dfrac{\text{atoms}}{\text{cm}^3}.$

$\dfrac{\text{Atom sites}}{\text{cm}^3} = \dfrac{4}{(4.049 \times 10^{-8})^3} = 6.03 \times 10^{22} \dfrac{\text{sites}}{\text{cm}^3}.$

(a) Approx. 1 out of 600 sites is vacant; (b) $0.01 \times 10^{22} = 10^{20}$ vacancies/cm^3.

O^{2-}	Fe^{2+}	O^{2-}	Fe^{2+}	O^{2-}	Fe^{2+}	O^{2-}	Fe^{2+}
Fe^{2+}	O^{2-}	Fe^{2+}	O^{2-}	Fe^{2+}	O^{2-}	Fe^{2+}	O^{2-}
O^{2-}	Fe^{3+}	O^{2-}	Fe^{2+}	O^{2-}	$\square$	O^{2-}	Fe^{2+}
Fe^{2+}	O^{2-}	$\square$	O^{2-}	Fe^{3+}	O^{2-}	Fe^{3+}	O^{2-}
O^{2-}	Fe^{3+}	O^{2-}	Fe^{2+}	O^{2-}	Fe^{2+}	O^{2-}	Fe^{2+}
Fe^{2+}	O^{2-}	Fe^{2+}	O^{2-}	Fe^{2+}	O^{2-}	Fe^{2+}	O^{2-}

FIG. 4–9. Nonstoichiometric compound (Fe$_{<1}$O). The charge balance is maintained by the presence of a cation vacancy. (Compare with the structure of the stoichiometric compound MgO in Fig. 3–10.)

Nonstoichiometric compounds. Either vacancies or interstitialcies must exist in those phases which are not rational compounds. For example, wüstite (Fe$_{<1}$O) has the same basic lattice as MgO and NaCl (Fig. 3–10). However, in this compound there is an equilibrium number of ferric ions:

$$Fe^{2+} \leftrightarrows Fe^{3+} + e^-. \tag{4-1}$$

A cation vacancy must be present for every two Fe^{3+} ions which are present in order to maintain electronic balance (Fig. 4–9). Thus we may write

$$3Fe^{2+} = 2Fe^{3+} + \square, \tag{4-2}$$

as a structural equation where the symbol, $\square$, indicates a vacancy.

Example 4–5

In our example of wüstite (Fig. 4–9), the ratio of Fe^{3+} to Fe^{2+} may be as high as 0.5. (a) With this ratio, what fraction of the normal cation sites is vacant? (b) What is the weight fraction of oxygen in this composition?

Answer: Basis: 100 Fe^{2+} ions.

(a)   50 Fe^{3+} ions and 25 $\square$.
            Total cation sites $= 100 + 50 + 25 = 175.$
            Vacancy fraction $= 25/175 = 0.14.$

(b)
$$100 \text{ Fe}^{2+} \text{ ions} = 100 \text{ O}^{2-} \text{ ions}$$
$$\underline{50 \text{ Fe}^{3+} \text{ ions} = 75 \text{ O}^{2-} \text{ ions}}$$
$$150 \text{ Fe} \quad \text{ions} \qquad 175 \text{ O}^{2-} \text{ ions}$$

Weight of oxygen $= (175)(16.0/\text{AN}) = 2800/\text{AN}.$
Weight of iron $= (150)(55.8/\text{AN}) = 8370/\text{AN}.$

Therefore, weight fraction of oxygen $= \dfrac{2800/\text{AN}}{(2800 + 8370)/\text{AN}} = 0.251.$

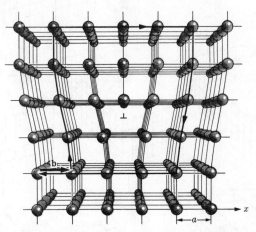

FIG. 4–10. Edge dislocation. A linear defect occurs at the edge of an extra plane of atoms. (Guy, A. G., *Elements of Physical Metallurgy*, Reading, Mass.: Addison-Wesley, 1959, page 110.)

4–8 Line defects (dislocations). The most common type of line defect within a crystal is a dislocation. An *edge dislocation* is shown in Fig. 4–10. It may be described as an edge of an extra plane of atoms within a crystal structure. Zones of compression and of tension accompany an edge dislocation (Fig. 4–11) so that there is a net increase in energy along the dislocation. The displacement distance for atoms around the dislocation is called the *Burgers vector*. This vector is at right angles to the edge dislocation line.

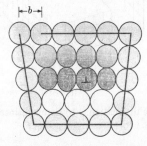

FIG. 4–11. Dislocation energy. Atoms are under compression (darker) and tension (lighter) adjacent to the dislocation. The displacement vector (Burgers vector) is perpendicular to the dislocation line.

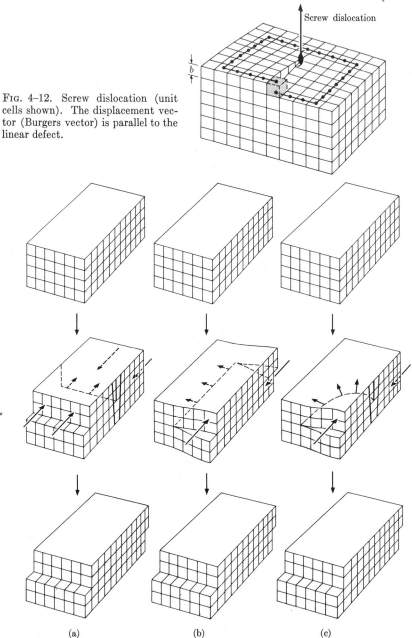

FIG. 4–12. Screw dislocation (unit cells shown). The displacement vector (Burgers vector) is parallel to the linear defect.

FIG. 4–13. Dislocation formation by shear. (a) Edge dislocation. (b) Screw dislocation. (c) Dislocation loop with edge and screw components.

A *screw dislocation* has its displacement, or Burgers vector, parallel to the linear defect (Fig. 4–12). Shear stresses are associated with adjacent atoms; therefore, extra energy is involved here as in the previously cited edge dislocations.

Dislocations of both types are closely associated with crystallization. Edge dislocations, for example, arise when there is a slight mismatch in the orientation of adjacent parts of the growing crystal so that an extra row of atoms is introduced or eliminated. As shown in Fig. 4–12, a screw dislocation provides for easy crystal growth because additional atoms and unit cells can be added to the "step" of the screw. Thus the term screw is very apt, because the step swings around the axis as growth proceeds.

Dislocations are associated with deformation as well as with crystallization. We see this in Fig. 4–13, where shear is seen to introduce either an edge dislocation or a screw dislocation. Both lead to the same final displacement and are in fact related through the dislocation loop which forms.

4–9 Boundaries. *Surfaces.* Crystalline imperfections may extend in two dimensions as a boundary. The most obvious boundary is the external *surface*. Although we may visualize a surface as simply a terminus of the crystal structure, we should quickly appreciate the fact that the atoms on the surface are not fully comparable to the atoms within a crystal. The surface atoms have neighbors on only one side (Fig. 4–14); therefore they have higher energy than do the internal atoms. This energy may be rationalized with Fig. 2–18 by noting that if additional atoms were to be deposited onto the surface atoms, energy would be released just as it was for the combination of two individual atoms. However, we find our best visible evidence of this surface energy in the case of liquid drops which have spherical shape to minimize the surface area (and therefore the surface energy) per unit volume. Surface adsorption provides additional evidence of the energy differential at the surface.

Surface

FIG. 4–14. Surface atoms (schematic). Since these atoms are not entirely surrounded by others, they possess more energy than internal atoms.

Grain boundaries. Although a material such as copper in an electric wire may contain only one phase, it contains many crystals of various orientations. These individual crystals are called *grains*. The shape of a grain in a solid is usually controlled by the presence of surrounding grains. Within any particular grain, all of the atoms are arranged with one orientation and one pattern, characterized by

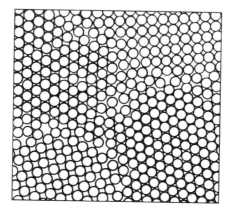

FIG. 4–15. Grain boundaries. Note the area of disorder at the boundary. (Clyde Mason, *Introductory Physical Metallurgy.* Cleveland: American Society for Metals, 1947.)

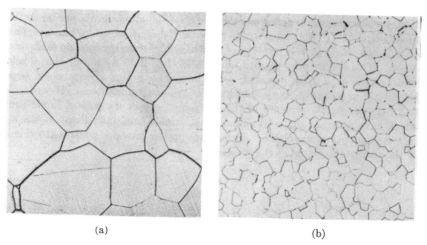

(a)   (b)

FIG. 4–16. Grain boundaries. (a) Molybdenum (×250) (O. K. Riegger). (b) High-density periclase, MgO (×250). (Gardner, R. E., and G. W. Robinson, Jr., "Improved Method for Polishing Ultra-High Density MgO," *Journ. Amer. Ceram. Soc.,* **45**, 1962, page 46.)

the unit cell. However, at the *grain boundary* between two adjacent grains there is a transition zone which is not aligned with either grain (Fig. 4–15).

When a metal is observed under a microscope, although we cannot see the individual atoms illustrated in Fig. 4–15, we can quite readily locate the grain boundaries if the metal has been treated by *etching*. First the metal is smoothly polished so that a plane, mirrorlike surface is obtained, and then it is chemically

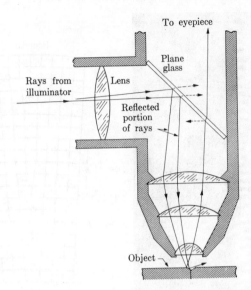

FIG. 4-17. Grain boundary observation. The metal has been polished and etched. The corroded boundary does not reflect light through the microscope. (Bruce Rogers, *The Nature of Metals*. Cleveland: American Society for Metals, 1951.)

attacked for a short period of time. The atoms in the area of transition between one grain and the next will dissolve more readily than other atoms and will leave a line which can be seen with the microscope (Fig. 4-16); the etched grain boundary does not act as a perfect mirror as does the remainder of the grain (Fig. 4-17).

We may consider that the grain boundary is two-dimensional, although it actually has a finite thickness of 2 to 10 or more atomic distances. The mismatch of the orientation of adjacent grains produces a less efficient packing of the atoms along the boundary. Thus the atoms along the boundary have a higher energy than those within the grains. This accounts for the more rapid etching along the boundaries described above. The higher energy of the boundary atoms is also important for the nucleation of polymorphic phase changes (Section 3-18). The lower atomic packing along the boundary favors atomic diffusion (Section 4-13), and the mismatch between adjacent grains interferes with the progression of dislocation movements (Fig. 4-13).

• *Tilt boundaries.* There is a second type of boundary which is sufficiently distinct from those shown in Fig. 4-16 to warrant separate discussion. It is called a small-angle, or *tilt*, boundary and is in reality a series of aligned dislocations (Fig. 4-18). There is relatively little energy associated with this type of boundary; however, it has importance because it tends to anchor dislocation movements which would normally contribute to plastic deformation.

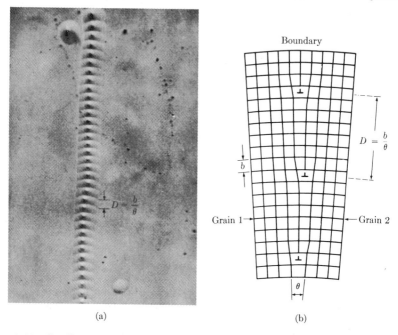

(a)   (b)

FIG. 4–18. Small-angle boundary. (a) Germanium crystal etched to show the ends of edge dislocations (×1000). (b) Schematic representation, showing only the unit cells. The angle θ has been exaggerated. (Courtesy F. L. Vogel, Jr.)

• Example 4–6

The small-angle boundary shown in Fig. 4–18 is essentially the (111) plane of germanium with the displacement vector in the [111] direction. Determine the angle across this boundary from the dislocation spacing as indicated by the etch pits.

Answer: Germanium has the structure of diamond (Fig. 2–10b).

The displacement vector is in the [111] direction to give a displacement value of d_{111} of $4(2R)/3 = 8(1.225)/3 = 3.26$ A.

With a (×1000) magnification, the etch pits are about 0.0025 mm (25,000 A) apart. Thus

$$\sin \theta = 3.26/25,000 = 0.00013;$$
$$\theta = 27''.$$

ATOM MOVEMENTS

4–10 Introduction. The atoms of a crystal become static only at absolute zero (−273°C). Under that condition the atoms settle down to their lowest energy positions among their neighbors (Fig. 2–18). As the temperature is increased, thermal vibrations displace the atoms in a random manner about these low-energy positions.

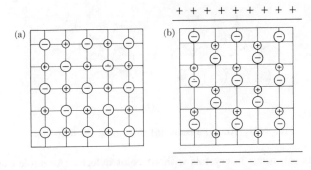

FIG. 4–19. Ionic displacement in an electric field (a) without external field; (b) with external field.

Atomic displacements can also occur under electric or magnetic fields if the charges of the atoms respond to the field. For example, atoms in the form of ions are easily displaced in an electric field, as shown in Fig. 4–19. Thermal vibrations will be superimposed over these displacements, but the center of movement has been shifted from the normal position.

Atomic movements to new locations will result when the temperature or field is high enough to provide energy to lift the atom out of its original lattice point. This will be the subject of the next sections.

4–11 Mechanisms of atom movements. Many of the atomic movements within solids involve point defects. The vacancy mechanism requires little energy and moves an atom from an occupied site into an adjacent vacant site. The interstitial mechanism moves atoms among the neighboring atoms of the crystal structure (Fig. 4–20).

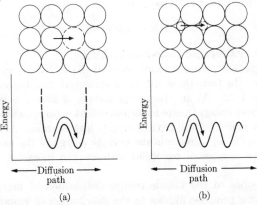

FIG. 4–20. Atom movements. (a) Vacancy mechanism. (b) Interstitial mechanism. Additional energy is required if the normal interatomic distance is *either* increased *or* decreased. (Cf. Fig. 2–18b.)

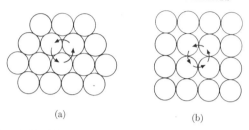

FIG. 4–21. Ring diffusion: (a) three-ring, (b) four-ring.

Movements can occur in crystals without point defects. A simple exchange of the two nearest neighbors is theoretically possible; however, it is probably less common than ring diffusion, which involves the simultaneous movements of 3 or 4 atoms (Fig. 4–21).

Any particular atom has equal probability for movement in each of the three coordinate directions. A net amount of diffusion occurs only when there is a gradient in concentration, potential, or pressure (Section 4–13).

• **4–12 Thermal energy distribution.** The total kinetic energy KE of a gas increases in proportion to the temperature T, so that the equation,

$$KE = \tfrac{3}{2}RT, \tag{4-3}$$

is appropriate. The R of this equation is the same gas constant that is usually encountered in introductory chemistry courses. Its value and units are 1.987 cal/mole·°C. For our purposes, it is advantageous to look at individual molecules and thus replace R with kN where N is Avogadro's number, 6.02×10^{23} atoms/mole, and k is 0.33×10^{-23} cal/molecule·°C. This is more commonly converted to 1.38×10^{-16} erg/molecule·°K, so that

$$KE = (\tfrac{3}{2}kT)N. \tag{4-4}$$

This latter value of k is called *Boltzmann's constant*.

The above equation does not imply that all the molecules within a gas have the same energy. In fact, there will be a statistical distribution of energies as indicated in Fig. 4–22. At any particular instant of time a very few molecules will have nearly zero energy; many molecules will have energies near to the average energy, and some molecules will have extremely high energies. As the temperature increases, there is (1) an increase in the average energy of the molecules, and (2) an increase in the number of molecules with energies in excess of any specified value.

The above applies to the kinetic energy distribution of molecules in a gas. However, the same principle applies to the distribution of vibrational energy of atoms in a liquid or solid. Specifically, at any particular instant of time, a very few atoms will have zero energy; many atoms will have energies near the average energy, and some atoms will have extremely high energies.

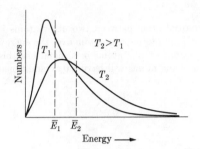 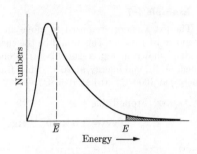

FIG. 4–22. Energy distribution. Both the average energy $\overline{E}$ and the fraction with energies in excess of a specified level are increased as the temperature T is increased.

FIG. 4–23. Energies. The ratio of the number of high-energy atoms (shaded) to total number of atoms is an exponential function of $(-E/kT)$ when $E \gg \overline{E}$.

Our interest will be directed toward those atoms which have high energies. Very often we should like to know the probability of atoms possessing more than a specified amount of energy, e.g., what fraction of the atoms has energy greater than E of Fig. 4–23. The statistical solution to this problem has been worked out by Boltzmann as follows:

$$\frac{n}{N_{\text{tot}}} = f(e^{-(E-\overline{E})/kT}), \qquad (4\text{–}5)$$

where k is the previously described Boltzmann's constant of 1.38×10^{-16} erg/°K. The number n of atoms with an energy greater than E out of the total number N_{tot} which are present is a function of the temperature T. This equation is applicable when E is considerably in excess of the average energy $\overline{E}$, so that the equation reduces to

$$\frac{n}{N_{\text{tot}}} = Me^{-E/kT}, \qquad (4\text{–}6)$$

where M is a constant. As presented, the value of E must be expressed in ergs/atom; however, conversions may be made from other units by means of Table 4–2.

TABLE 4–2

CONVERSION RELATIONSHIPS

R =	1.987 cal/mole·°K
k =	1.38×10^{-16} erg/atom·°K
1 cal =	4.185×10^{7} ergs
1 erg =	0.624×10^{12} ev
1 gm atomic weight =	6.02×10^{23} atoms
1 cal/mole·°C =	0.694×10^{-16} erg/atom·°K

Example 4–7

The extra energy required to move an interstitial atom between two other atoms is found to be 1.0 ev. [This would be the energy required to move an atom over the energy "ridge" shown in Fig. 4–20(a).] (a) If one atom out of 10^{20} atoms in a metal has this much additional energy at 20°C, what fraction of the atoms will have 1.0 ev additional energy at 1000°C? (b) at 1050°C?

Answer: From Table 4–2,

$$1 \text{ ev} = 1.6 \times 10^{-12} \text{ erg,}$$

(a) $$M = \frac{n/N_{\text{tot}}}{e^{-E/kT}},$$

$$\ln M = -(2.3)(20) + \frac{1.6 \times 10^{-12}}{(1.38 \times 10^{-16})(293)} = -46 + 39.4 = -6.6.$$

At 1000°C,

$$\ln \frac{n}{N_{\text{tot}}} = -6.6 - \frac{1.6 \times 10^{-12}}{(1.38 \times 10^{-16})(1273)} = -6.6 - 9.1 = -15.7;$$

$$\frac{n}{N_{\text{tot}}} = \frac{1}{6,500,000}.$$

(b) At 1050°C,

$$\ln \frac{n}{N_{\text{tot}}} = -6.6 - \frac{1.6 \times 10^{-12}}{(1.38 \times 10^{-16})(1323)} = -15.35;$$

$$\frac{n}{N_{\text{tot}}} = \frac{1}{4,500,000}.$$

[Note: Although the above example shows that there is only a remote probability that an atom will have the energy necessary for the indicated atom movement, we must recall that a cubic centimeter contains about 10^{23} atoms. Therefore, at any particular point of time, a significant number of atoms may have this required energy, and thus a considerable number of atom movements can occur.]

4–13 Atomic diffusion. In uniform surroundings, each of the six atoms (of three dimensions) adjacent to the vacancy of Fig. 4–20(a) has an equal probability of moving into the hole. Stated conversely, the vacancy has an equal probability of moving in the six coordinate directions. Likewise, the interstitial atom of Fig. 4–20(b) has an equal probability of moving in the six coordinate directions.

Activation energy. If the atoms are to change locations, the "energy ridges" of Fig. 4–20 must be overcome. The energy required to overcome them (along with the energy of defect formation) is called the activation energy of diffusion. As shown in Fig. 4–20(a), energy is required to pull the atom away from its present neighbors; with interstitial diffusion, energy is required to force the atom into closer contact with neighboring atoms as it moves among them. The activation energy varies with a number of factors. For example, a small atom has a lower activation energy than a large atom or a molecule. Likewise, interstitial movements require more energy than vacancy movements. Finally, high activation

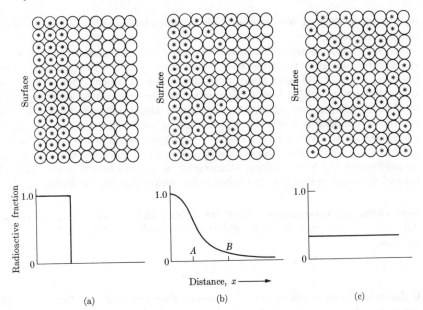

FIG. 4-24. Self-diffusion. Here radioactive nickel (Ni^{59}) has been plated onto the surface of nonradioactive nickel. (a) Time, $t = t_0$. (b) Diffusion gradient, $t_0 < t < t_\infty$. (c) Homogenized, $t = t_\infty$.

energies are required for diffusion in high-melting-point, strongly bonded materials such as tungsten, boron carbide, and corundum (Al$_2$O$_3$).

Self-diffusion. Normally, no net diffusion is observed in a pure, single-phase material, because the atom movements are random, and the atoms are all identical. However, through the use of radioactive isotopes, it is possible to identify the diffusion of atoms within their own structure, i.e., *self-diffusion.* For example, radioactive nickel (Ni^{59}) can be plated onto the surface of normal nickel. With time, and depending on the temperature, there is progressive self-diffusion of the tracer isotopes into the bulk of the nickel [and a counterdiffusion of the untagged atoms toward the surface (Fig. 4-24)]. The mechanisms of diffusion include all those shown in Figs. 4-20 and 4-21, as well as diffusion along grain boundaries where the structure is more open (Fig. 4-15).

Concentration gradients. The homogenization process shown in Fig. 4-24 must be interpreted as follows. Although there is equal probability that an individual atom will move in each direction, the concentration gradient favors a net movement of the tracer atoms toward the right. At point A in Fig. 4-24(b), there are more tagged atoms than there are at point B. Thus, even with the same probability per atom for the tagged atoms at A to move right as for the tagged atoms at B to move left, the difference in numbers produces a differential in movements and increases the uniformity and the randomness in the structure. (A converse description would have been written if our attention had been focused on the non-radioactive atoms.)

The description of self-diffusion and the counter-diffusion shown in Fig. 4–24 can also be applied to the presence of solute atoms within a solid solution. For example, if nickel had been plated onto the surface of copper, atomic diffusion would bring about nickel homogenization within the copper after sufficient time at elevated temperature. However, the rate of nickel diffusion down the concentration gradient is higher in copper than in nickel because the activation energy needed to move a nickel atom among copper atoms is less than that required to move nickel atoms among nickel atoms. [This difference would be anticipated because the lower melting temperature of copper (1083°C versus 1455°C for nickel) indicates that the Cu-Cu bonds are weaker than the Ni-Ni bonds.]

4–14 Diffusion coefficients.   Both the atomic and the statistical aspects of diffusion may be summed up by diffusion equations, called Fick's Laws. The first law,

$$J = -D \frac{dC}{dx},$$ (4–7a)

is important to us; it states that the amount of material, i.e., the flux J moving across a unit surface in unit time, is proportional to the concentration gradient dC/dx. The proportionality constant D is called the *diffusion coefficient*, and is expressed in cm^2/sec as shown below:

$$\frac{atoms}{cm^2 \cdot sec} = \frac{(cm^2/sec)(atoms/cm^3)}{cm}.$$ (4–7b)

The negative sign of Eq. (4–7a) indicates that the flux is in a down-gradient direction.

The second diffusion law, which relates the change in concentration with time, dC/dt, states that

$$\frac{dC}{dt} = D \left(\frac{d^2C}{dx^2} \right).$$ • (4–8)

From this law it is easy to appreciate why the final stages of homogenization (Fig. 4–24) are slow. The rate decreases as the concentration gradient is erased.

Diffusion coefficients vary with the nature of the solute **atoms**, with the nature of the solid structure, and with changes in temperature. Several examples are given in Table 4–3. Some reasons for the various values of Table 4–3 are: (1) Higher temperatures provide higher diffusion coefficients, because the atoms have higher thermal energies and therefore greater probabilities of being activated over the energy barrier between atoms (Fig. 4–20). (2) Carbon has a higher diffusion coefficient in iron than does nickel in iron because the carbon atom is a small one (Appendix D). (3) Copper diffuses more readily in aluminum than in copper because the Cu-Cu bonds are stronger than the Al-Al bonds (as evidenced by their melting temperatures). (4) Atoms have higher diffusion coefficients in bcc iron

TABLE 4–3

DIFFUSION COEFFICIENTS
(Calculated from data in Table 4–4.)

Solute	Solvent (host structure)	Diffusion coefficient, cm^2/sec	
		500°C (930°F)	1000°C (1830°F)
1. Carbon	fcc iron	$(10^{-10.3})*$	$10^{-6.5}$
2. Carbon	bcc iron	$10^{-7.2}$	$(10^{-5.2})$
3. Iron	fcc iron	$(10^{-19.5})$	$10^{-11.8}$
4. Iron	bcc iron	$10^{-16.1}$	$(10^{-9.5})$
5. Nickel	fcc iron	$(10^{-19.0})$	$10^{-11.6}$
6. Manganese	fcc iron	$(10^{-19.6})$	$10^{-12.0}$
7. Zinc	Copper	$10^{-12.2}$	$10^{-8.0}$
8. Copper	Aluminum	$10^{-9.3}$	Melts
9. Copper	Copper	$10^{-15.1}$	$10^{-8.8}$
10. Silver	Silver (crystal)	$10^{-12.9}$	Melts
11. Silver	Silver (grain boundary)	$10^{-6.9}$	Melts
12. Carbon	hcp-titanium	$10^{-11.5}$	$(10^{-6.8})$

* Parentheses indicate that the phase is metastable.

than in fcc iron because the former has a lower atomic packing factor (0.68 versus 0.74). (We shall observe later that the fcc structure has larger interstitial holes; however, the passageways between the holes are smaller than in the bcc structure.) (5) The diffusion proceeds more rapidly along the grain boundaries because this is a zone of crystal imperfections (Fig. 4–15).

• **Example 4–8**

Carbon was diffused into the surface of a rod of fcc iron (density, 7.8 gm/cm^3) so that the following gradient exists at 1000°C:

Location below surface, cm	0.00	0.02	0.04	0.06	0.08	0.10	0.12	0.14	0.16
Carbon, w/o	1.20	0.94	0.75	0.60	0.50	0.42	0.36	0.32	0.30

(a) At 1000°C, how many carbon atoms per minute pass the location 0.01 cm below the surface of a rod 6 in. long by 1.0 in. dia.? (b) The 0.10 location? (c) What happens to the extra carbon of answer (a)?

Answer: Let us first determine the surface of the rod. We have

$$\text{Surface area} = 6\pi \text{ in}^2 = 122 \text{ cm}^2.$$

Also,

$$\frac{dm/dt}{A} = J = -D\frac{dC}{dx}, \qquad \Delta m = -DA\frac{\Delta C}{\Delta x}\Delta t.$$

(a) At 0.00 cm,

$$1.20 \text{ w/o} = 0.0936 \frac{\text{gm}}{\text{cm}^3},$$

$$\left(\frac{0.0936}{12}\right)(0.6 \times 10^{24}) = 4.68 \times 10^{21} \frac{\text{atoms}}{\text{cm}^3}.$$

At 0.02 cm,

$$0.94 \text{ w/o} = 3.67 \times 10^{21} \frac{\text{atoms}}{\text{cm}^3},$$

$$\Delta m = -\frac{10^{-6.5} \text{ cm}^2}{\text{sec}} 122 \text{ cm}^2 \left[\frac{(4.68 - 3.67) \times 10^{21} \text{ atoms/cm}^3}{0.02 \text{ cm}}\right] \cdot 60 \text{ sec}$$

$$= -\frac{(3.1 \times 10^{-7})(1.22 \times 10^2)(1.01 \times 10^{21})(60)}{0.02} = -11.5 \times 10^{19} \text{ atoms}.$$

TABLE 4–4

DIFFUSION CONSTANTS*
($\log D = \log D_0 - Q/2.3RT$)

Solute	Solvent (host structure)	D_0, cm^2/sec	Q, cal/mole
1. Carbon	fcc iron	0.21	33,800
2. Carbon	bcc iron	0.0079	18,100
3. Iron	fcc iron	0.58	67,900
4. Iron	bcc iron	5.8	59,700
5. Nickel	fcc iron	0.5	66,000
6. Manganese	fcc iron	0.35	67,500
7. Zinc	copper	0.033	38,000
8. Copper	aluminum	2.0	33,900
9. Copper	copper	11.0	57,200
10. Silver	silver (crystal)	0.72	45,000
11. Silver	silver (grain boundary)	0.14	21,500
12. Carbon	hcp-titanium	2.24	41,600

* Principally from Guy, A. G., *Physical Metallurgy for Engineers*, Reading, Mass.: Addison-Wesley (1962) page 251.

The answer is negative because the atoms move toward the lower concentrations.

(b) At 0.08 cm,

$$0.50 \text{ w/o} = 1.95 \times 10^{21} \, \frac{\text{atoms}}{\text{cm}^3}.$$

At 0.12 cm,

$$0.36 \text{ w/o} = 1.40 \times 10^{21} \, \frac{\text{atoms}}{\text{cm}^3},$$

$$\Delta m = -\frac{(10^{-6.5})(113)(0.55 \times 10^{21})(60)}{0.04} = -2.9 \times 10^{19} \text{ atoms}.$$

(c) The weight percentage of carbon in the subsurface iron is increasing.

• *Diffusion coefficient versus temperature.* The discussion in Section 4–12 related the distribution of thermal energy to temperature. It was noted in Eq. (4–6) that the numbers of atoms which have more than a specified amount of energy increase as an exponential function of temperature. Thus it is only natural that the diffusion coefficient will have a similar relationship:

$$D = D_0 e^{-Q/RT},$$

or

$$\ln D = \ln D_0 - \frac{Q}{RT}, \tag{4–9}$$

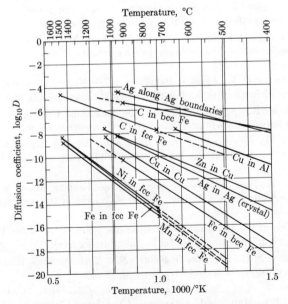

FIG. 4–25. Diffusion coefficients versus temperature. (See Example 4–9.)

where R has the previous meaning of 1.987 cal/mole·°K, temperature is in °K, D is the diffusion coefficient, Q is an activation energy for diffusion, and D_0 (or ln D_0) is a constant which includes several factors that are essentially unaffected by temperature. Included in this constant are such items as the jump distance and the vibration frequency of the atom, both of which contribute to the movement efficiency of those atoms which do have enough energy for diffusion jumps. The values of D_0 and Q are unique for each diffusion system. Table 4–4 provides these values for the several diffusion couples which are shown in Table 4–3.

• **Example 4–9**

Plot the values of the diffusion coefficients versus temperature for the diffusion couples of Tables 4–3 and 4–4.

Answer: See Fig. 4–25. [*Note:* when log D is plotted versus reciprocal temperature, the slope of the curve is $-Q/2.3R$, and log D_0 is the value of log D at $1/T = 0$.]

References for Further Reading

4–1. ADDISON, W. E., *Structural Principles in Inorganic Compounds.* New York: John Wiley & Sons, 1961. Paperback. Chapter 8 presents defects in the solid state. Emphasis is directed to nonstoichiometric compounds.

4–2. A.S.T.M., *Major Effects of Minor Constituents on the Properties of Materials,* S.T.P. 304. Philadelphia: American Society for Testing and Materials, 1961. A series of five articles on the effect of impurities on properties. For the advanced undergraduate.

4–3. AZÁROFF, L. V., *Introduction to Solids.* New York: McGraw-Hill, 1960. Chapter 5 discusses imperfections in the packings and movements of atoms. Advanced undergraduate level.

4–4. BIRCHENALL, C. E., *Physical Metallurgy.* New York: McGraw-Hill, 1959. Diffusion is discussed in Chapter 9. For the advanced undergraduate and the instructor.

4–5. CHALMERS, B., *Physical Metallurgy.* New York: John Wiley & Sons, 1959. Chapter 4 discusses imperfections in crystals. Advanced undergraduate level.

4–6. GUY, A. G., *Elements of Physical Metallurgy.* Reading, Mass.: Addison-Wesley, 1959. Chapter 11 gives a thorough presentation of diffusion in metals. Advanced undergraduate level.

4–7. GUY, A. G., *Physical Metallurgy for Engineers.* Reading, Mass.: Addison-Wesley, 1962. Chapter 8 introduces diffusion. It also makes use of the error function for unsteady state transfer.

4–8. JASTRZEBSKI, Z. D., *Engineering Materials.* New York: John Wiley & Sons, 1959. Diffusion is introduced in Chapter 3. Introductory level.

4–9. SHEWMON, P. G., *Diffusion in Solids.* New York: McGraw-Hill, 1963. A concise treatise on diffusion. For the instructor.

4–10. WULFF, J., *et al., Structures and Properties of Materials.* Cambridge, Mass.: M.I.T. Press, 1963. Multilithed. Chapter 6 of Vol. I and Chapter 5 of Vol. II present imperfections and diffusion at an introductory level.

Problems

4-1. An alloy contains 85 w/o copper and 15 w/o tin. Calculate the atomic percent (a/o) of each element.

Answer: 8.7 a/o Sn; 91.3 a/o Cu

4-2. There is 5 a/o magnesium in an Al-Mg alloy. Calculate the w/o magnesium.

4-3. Consider Fig. 4-5. to be an interstitial solution of carbon in fcc iron. What is the w/o carbon present?

Answer: 6% carbon. [*Note:* In reality, the maximum solubility is 2%C.]

4-4. Consider Fig. 4-2 to be a substitutional solid solution of cadmium and magnesium. What is the w/o Cd present if (a) Cd is the more prevalent atom? (b) Mg is the more prevalent atom?

4-5. (a) An alloy containing 75 w/o Cu and 25 w/o Zn has _____ a/o Cu and _____ a/o Zn. (b) How much would each unit cell of this alloy weigh? (c) The density of this brass is 8.5 gm/cm^3. What is the volume, and (d) what is the mean lattice constant of each unit cell?

Answer: (a) 75.6 a/o Cu, 24.4 a/o Zn; (b) 4.25×10^{-22} gm/uc; (c) 5×10^{-23} cm^3/uc; (d) 3.68 A

4-6. An alloy contains 80 w/o Ni and 20 w/o Cu in substitutional fcc solid solution with $a = 3.54$ A. Calculate the density of this alloy.

4-7. If 1.0% carbon, by weight, is present in an fcc iron, what percent of the unit cells have carbon atoms?

Answer: 19% of the unit cells have carbon.

4-8. Determine the radius of the largest atom which can be located in the interstices of bcc iron without crowding. [*Hint:* The center of the largest hole is located at $\frac{1}{2}$, $\frac{1}{4}$, 0.]

4-9. Calculate the radius of the largest atom which can exist interstitially in fcc iron without crowding. [*Hint:* Sketch the (100) face of several adjacent unit cells.]

Answer: 0.53 A

4-10. A copolymer contains 67 mer % vinyl alcohol and 33 mer % ethylene. What is (a) the a/o carbon? (b) the w/o carbon?

4-11. A copolymer of vinyl chloride and vinyl acetate contains equal mer percents of each. What is the w/o of each?

Answer: 42.1 w/o vinyl chloride, 57.9 w/o vinyl acetate

4-12. If all the iron ions of Fig. 4-6 were changed to Ni ions, what would be the w/o MgO?

4-13. (a) What is the w/o FeO in the solid solution of Fig. 4-6? (b) the w/o Fe^{2+}? (c) of O^{2-}?

Answer: (a) 51 w/o (b) 39.8 w/o (c) 30.8 w/o

4-14. In copper at 1000°C, one out of every 473 lattice sites is vacant. If these vacancies remain in the copper when it is cooled to 20°C, what will be the density of the copper?

4-15. What is the density of Fe$_{<1}$O, if the Fe^{3+}/Fe^{2+} ratio is 0.14. [Fe$_{<1}$O has the structure of NaCl; and $(r_{Fe} + R_O)$ averages 2.15 A.]

Answer: 5.72 gm/cm^3

4–16. (a) What is the length of the Burgers vector in the [112] direction of iron? (b) of nickel?

4–17. (a) What is the direction and length of the shortest Burgers vector on the (110) plane of aluminum? (b) the shortest Burgers vector on the (110) plane of MgO?

Answer: (a) [$1\bar{1}0$], 2.862 A (b) [$1\bar{1}0$], 2.97 A

4–18. (a) What is the direction and length of the shortest Burgers vector on the (100) plane of aluminum? (b) the shortest Burgers vector on the (100) plane of MgO?

• 4–19. Small-angle (tilt) boundaries are present in some copper because extra (100) planes of atoms give a series of aligned edge dislocations. If the tilt boundary accounts for a 1° mismatch between the adjacent crystal areas, how many angstroms are there between succeeding dislocations?

Answer: 206 A

• 4–20. Repeat Problem 4–19, with the tilt boundary originating from extra (110) planes.

• 4–21. At 800°C, 1 out of 10^{10} atoms, and at 900°C, 1 out of 10^9 atoms has appropriate energy for movements within a solid. (a) What is the activation energy in cal/mole? (b) At what temperature will 1 out of 10^8 atoms have the required amount of energy?

Answer: (a) 57,000 cal/mole (b) 1027°C

• 4–22. Select a random plane in polycrystalline silver and assume that (1) the grains are cubic, and (2) the grain boundary is 50 atoms wide. (a) What grain size would permit the same number of silver atoms to cross this plane within the grains as cross the plane along the boundaries at 500°C? (b) at 900°C? [*Hint:* the random plane lies within the boundary zone in proportion to the volume of the boundary zone.]

4–23. Zinc has diffused into copper and assumed a gradient of approximately: w/o Zn = $10/(x + 0.1)$, where x is the number of cm from surface S. (a) At 500°C, how many Zn atoms per second cross a plane which is parallel to S, but 1 mm below the surface? 1 cm below the surface? (b) The same, but at 1000°C?

Answer: (a) 1.5×10^{11} atoms/cm²·sec at 0.1 cm, 4×10^9 atoms/cm²·sec at 1 cm; (b) 2×10^{15} atoms/cm²·sec at 0.1 cm, 6×10^{13} atoms/cm²·sec at 1 cm.

4–24. Repeat Problem 4–23, for Cu atoms [w/o Cu = $100 - 10/(x + 0.1)$].

• 4–25. Aluminum is to be diffused into a silicon single crystal. At what temperature will the diffusion coefficient be 10^{-10} cm²/sec? [$Q = 73,000$ cal/mole and $D_0 = 1.55$ cm²/sec.]

Answer: 1296°C

4–26. At 800°C, $D = 10^{-13}$ cm²/sec for the self-diffusion of germanium in its own structure. The diffusion coefficient of copper in germanium is 3×10^{-9} cm²/sec. Account for the difference of more than 30,000/1.

• Problems preceded by a bullet are based, in part, on optional sections.

5

electronic structures
and processes

5–1 Introduction. Electromagnetic fields interact with the charged particles in materials to produce (1) *conductivity*, (2) *dielectric polarization*, and (3) *magnetic characteristics*. These controllable results are useful to the engineer because they permit him to design electrical circuits for power supplies, communications, and equipment controls. The charged particles in the materials, the *ions* and *electrons*, normally have vibrational movements that are wavelike in character. Electric and magnetic fields superimpose directional forces of attraction onto these movements so that they are no longer entirely random.

The extent to which dielectric and magnetic behavior and conductivity may be varied is affected by (1) the energies of the electrons in the valence (outer) shells of the atoms, (2) the spin of the electrons in the atoms, and (3) the crystalline or the amorphous structure of the material. Knowledge of these relationships permits prediction of the electric and magnetic properties of a material so that trial-and-error selection is not necessary. For example, recent advances in semiconductor applications for such equipment as transistors and solar batteries originated in the theoretical predictions of the behavior of electrons in materials.

ELECTRICAL CONDUCTIVITY

5–2 Definitions. Electrical conductivity is the movement of electrical charge from one location to another. Since the charge may be carried by ions or electrons, whose *mobility* varies in different materials, there is a full "spectrum" of conductivities, ranging from highly conducting metals to nearly perfect insulators (Fig. 5–1).

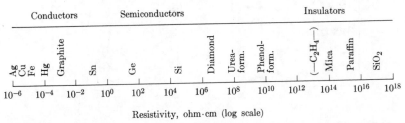

Fig. 5–1. Resistivity spectrum. Semiconductors have intermediate resistivity that may be altered appreciably by minor changes in their electronic structure. Resistivity is the reciprocal of conductivity.

In *ionic conductivity*, the carriers may be either negative or positive ions. In *electronic conductivity*, the carriers are electrons or electron "holes" (Section 5–6). The charge per electron is 1.6×10^{-19} coulomb (i.e., ampere-seconds). Since ions contain either a deficiency or an excess of electrons, the charge per ion is an integral multiple of 1.6×10^{-19} coulomb.

Conductivity, σ, may be expressed as a product of (1) the number of charge carriers n in a material, (2) the charge q carried by each, and (3) the mobility μ of the carriers. That is,

$$\sigma = nq\mu, \tag{5-1}$$

where the units are

$$\frac{1}{\text{ohm·cm}} = \left(\frac{\text{carriers}}{\text{cm}^3}\right)\left(\frac{\text{coulombs}}{\text{carrier}}\right)\left(\frac{\text{cm/sec}}{\text{volt/cm}}\right).$$

Since coulombs equal ampere-seconds and volts equal ampere-ohms, the above units balance. The mobility of a carrier is its net velocity per unit voltage gradient.

5–3 Ionic conductivity.   It was shown in Fig. 4–20 that atoms and ions can be moved from one lattice site to another. The probability of such movement is low unless the temperature is high. At high temperatures a small fraction of the atoms may possess sufficient energy to pass over the "energy ridge" that was shown. Ions have a greater opportunity to be moved over the "energy ridge" when they move with the electric field. This increased probability results from the fact that the ion is accelerated and receives more energy as it vibrates in the favorable direction of the electric field. Conversely, it is decelerated as it moves in the unfavorable direction so that the probability of an "ion jump" in the reverse direction is reduced. The result is a net ion movement in one direction, which gives ionic conductivity.

The ionic conductivities in solids are naturally low because there is only a very low probability that the energy will be available for the ion jumps. Ionic conductivity is higher in liquids, for reasons that are self-evident, since the place-

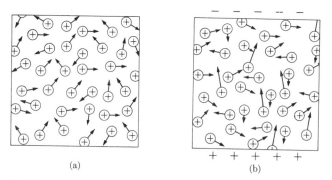

(a)   (b)

Fig. 5–2. Positive ion movement. (a) In the absence of an external electric field, the movements of these ions are random. (b) The presence of an external field results in a net movement of the positive ions toward the negative electrode.

ment of neighboring atu.
is required for ion moveme
statistical balance of the mov.

Example 5-1

At 550°C the conductivity of solid N.
because the Na^+ ions are smaller than Cl
bility of the Na^+ ions under these conditions ii

Answer:

$$n = \frac{4Na^+/unit}{[(2)(0.98 + 1.81) \times 10^{-8}]^3}$$

$$= 2.3 \times 10^{22} \text{ carriers/cm}^3.$$

From Eq. (5-1),

$$\mu_i = \frac{\sigma}{qn} = \frac{2.0 \times 10^{-6}/\text{ohm·cm}}{(1.6 \times 10^{-19} \text{ amp·sec})(2.3 \times 10^{22}/\text{cm}^3)}$$

$$= 5.5 \times 10^{-10} \frac{\text{cm}^2}{\text{volt·sec}}.$$

- *Ionic conductivity versus temperature.* Ionic conductivity increases at higher temperatures because the mobility of the ions is increased through increased diffusion rates. As expected, there is a relationship between ionic mobility, μ_i and the diffusion coefficient, D, of Eq. (4-9).

$$\mu_i = \frac{qD}{kT}, \tag{5-2a}$$

where q is the electric charge, k is Boltzmann's constant, and T is absolute temperature. The units are:

$$\frac{\text{cm/sec}}{\text{volt/cm}} = \frac{(\text{amp·sec})(\text{cm}^2/\text{sec})}{(\text{erg}/°K)(°K)}. \tag{5-2b}$$

A final unit balance is possible because 1 erg $= 10^{-7}$ joule $(= 10^{-7}$ volt·amp·sec).

5-4 Electronic conductivity.

Certain comparisons may be made between ionic and electronic conductivities. (1) In each case, a charge of 1.6×10^{-19} coulomb is involved. (2) This charge is accelerated as it moves in one direction in the electric field, and decelerated as it reverses its direction. (3) Both the ion and the electron have a mobility which was defined in Section 5-2 as the net velocity (cm/sec) that arises from a specific potential gradient (volt/cm).

Metals. Valance electrons in metals are not anchored to any specific atom (Section 2-9). Thus their energy permits them to move among the atoms in all directions of the crystal structure with equal velocity (Fig. 5-3a). However, if an electric field is superimposed on the material, those electrons moving toward the positive pole are given added energy and are accelerated (Fig. 5-3b). As the electron moves in this direction it will sooner or later encounter the local electric fields around atoms and either be deflected or reflected. Any resulting movement toward the negative electrode consumes energy, and therefore the velocity in that

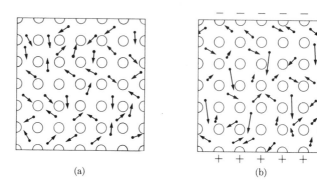

(a)   (b)

FIG. 5–3. Electron movements in metals. (a) When there is no external electric field, the movements of electrons in a metal crystal are random. (b) Within an external electric field, electrons are accelerated when they move toward the positive plate and decelerated when they move toward the negative plate. The net movement of electrons is toward the positive plate.

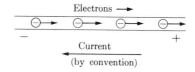

FIG. 5–4. Electric current. Since an electric field accelerates the movements of electrons and ions in one direction and decelerates them in the opposite direction, a net electron movement is produced. By convention, the direction of the current is considered to be opposite to that of the electrons.

direction is decreased. The net effect is an electron movement toward the positive pole (Fig. 5–4).

Because of its small mass per unit charge, an electron exhibits significant and rapid changes in velocity as it responds to the electric field. The limiting factor on the mobility of the electron is the number of deflections or reflections which occur. Longer mean free paths between changes in direction permit more acceleration *and* deceleration, so that the drift velocity and electron mobility increase. When we study metals in Chapter 6, we shall see that factors such as thermal agitation, impurities, and plastic deformation all reduce the conductivity of a metal, because these imperfections mean that there are irregularities in the electrical fields within a metal. Irregularities reduce the mean free paths of electrons, the mobility of an electron, and finally the electrical conductivity.

5–5 Insulators. We have already concluded that both ionically and covalently bonded materials are extremely poor conductors because the electrons are not free to leave their host atoms (Section 2–16). There is an analogy between electron movements in insulators and atom movements in materials (Section 4–11). If we use carbon in the form of diamond as an example (Fig. 5–5), it can be shown that

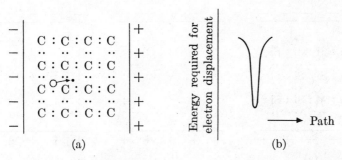

FIG. 5–5. Electron movements in a covalent solid (diamond). (a) Two-dimensional representation (cf. Fig. 2–10). (b) Energy required for electron movement. The low-energy point for each electron is within the covalent bond pair. The depth of this energy trough is more than 6 ev in diamond.

more than six ev of energy must be supplied to remove each electron from its low-energy position so that it may transport a charge. The probability that an electron will receive the energy necessary to move it from its stable position is extremely low. Higher temperatures can give some additional energy to the electrons; however, even with this added amount of energy, there is only a small chance for electron movements, and the resistivity in diamond remains high.

The energy requirements for electron movements are not the same in all covalent solids. For example, silicon, germanium, and gray tin all have the same structure as diamond (Fig. 2–10), but have higher conductivities (and thus lower resistivities), as shown in Table 5–1. The conductivity which does exist in these solids is called *intrinsic conduction* because it is a result of electron movements in pure materials. Electronic imperfections are formed which may be compared to the Frenkel defect of Fig. 4–8(e). Specifically, a charge is displaced from the lowest energy position.

TABLE 5–1

ENERGY REQUIREMENTS VERSUS RESISTIVITY

Element	Energy, ev	Resistivity, at 68°F, ohm·cm
C (diamond)	> 6.0	> 10^6
Si	1.0	6×10^4
Ge	0.7	50
Sn (gray)	0.08	< 1

5–6 Semiconductors. By definition, semiconductors have a resistivity between that of conductors and that of insulators (Fig. 5–1). However, for a semiconductor to be useful in an electronic circuit, its resistivity must be within one or two orders of magnitude of 1 ohm·cm. Thus the intrinsic conduction of germanium

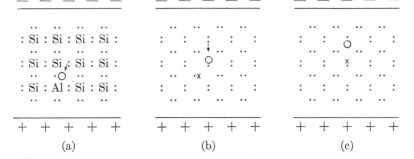

FIG. 5–6. Silicon plus aluminum. Aluminum contains three valence electrons. Its presence in the structure leaves an electron "hole" in the covalent bonds of the diamond-cubic structure. As the electron moves into the hole, new holes are opened up. As a result, the "holes" move toward the negative electrode.

and silicon (about 10^{-2} and 10^{-4} ohm·cm^{-1}, respectively) has limited usefulness in electronic circuits.

The conductivity of a material may be increased through the addition of electronic imperfections. For example, consider silicon which contains an impurity atom of aluminum (Fig. 5–6). Silicon has the same cubic structure as carbon does in diamond (Fig. 2–10). The presence of an aluminum atom leaves an electron vacancy or an *electron hole* within the structure. Adjacent electrons can move into this position when an electric field is applied across the material. Of course, as an adjacent electron moves into this hole, the hole moves toward the negative electrode. In this case the electron hole is considered to be a positive charge carrier giving rise to a *p-type* semiconduction.

Extrinsic conduction arising from the presence of an electronic imperfection may be *p*-type, or it may be of an *n-type*. If phosphorus is present in place of aluminum within the silicon structure, the fifth valence electron is not in a low-energy covalent bond (Fig. 5–7). Therefore, only a small amount of additional energy is needed to accelerate the electron as it moves across an electric field.

Example 5–2

A silicon semiconductor contains 0.00001 a/o aluminum and has a resistivity of 2.45 ohm·cm. (a) How many electron holes are there per cm^3? (b) What is their mobility?

Answer: (a) There is 1 electron hole per aluminum atom; therefore there is 1 electron hole per 10^7 silicon atoms. From Appendix D:

$$\text{Si atoms/cm}^3 = \frac{(2.4 \text{ gm/cm}^3)(6.02 \times 10^{23} \text{ atoms/mole})}{28.1 \text{ gm/mole}} = 5.13 \times 10^{22}/\text{cm}^3;$$

$$\text{holes/cm}^3 = 5.13 \times 10^{15}/\text{cm}^3.$$

(b)
$$\mu = \frac{1}{\rho q n} = \frac{1}{(2.45 \text{ ohm·cm})(1.6 \times 10^{-19} \text{ coul})(5.13 \times 10^{15}/\text{cm}^3)}$$

$$= 500 \frac{\text{cm}^2}{\text{ohm·coul}} = 500 \frac{\text{cm/sec}}{\text{volt/cm}}.$$

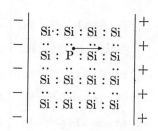

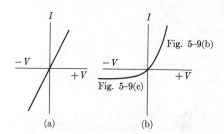

FIG. 5–7. Silicon plus phosphorus. Because phosphorus has five valence electrons, one electron cannot fit into the covalent bond of the regular diamond structure. It is thus in a high-energy position and requires very little additional energy to be accelerated across the electric field.

FIG. 5–8. Amperage versus voltage. (a) Ohmic conductor. The current is not sensitive to the potential direction. (b) Asymmetrical conductor. A current response is a function of both the potential direction and the potential.

• *Junctions.* We have had semiconductors in the form of radio "crystals" for some time. However, the controlled use of semiconductors has become much more important within recent years with the increased understanding of the conduction mechanism. Our attention will be directed briefly to the p-n junction as an example of one of many semiconductor devices.

The p-n junction is a diode rectifier because it has asymmetrical current/voltage characteristics. This is shown in Fig. 5–8(b) where a comparison is made with an ohmic conductor. In an ohmic conductor, the value of dV/dI is constant (equal to resistance). Most semiconductors have nonlinear resistance characteristics, particularly if the direction of the voltage gradient is reversed. The resulting asymmetry is used for a rectification, as indicated in Fig. 5–9. The junction per-

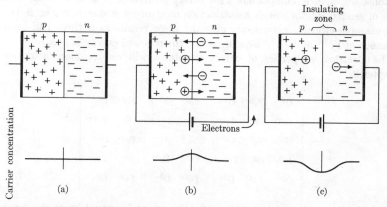

FIG. 5–9. Examples of p-n junctions. (a) No potential gradient; (b) and (c) opposing potential gradients. In (c) the charge carriers are removed from the junction so that an insulating zone remains. (Minus signs indicate electron carriers; plus signs indicate electron-hole carriers.)

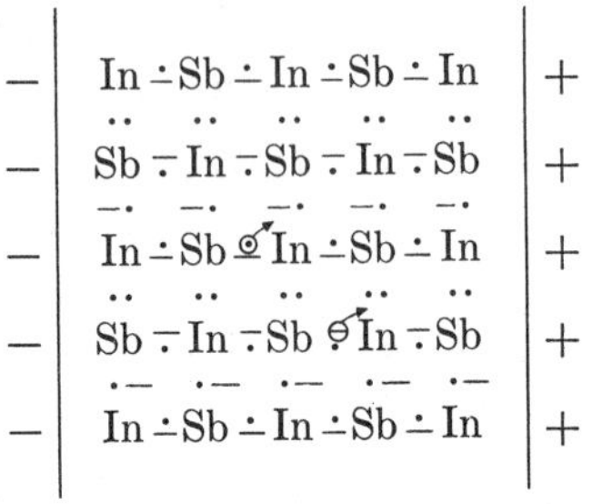

$$
\begin{array}{c|c}
- & \text{In} \div \text{Sb} \div \text{In} \div \text{Sb} \div \text{In} \\
- & \text{Sb} \mp \text{In} \mp \text{Sb} \mp \text{In} \mp \text{Sb} \\
- & \text{In} \div \text{Sb} \ \text{In} \div \text{Sb} \div \text{In} \\
- & \text{Sb} \mp \text{In} \mp \text{Sb} \ \text{In} \mp \text{Sb} \\
- & \text{In} \div \text{Sb} \div \text{In} \div \text{Sb} \div \text{In} \\
\end{array}
\begin{array}{c}
+ \\ + \\ + \\ + \\ + \\
\end{array}
$$

FIG. 5-10. Group III–V covalent semiconductor. Indium is a Group III element, antimony a Group V one. InSb averages four valence electrons per atom, and therefore has the characteristics of silicon or diamond (Fig. 5–5). The dots indicate electrons originally from Sb, and the dashes those originally from In.

mits charge movements in one direction but not in the other, because an insulating zone is formed. In effect, the carriers have been displaced from the junction zone and movements in opposition to the field are required to transfer charge.

• *Compound semiconductors.* Semiconduction need not be limited to the Group IV elements. The same electronic structures can be developed by combinations of Group III and Group V elements. Figure 5–10 shows one example of a III-V compound of indium and antimony. The galena (PbS) of the early crystal sets is a II-VI semiconductor. Basically, the requirement for a satisfactory covalent semiconductor compound is that it have an average of four electrons per atom. Therefore it is possible to devise such semiconductors as I-III-VI$_2$ or II-V$_2$ compounds, but there are limitations. If the elements are strong ion formers, the necessary covalent bond cannot be maintained. Thus, I-VII compounds, such as sodium chloride, and II-VI compounds, such as magnesium oxide, are too highly ionic to be good semiconductors. Silver iodide forms a weak I-VII compound because neither element has strong ionizing characteristics.

Nonstoichiometric compounds with defect structures (Fig. 4–9) form another type of semiconductor. Such a conduction mechanism is shown in Fig. 5–11. In this example electron movements give the same results as if there had been an exchange of Fe^{2+} and Fe^{3+} ions; however, the required energy is less.

The electrical properties of defect structures will receive more attention in Chapter 8.

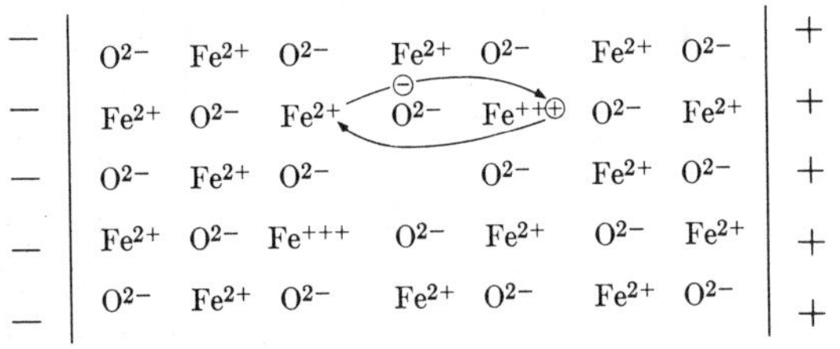

$$
\begin{array}{c|ccccccc|c}
- & O^{2-} & Fe^{2+} & O^{2-} & Fe^{2+} & O^{2-} & Fe^{2+} & O^{2-} & + \\
- & Fe^{2+} & O^{2-} & Fe^{2+} & O^{2-} & Fe^{++} \oplus & O^{2-} & Fe^{2+} & + \\
- & O^{2-} & Fe^{2+} & O^{2-} & & O^{2-} & Fe^{2+} & O^{2-} & + \\
- & Fe^{2+} & O^{2-} & Fe^{+++} & O^{2-} & Fe^{2+} & O^{2-} & Fe^{2+} & + \\
- & O^{2-} & Fe^{2+} & O^{2-} & Fe^{2+} & O^{2-} & Fe^{2+} & O^{2-} & + \\
\end{array}
$$

FIG. 5-11. Defect semiconductor (Fe$_{<1}$O). Charge can be carried by an electron moving from one iron ion to another. This has the same effect as an interchange of the Fe^{2+} and Fe^{3+} ions.

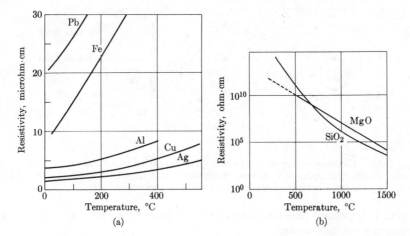

FIG. 5–12. Electronic resistivity versus temperature. (a) Metals. Resistivity increases with temperature. (b) Ceramic compounds. Resistivity decreases with temperature. (Note that there is a difference in scales.)

5–7 Electronic resistivity versus temperature.   There is a contrast between the temperature dependence of resistivity in metals and in materials containing semimetallic or nonmetallic elements.   In metals, where there are numerous free electrons, higher temperature introduces greater thermal agitation, which reduces the mean free path of electron movement with a consequent reduction in electron mobility and an increase in resistivity.   The value of $d\rho/dT$ is positive in a metal (Fig. 5–12a).   The values for $d\rho/dT$ are negative in other materials because an increase in temperature supplies the thermal energy which frees additional charge carriers (Fig. 5–12b).

ELECTRON ENERGIES

5–8 Introduction.   With minor modifications, the explanation in the preceding section is the classical one for describing electronic conductivity.   It is quite useful in this form; however, there are certain shortcomings.   Why, for example, are there such major differences between the conductivities of metals and insulators? How can magnetic behavior of materials be explained?   What accounts for the luminescence of certain materials?   To account for these and other features of electrical behavior, we must consider the energy characteristics of electrons.

Energy levels.   Individual atoms may be described as having energy shells.   A highly simplified sketch such as shown in Fig 5–13(a) is commonly used.   The refinement of the energy relationships showing sub-shells (Fig. 5–13b and c) is often desirable because it permits us to use the fact that only two electrons can share the same energy level.   The simplified version of this sketch (Fig. 5–13c) will be used in subsequent figures.

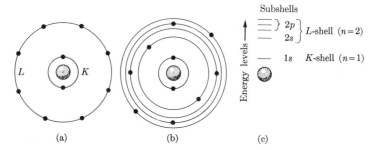

FIG. 5–13. Electron energy levels (neon). (a) Simplified energy shells. (b) Energy levels. Shells contain more than one energy subshell if they have more than two electrons. (c) Energy-level plot of the subshells within an individual atom.

Several important principles may be stated about the energies of the electrons *within any one isolated atom:*

(1) There are specific electronic energy levels around each atom (Fig. 5–13c). Electrons cannot occupy spaces between these levels.

(2) Electrons fill the lowest energy levels first. A specific quantity of energy, called a *quantum* of energy, must be supplied to move an electron to the next higher level.

(3) At most, only two electrons may occupy any one energy level (Fig. 5–13b).

(4) These two electrons with equal energy values are "mirror images" of each other; that is, their characteristics indicate that one "spins" in one direction and the other in the opposite direction (Fig. 5–14).

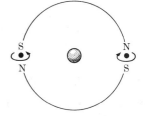

FIG. 5–14. Electron spins. Two electrons may occupy the same level because they have opposite magnetic characteristics. This can be most simply described as electron "spins" in opposite directions.

The above principles and Fig. 5–13 apply to individual atoms which are far enough from other atoms to behave independently. In such a situation the electrons in like levels of identical atoms have equal amounts of energy (Fig. 5–13c).

5–9 Energy bands. The outermost (valence) electrons of adjacent atoms interact when the atoms are brought into close proximity (e.g., in a crystal).* Since no more than two interacting electrons may have the same energy level, new levels must be established (Fig. 5–15) which are discrete, but only infinitesimally

---

* Nonvalence electrons do not interact significantly at any realizable interatomic distance because they are too closely associated with their nuclei.

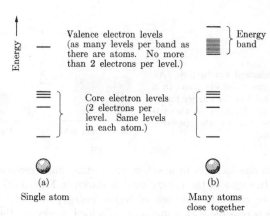

FIG. 5–15. Energy bands (sodium). When atoms are close together, the valence electrons interact. No more than two may have one energy level. Therefore many discrete levels exist in the valence energy bands.

different. This group of related levels in a polyatomic material is called an *energy band* and corresponds to an energy level in a single atom. Each band contains *as many discrete levels as there are atoms in the crystal*. Because the alkali metals have a valence of one, their energy bands are only half full (Fig. 5–16). Each level in the lower half of the band contains two electrons.

Alkaline earth metals (e.g., beryllium, magnesium, and calcium) have two valence electrons per atom. This number is sufficient to fill the first energy band with two electrons in each level. However, there is an overlapping because the lowest levels in the second band require less energy than the highest levels in the first band, so some electrons "overflow" into levels in the second band (Fig. 5–17).

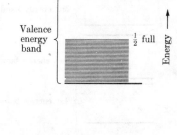

FIG. 5–16. Energy band of sodium. There are as many energy levels in a band as there are atoms. Since each energy level may contain two electrons (opposite spins), and since sodium has only one valence electron per atom, the valence energy band is only half filled.

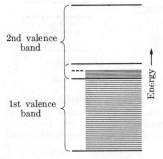

FIG. 5–17. Energy bands of magnesium. Nominally, all the valence electrons could go into the first valence band because magnesium is divalent. However, there is an overlap; therefore less energy is required for electrons to reach some levels in the second band than to reach the top levels in the first band. The positions of lowest energy are filled first.

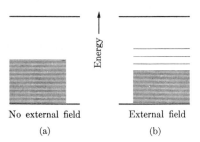

FIG. 5–18. Electrical conduction. An external field can raise electrons to a higher energy level in the energy band. This permits acceleration of the valence electrons toward the positive plate (Fig. 5–3b).

No external field   External field
(a)   (b)

To move from one location to another, an electron must receive extra energy (Section 5–4). In terms of the energy models shown in Figs. 5–16 and 5–17, the electrons must be raised to positions of higher energy, since the low levels are filled first. This is possible with a minimum of added energy for the alkali metals because there are vacant levels in the energy band immediately above the filled levels (Fig. 5–18). The alkaline earth metals also have vacant levels which extend into the second energy band (Fig. 5–17).

An external electric field can supply the small amount of energy required to raise an electron to the next level within the band, and this added energy permits movement toward the positive pole (Figs. 5–3b and 5–4). Since the raising of some electrons to higher energy levels also opens up lower levels which were formerly occupied, electrons moving against the external electric field can be decelerated to a lower energy level. This also contributes to the net movement of the electrons in the one direction.

Energy gaps. The adjacent energy bands in materials do not always overlap, so that an *energy gap* may be present (Fig. 5–19a). This situation does not affect

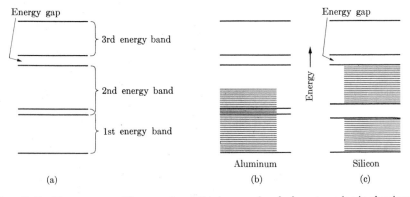

Energy gap

3rd energy band

2nd energy band

1st energy band

(a)

Aluminum
(b)

Energy gap

Silicon
(c)

FIG. 5–19. Energy gaps. The second and third energy bands do not overlap in aluminum or in silicon. This does not affect the conductivity of aluminum since there are many vacant energy levels in the second band, to which electrons can move readily. In silicon, however, a strong electric field is required to raise electrons to a higher energy level; therefore pure silicon is a poor conductor.

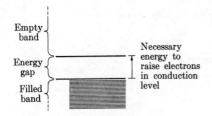

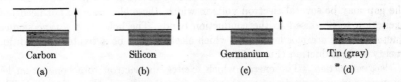

Fig. 5–20. Energy gap and conduction. To provide conduction, the electrons must be given sufficient additional energy to be raised to the next band.

the conductivity of the material if there are still vacant levels within the energy band. For example, aluminum, with energy gaps between the second and third bands (Fig. 5–19b), has excellent conductivity because its outer electrons can be energized by small electric fields. However, since silicon, with four valence electrons per atom, has no vacant levels in the first two energy bands (Fig. 5–19), the only possible way to move a silicon electron to a higher level is to supply enough energy to raise it across the gap to the next higher band (Fig. 5–20). This requires a very strong electric field. Therefore silicon is not a good conductor and has relatively high resistivity.

Energy gaps vary in size from material to material. Figure 5–21, which makes a schematic comparison in the size of energy gaps of certain materials, may be compared with Table 5–1. Since each of these elements is in the fourth group of the periodic table, and each possesses the same diamond-cubic structure (Fig. 2–10), we may conclude that the difference in resistivity is directly associated with the size of the energy gap.

• *Intrinsic and extrinsic semiconductors.* If the number of electrons able to jump to the conduction band because of thermal energy is sufficient to provide semiconduction, the energy gap must be only a few kT (1 kT = 0.025 ev at 20°C). Semiconductors with this characteristic are called *intrinsic.* The number n_i of charge carriers in an intrinsic semiconductor is related to the size of the energy gap E_g, and to the temperature, as follows:

$$n_i = Se^{-E_g/2kT}, \qquad (5\text{–}3)$$

where S is a constant over small temperature variations. There are twice as many intrinsic carriers as electrons which jump the energy gap, because each electron

| Carbon | Silicon | Germanium | Tin (gray) |
| (a) | (b) | (c) | (d) |

Fig. 5–21. Energy gaps in Group IV elements. All these elements can have the same structure since they all have filled bands. Because tin has the smallest energy gap, it requires a smaller electric field to raise its electrons to a conducting level in the next band, and its resistivity is low. (Cf. Table 5–1.)

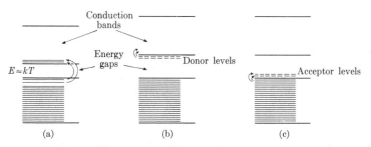

FIG. 5–22.   Energy bands in semiconductors.   (a) Intrinsic semiconductor.   (b) Extrinsic semiconductor (*n*-type).   (c) Extrinsic semiconductor (*p*-type).

which moves to the conduction band leaves a hole in the lower band to receive conduction (Fig. 5–22a).

- **Example 5–3**

   An intrinsic semiconductor has a resistivity of 1.20 ohm·cm at 20°C and 1.08 ohm·cm at 50°C. Estimate the size of the energy gap. (Assume negligible change in mobility over this small temperature range.)

   Answer:

$$n = \frac{1}{\rho q \mu} = S e^{-E_g/2kT},$$

$$\frac{n_{20°}}{n_{50°}} = \frac{1.08 q \mu}{1.20 q \mu} = \frac{S e^{-E_g/2k(293)}}{S e^{-E_g/2k(323)}},$$

$$\ln 0.9 = -0.1054 = \frac{-E_g(\frac{1}{293} - \frac{1}{323})}{2(1.38 \times 10^{-16})},$$

$$E_g = 8.8 \times 10^{-14} \text{ erg} = 0.055 \text{ ev}.$$

An *extrinsic*, or impurity, semiconductor may have a greater energy gap as such; however, the impurities provide intermediate energy levels in which electrons can reside. The extra electrons (Fig. 5–7) in an *n*-type semiconductor are present in so-called *donor* levels near the top of the energy gap (Fig. 5–22b). Thus, although the gap may be several electron volts in width, these electrons do not need much excitation to be raised to the conduction band. The holes of a *p*-type semiconductor provide *acceptor* levels into which electrons can be activated for additional energy and conduction (Fig. 5–22c).

- *Photoconduction.* The energy which excites an electron to a conduction level may come from an electromagnetic source as well as from a thermal source. Thus, light rays (or more correctly, a photon) can increase the conductivity of a semiconductor just as thermal energy may. A material which is adapted to this purpose is called a photoconductor.

MAGNETIC BEHAVIOR

5–10 Introduction. Some materials, such as iron, are markedly magnetic, and others are not. In fact, one of the simple techniques for separating ferrous and nonferrous substances is a comparison of their magnetic properties. Although iron has few equals, it is not the only material with strong magnetic characteristics. Cobalt, nickel, and gadolinium are highly magnetic; furthermore, many specialized alloys have useful magnetic properties.

Most elements and materials are not entirely devoid of magnetic characteristics. The majority of metals are paramagnetic (very weakly attracted to a magnet); the rest of the metals and all nonmetals are diamagnetic (very weakly repelled by a magnet). Since the magnetic characteristics of paramagnetic and diamagnetic materials are less than one-millionth as effective as those of the iron-cobalt-nickel group, they have only limited engineering significance at the present time.

5–11 Ferromagnetism. The historic and commercial importance of iron as a magnetic material has led to the name *ferromagnetism* for the strongly magnetic properties possessed by the iron group of transition elements.

Ferromagnetism is a result of the electron structure within atoms. We recall that at most two electrons can occupy each energy level of an isolated atom (Fig. 5–13), and that the same holds true for atoms in a crystal structure (Fig. 5–15). These two electrons have "spins" in opposite directions (Fig. 5–14), and since each spinning electron is equivalent to a moving charge, each electron acts as an extremely small magnet, with accompanying north and south poles.

Generally speaking, in a material with an even number of electrons, as many electrons spin in one direction as in the other (Fig. 5–23a), and the net effect is a magnetically insensitive structure. However, in an element with unfilled subvalence shells, more electrons spin in one direction than in another (Fig. 5–23b). Therefore, these elements have a net magnetic moment and act as small magnets. In α-iron, cobalt, nickel and gadolinium, these magnetic moments are sufficiently strong and the atoms are sufficiently close together for there to be spontaneous magnetic alignment of adjacent atoms. These conditions produce *ferromagnetism*. Although only the above pure materials are ferromagnetic, manganese and γ-iron almost meet the requirements, so that we find that other metals, such as MnBi alloys, also have structures which are ferromagnetic. Likewise, various ceramic phases are magnetic, such as $NiFe_2O_3$ and $BaFe_{12}O_{19}$.

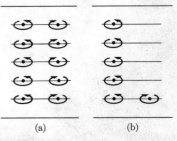

(a)   (b)

FIG. 5–23. Atomic magnetism. (a) Diamagnetic. (b) Magnetic. In those atoms with unfilled electron shells more electronic spins are aligned in one direction than in the opposite direction, so that the atom contains a magnetic moment.

S	S	S	N	N	N					
N	N	N	S	S	S	S N	S N	S N	S N	S N
S	S	S	N	N	N	N				
N	N	N	S	S	S	S	S N	S N	S N	S N
S	S	S	N	N	N	N	N			
N	N	N	S	S	S	S	S	S N	S N	S N
S	S	S	N	N	N	N	N	N		
N	N	N	S	S	S	S	S	S	N	S N
S	S	S	N	N	N	N	N	N	N	
N	N	N	S	S	S	S	S	S	S	S
S	S	S	N	N	N	N	N	N	N	N
N	N	N	S	S	S	S	S	S	S	S
S	S	S	N	N	N	N	N	N	N	N
N	N	N	S	S	S	S	S	S	S	S
S	S	S	N	N	N	N	N	N	N	N
N	N	N	S	S	S	S	S	S	S	S
S	S	S	N	N	N	N	N	N	N	N
N	N	N	S	S	S	S	S	S	S	S
S	S	S	N	N	N	N	N	N	N	N
N	N	N	S	S	S	S	S	S	S	S

Fig. 5-24. Magnetic domains. Domains, like grains, contain many unit cells; however, adjacent domains are crystallographically related. Dashed lines indicate domain boundaries.

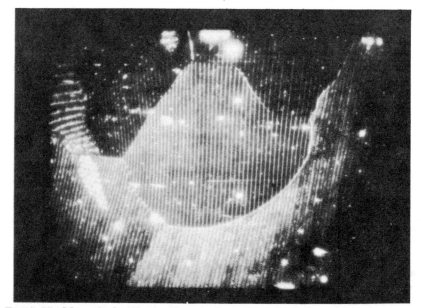

Fig. 5-25. Magnetic domains in silicon ferrite (×25). The domains are made apparent under the microscope by the use of very fine iron powder on the polished metal surface. The powder can be observed at the domain boundaries. (L. S. Dijkstra and U. M. Martius, "Domain Pattern of Silicon Iron Under Stress," *Reviews of Modern Physics*, **25,** 146–50, 1953.)

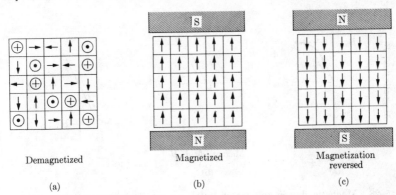

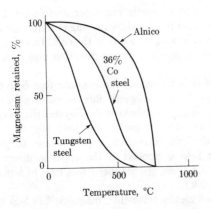

Demagnetized	Magnetized	Magnetization reversed
(a)	(b)	(c)

Fig. 5-26. Domain alignment. An external magnetic field can align ferromagnetic domains. When the domains are aligned the material is magnetized.

Fig. 5-27. Magnetization versus temperature. An increase in thermal activity permits return to a randomized domain structure. (Adapted from J. K. Stanley, *Metallurgy and Magnetism*. Cleveland: American Society for Metals, 1948.)

Domain structures. Since adjacent ferromagnetic atoms align themselves so that their orientations are in the same direction, a crystal or grain contains *magnetic domains* (Fig. 5-24). Domains usually do not have dimensions greater than 0.002 inch (Fig. 5-25). In an unmagnetized ferromagnetic material, domains are randomly oriented, and consequently their effects are cancelled out. However, if the domains are aligned by a magnetic field, the material becomes magnetic (Fig. 5-26). The alignment of all the domains in one direction provides an additive effect which may or may not be permanent after the external magnetic field is removed. The terms "magnetically hard" and "magnetically soft" are used to indicate whether the magnetic alignment is permanently retained, and inasmuch as a mechanically hard material is likely to be a magnetically hard material, the terms are apt. The residual strains of a hardened material prevent the randomization of the domains. A material will usually lose its ordered magnetic domain when it is annealed (Fig. 5-27), since thermal activity promotes randomization of the domain alignments.

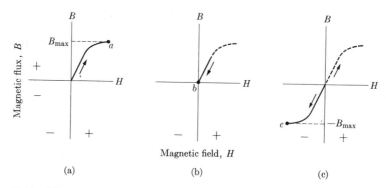

Fig. 5–28. Magnetic flux in an ideally "soft" magnet. Demagnetization occurs immediately upon removal of the magnetizing field. No energy is consumed. Such a material would not heat magnetically in a transformer coil.

5–12 Alternating magnetic fields. The magnetic characteristics required in electrical components in equipment are often produced by passing current through a coil with a magnetic core that increases the magnetic flux in the coil. In alternating-current equipment, the core is first magnetized in one direction and then in the other as the current is reversed.

In Fig. 5–28(a), as the *magnetic field* H is increased, the *magnetic flux* B in the ideally soft magnetic material is increased. The magnetic flux increases with the magnetic field until *magnetic saturation*, B_{max}, is approached. Beyond this point, an increase of magnetizing field increases the magnetic flux only slightly. If the magnetizing field is removed, the magnetic flux will decrease to zero (Fig. 5–28b). When the magnetizing field is applied in the opposite direction during the negative part of an alternating cycle, the magnetic flux rises to a maximum in the opposite direction (Fig. 5–28c).

Hysteresis. In a material which is not ideally reversible, magnetic flux lags the reversal of the magnetizing field. Thus in Fig. 5–29(a) the removal of the magnetizing field still leaves some residual magnetism B_r in the material.* Not until the field is reversed by application of a field H_c (*coercive force*) is the magnetic flux completely removed (Fig. 5–29b). The negative part of the alternating cycle produces an identical but opposite lag (Fig. 5–29c).

The lag just described is of prime interest to an electrical engineer. A material with a high coercive field H_c consumes energy in realigning the magnetic domains from one direction to the opposite direction. Such energy shows up in the material as heat and is lost. The amount of energy consumed is proportional to the area within the hysteresis loop. [Compare Fig. 5–29(c) with the hysteresis loops in Fig. 8–28.] Thus, except for permanent magnets, a magnetic material that behaves like that depicted in Fig. 5–28 is desirable.

---

* The material for permanent magnets is chosen so that the value of B_r is nearly equal to B_{max}.

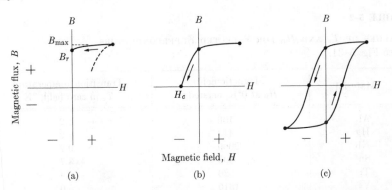

FIG. 5-29. Magnetic flux in a "hard" magnet. Removal of the magnetizing field H does not remove the magnetic flux B. An opposite coercive force, H_c, must be applied to remove the magnetic flux. (Compare with ferroelectric behavior in Fig. 8-28.)

Since materials which are strain-free are also magnetically soft, metals used as core materials in electrical coils usually have a single phase and are carefully annealed so as to produce as low a residual magnetic flux, B_r, as possible. Crystal orientation also affects the magnetic characteristics of a material, as is shown in Fig. 5-30 for three different crystal directions. In iron, the [100] direction requires the least magnetic field H to reach the fully magnetized state B_{max}. Nickel and cobalt are most readily magnetized in the [111] and the [0001] directions, respectively. By appropriate forming and heat treatments, the metallurgist can prescribe methods to produce preferred orientations (Chapter 6) in sheet metal. These "grain-oriented" steels may be incorporated into the designs so as to take full advantage of the effects of crystal orientation.

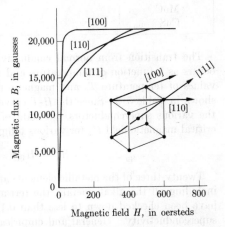

FIG. 5-30. Magnetic flux versus crystal direction. Effect of applying a magnetizing field in each of three crystallographic directions in a single crystal of iron. Full magnetization is easily obtained in the [100] direction. (A. G. Guy, *Elements of Physical Metallurgy.* Reading, Mass.: Addison-Wesley, 1959.)

• **5-13 Superconductivity.** At low temperatures certain metals and a large number of intermetallic compounds possess *superconductivity*, having zero resistivity and undetectable magnetic permeability. Although the origin of these properties is not understood, they have considerable engineering interest, for obvious reasons.

TABLE 5-2

VALUES OF T_c AND H_0 FOR SELECTED SUPERCONDUCTORS
(See Fig. 5-31.)

Material	Magnetic field H_0 at 0°K, oersteds	Transition temperature T_c in zero field, °K
Al	106	1.2
Hg	413	4.2
Nb	2000	9.2
Sn	305	3.7
Ti	20	0.4
V	1310	5.0
Nb$_3$Sn	5000	18.1
V$_3$Si		17.1
NbN		16.0
MoC		8.0
CuS		1.6

The transition from normal conductivity to superconductivity is abrupt and occurs as a function of temperature and magnetic field (Fig. 5-31). The critical values of temperature T_c and magnetic field H_0 for several superconductors are shown in Table 5-2. Since the H-T curve of Fig. 5-31 is essentially parabolic for the various superconductors, the data of Table 5-2 permit a calculation of the critical magnetic field H_c for various temperatures T:

$$H_c = H_0[1 - (T/T_c)^2]. \tag{5-4}$$

Twenty-three of the metallic elements are known to be superconductive. Others, including all the alkali metals, the ferromagnetic metals, and the noble metals, have been checked down to less than 0.1°K with no evidence of a transition to superconductivity. General and empirical rules reveal that superconduction occurs most readily (1) among those metals with low conductivities of the normal type, and (2) among those metals with 3, 5, or 7 valence electrons. These generalizations have led to the formulation of many intermetallic compounds with high transition temperatures. Several of these are listed in Table 5-2.

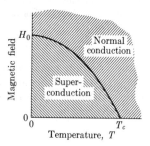

FIG. 5-31. Conditions for superconduction. Zero resistivity and negligible magnetic permeability occur when superconducting metals are in low magnetic fields at low temperatures.

TABLE 5–3

FACTORS AFFECTING THE INDEX OF REFRACTION

Material	Composition	Density	Index of refraction
Quartz	SiO_2	2.65	1.544–1.553
Tridymite	SiO_2	2.28	1.469–1.471
Cristobalite	SiO_2	2.32	1.484–1.487
Vitreous silica	SiO_2	2.20	1.46
		Anion radius	
Villiaumite	NaF	1.33	1.336
Halite	NaCl	1.81	1.544

From L. H. Van Vlack, *Physical Ceramics for Engineers*, Reading, Mass.: Addison-Wesley, 1964.

OPTICAL BEHAVIOR

5–14 Opacity and transparency. The optical behavior of a material is related to its electronic structure. In general, materials with free electrons are opaque because the electrons absorb the electromagnetic energy of the light. The material need not have metallic conductivity, because the photons of radiant energy may be absorbed by an electron which is raised to a higher energy level, but remains within the vicinity of its host atom.*

The electrons of a structure can also react with electromagnetic radiation without absorbing the energy, so that the material remains transparent. We recall from Chapter 1 [Eq. (1–10)] that the index of refraction is an inverse measure of the velocity of light within a material as compared with its velocity in a vacuum. This interaction depends on the polarizability of the material (Section 2–11). Both molecular and electronic polarizability are important; however, in general only electronic polarizability (Fig. 2–15) responds rapidly enough ($> 10^{15}$ cps) to interact at the frequency of visible light. Since the index of refraction is dependent on electronic polarizability, we find two factors which contribute significantly to higher indices: (1) greater phase density (and therefore more dipoles per unit volume), and (2) the presence of atoms with higher atomic numbers (and therefore more electrons per atom). These effects may be indicated with ceramic examples. All four of the common silica polymorphs have the same composition (SiO_2), but have different indices of refraction, as indicated in Table 5–3. Thus this change in index of refraction is a function of density only. As a second example, sodium chloride has the same structure as sodium fluoride, but has a greater index of re-

---

* Translucency and opacity may also occur as a result of extensive internal reflections and refractions, e.g., ice in a snow bank, or gypsum plaster in a wall.

fraction because the Cl^- ion has more electrons and is larger and more polarizable than the F^- ion. Other crystals, which have (1) high atomic packing factors, (2) large atomic or molecular weights, and (3) highly polarizable ions, possess appreciably higher indices than those cited in Table 5–3. For example, the indices of closely packed MgO and Al_2O_3 crystals are considered to be high, with index values of 1.736 and 1.76, respectively. However, extreme cases include crystals such as PbS at 3.9.

• 5–15 Luminescence. Electrons may be activated to higher energy levels in a variety of manners, the most common being that of photon excitation. As the electron returns to its lower energy position, energy is released, usually in the form of another photon, producing luminescence (Fig. 5–32). Unless the excitation was by two steps, the reradiated energy is never greater than the energy of the incident radiation, i.e., the emitted photon never has a wavelength shorter than that of the initial photon.

The reradiation of luminescence is not instantaneous, but delayed by the electron's period of residence at the activated energy level. Since the reradiation occurs statistically, the intensity of luminescence, I_t, at any time t is related to the initial intensity as follows:

$$I_t/I_0 = e^{-t/\tau}, \qquad (5\text{--}5)$$

where τ is called the relaxation time for reradiation. If the relaxation time for luminescence is short compared to the time of our visual perception, the term *fluorescence* is used. On the other hand, if the relaxation time gives a noticeable delay or afterglow of luminescence, the term *phosphorescence* is used. Obviously, the distinction made between these two behaviors is related to the reaction speed of the sensing device.

Figure 5–32 illustrates *photoconduction* as well as luminescence, because the electron has been raised to the conducting band by photon activation. Before the electron returns to the lower energy level, it is free to be accelerated within an electric field and therefore conducts a charge. However, the energy absorption prior to luminescence may also involve nonconducting electrons; e.g., in transition elements, such as Mn, V, and Cr, the electrons may be raised to other energy

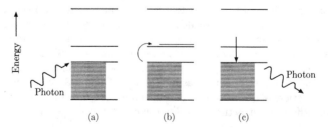

Fig. 5–32. Luminescence. Excitation arises from the absorption of energy from an external source, e.g., a photon. Energy is subsequently released by photon emission.

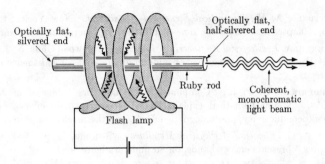

Fig. 5–33. LASER device (Light Amplification by Stimulated Emission of Radiation). Photon energy is absorbed by the ruby (Al_2O_3 plus Cr_2O_3) rod and reemitted as an intense, coherent, and monochromatic light beam.

levels in the unfilled subvalence shells (Fig. 5–23). Such a change affects the magnetic characteristics of the atom and of the total material. The return of the electron to the original energy value releases a photon and returns the atom to its original magnetic condition.

• *Lasers.* The reemission of photons from a luminescent material is a statistical function of time, as shown in Eq. (5–5). Thus the number of photons released spontaneously in any interval of time is directly proportional to the number of electrons which are excited at the time. Photon emission may be stimulated to occur earlier if the excited electron is encountered by a photon which has the same energy as the one to be released.

The stimulated emission just described has led to devices called *lasers* to amplify light beams. In brief, the flash lamp of Fig. 5–33 supplies photons which raise the chromium ions that have been dissolved in ruby (Al_2O_3) to a higher energy level. The photons (6943 and 7009 angstroms) which are reemitted spontaneously are then used to stimulate the emission of photons of the same wavelength from additional chromium ions, thus short-circuiting the time requirement of Eq. (5–5). One of the key features of the laser shown in Fig. 5–33 is the optically flat, reflecting ends of the ruby rod. They must reflect the emitted photons so that they may be used as further stimulation for the emission of additional photons. The reflected and re-reflected light beam thus builds up to a high intensity before emerging from the end of the rod as a coherent and extremely monochromatic light source.

References for Further Reading

5–1. Azároff, L. V., and J. J. Brophy, *Electronic Processes in Materials.* New York: McGraw-Hill, 1963. For the advanced undergraduate student and the instructor. The structure of materials is used to explain electronic and magnetic behavior.

5–2. Bozorth, R. M., "Ferromagnetism," *Recent Advances in Science.* New York: New York University Press (distributed by Interscience), 1956. Discusses the technical characteristics of ferromagnetic materials in a nonmathematical manner.

5-3. COTTRELL, A. H., *Theoretical Structural Metallurgy.* New York: St. Martin's Press, 1955. Chapter 5 discusses the zone (band) theory of metals at the advanced level.

5-4. DEKKER, A. J., *Electrical Engineering Materials.* Englewood Cliffs, N. J.: Prentice-Hall, 1959. For the electrical engineer at undergraduate level. Field theory knowledge is advantageous.

5-5. FREDERIKSE, H. P. R., "Compound Semiconductors," *Journal of Metals,* **10,** 346–50, 1958.   Nonmathematical explanation of electromagnetic effects, optical absorption, photoconductivity, photomagnetic effects, and thermoelectric power.

5-6. GUY, A. G., *Elements of Physical Metallurgy.* Reading, Mass.: Addison-Wesley, 1959. Chapter 3 presents energy bands, on an undergraduate level.

5-7. HUME-ROTHERY, W., *Atomic Theory for Students.* London: Institute of Metals, 1955. For the metallurgy student.

5-8. HUME-ROTHERY, W., *Electrons, Atoms, Metals and Alloys.* London: Institute of Metals, 1955. Chapter 27 discusses metals, insulators, and semiconductors. This book is in the form of a dialogue which includes questions and answers. The presentation is unusual, interesting, and gives a different slant on the technical matter.

5-9. KATZ, H. W., *Solid State Magnetic and Dielectric Devices.* New York: John Wiley & Sons, 1959. For the electrical engineering student. Field theory is required.

5-10. SCHAWLOW, A. L., "Optical Masers," *Scientific American,* **204,** 52–61, June 1961. Optical masers are now called lasers. This article is a good introduction to the subject.

5-11. SCHOCKLEY, W., "Transistor Physics," *American Scientist,* **42,** 41, 1954.   An excellent summary article at the introductory level.

5-12. SCHUMACHER, E. E., "Metallurgy Behind the Decimal Point," *Transactions A.I.M.E.,* **188,** 1097, 1950. Of interest to the metallurgical student who wants to know more about the effect of impurities on properties. Semiconductors serve as examples.

5-13. VON HIPPEL, A. R., *Dielectric Materials and Applications.* Cambridge, Mass. Technology Press of M.I.T. (and John Wiley & Sons), 1943. Contains graphs and tables which present the dielectric constants and power factors as a function of frequency and temperature for a very large number of insulating materials.

Problems

5-1. Silicon has a density of 2.40 gm/cm^3. (a) What is the concentration of the silicon atoms per cubic centimeter? (b) Phosphorus is added to silicon to make it an n-type semiconductor with a conductivity of 1 mho/cm and an electron mobility of 1700 $cm^2/$ volt·sec. What is the concentration of the conduction electrons per cubic centimeter?

Answer: (a) 5.15×10^{22} atom/cm^3 (b) 3.68×10^{15} carrier electrons/cm^3

5-2. (a) How many silicon atoms are there for each conduction electron in Problem 5-1(b)? (b) The lattice constant for silicon is 5.42 A, and there are 8 atoms per unit cell. What is the volume associated with each conduction electron? (c) How many unit cells per conduction electron?

5-3. Germanium used for transistors has a resistivity of 2 ohm·cm and an electron "hole" concentration of 1.9×10^{15} holes/cm^3. (a) What is the mobility of the electron holes in the germanium? (b) What impurity element could be added to germanium to create electron holes?

Answer: (a) 1640 cm^2/volts·sec (b) Al, In, Ga

5-4. Semiconducting germanium is formed by melting 3.22×10^{-6} gm of antimony with 100 gm of germanium. (a) Will the semiconductor be n-type or p-type? (b) Calculate the concentration of antimony (in atoms/cm^3) in the germanium.

• 5-5. What is the diffusion coefficient for Na$^+$ ions in NaCl at 550°C? The Na$^+$ ions account for 98% of the 2×10^{-6} (ohm·cm)$^{-1}$ conductivity. [*Note:* 1 watt·sec = 10^7 ergs.]

Answer: 3.8×10^{-11} cm^2/sec

• 5-6. At 727°C, 80% of the charge in NaCl is carried by the Na$^+$ ions (and 20% by the Cl$^-$ ions). What is the diffusion coefficient for the Na$^+$ ions if the total conductivity is 2.5×10^{-4} (ohm·cm)$^{-1}$?

• 5-7. Using the data from the previous problems, calculate the activation energy for Na$^+$ ion movements in NaCl.

Answer: 44,000 cal/mole

• 5-8. The diffusion coefficients for K$^+$ ions in KCl* are $10^{-5.15}$ at 1000°K and $10^{-6.35}$ at 500°K. (a) What is the diffusion coefficient of K$^+$ ions at 750°K (477°C)? (b) How much conductivity arises from the K$^+$ ion movements at this temperature?

5-9. Some Fe$_{<1}$O has an Fe^{3+}/Fe^{2+} ratio of 0.1; what is the mobility of the electron holes if this oxide has a conductivity of 1 (ohm·cm)$^{-1}$ and 99% of the charge is carried by the electron holes ($a = 4.3$ A)?

Answer: 1.4×10^{-3} cm^2/volt·sec

5-10. How many charge carriers are there per cubic centimeter in the previous problem? (a) Electron holes? (b) Cation vacancies?

5-11. What is the resistance of a copper wire 0.08 in. in diameter and 100 ft long if its resistivity is 1.7 microhm·cm?

Answer: 0.16 ohm

5-12. A maximum resistance of 1 ohm is permitted in a copper wire 25 ft long. What is the smallest wire diameter which can be used?

• 5-13. The first series of transition elements have magnetic moments with the following number of Bohr magnetons (electron spins): Ti, 2; V, 3; Cr, 5; Mn, 5; Fe, 4; Co, 3; and Ni, 2. Provide an explanation for these values on the basis of Fig. 5-23.

• 5-14. Estimate the critical magnetic field for superconductivity of niobium at 5°K.

• 5-15. A phosphorescent material is exposed to ultraviolet light. The intensity of emitted light decreases 20% in the first 37 min. after the ultraviolet light is removed. How long will it be after the uv light is removed before the emitted light has only 20% of the original intensity (a decrease of 80%)?

Answer: 265 minutes

5-16. The density of coesite (a high-pressure polymorph of SiO$_2$) is 2.9 gm/cm^3. On the basis of Table 5-3, predict its mean index of refraction.

5-17. Show why AlP is a semiconductor.

Answer: See Fig. 5-10.

• Problems preceded by a bullet are based, in part, on optional sections.

* KCl has the same structure as NaCl (Fig. 3-10).

6

metallic phases and their properties

6-1 Introduction. This chapter is the first of three which are concerned with single-phase materials. Metals, polymers (i.e., "plastics"), and ceramics will be discussed in sequence. Although a distinction is often made among these three major categories of materials, the boundaries are not sharp. Many times a material has characteristics intermediate between two or even three of the categories.

Our goal in this chapter is to learn how the properties of single-phase metals can be changed. This approach serves two purposes: (1) it permits the engineer to understand the limitations of metals, and (2) it provides him with procedures for adjusting their properties to his design specifications.

Single-phase metals have only one crystal structure; however, their compositions can be varied by solid solution and their grains can have various microstructures. The properties of single-phase metals can be adjusted by (1) *plastic deformation* and (2) *recrystallization.** These procedures are in turn influenced by the composition and geometry of individual grains.

SINGLE-PHASE METALS

6-2 Single-phase alloys. Single-phase metals used commercially may be pure metals with only one component. Examples of such metals were cited in Section 4-2, and included copper for electrical wiring, zinc for the coating on galvanized steel, and the aluminum used for housewares. However, in many cases a second component is intentionally added to the metal in order to improve the properties. Any such combination of metals is called an *alloy.*

Alloys are single-phase metals so long as the solid solubility limit is not exceeded. Brass, a single-phase alloy of copper and zinc, bronze, a similar alloy of copper and tin, and copper-nickel alloys are typical of metals we shall study in this chapter. Multiphase, or polyphase, alloys contain additional phases because the solid solubility limit is exceeded. The majority of our steels, as well as many other metals, are multiphase alloys. They will be discussed in later chapters.

Properties of single-phase alloys. The properties of alloys are different from those of pure metals. This is shown in Figs. 6-1 and 6-2 for brass and Cu-Ni solid solutions. The increase in strength and hardness is due to the presence of solute atoms which interfere with the movements of atoms in the crystals during plastic

---

* There are additional procedures for adjusting the properties of multiple-phase metals (see Chapter 11).

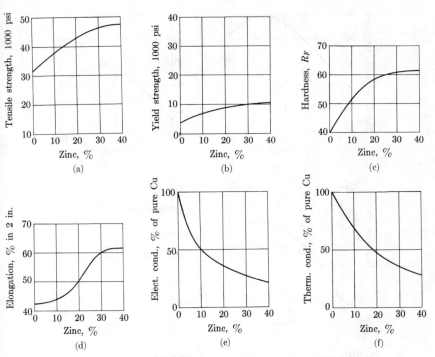

Fig. 6-1. Mechanical and physical properties of annealed brasses. (Adapted from ASM data.)

deformation. We shall observe later (Section 6-5) that this interference exists because dislocation movements (Fig. 4-13) are stabilized by alloying elements.

Very small amounts of impurities reduce the electrical conductivity of a metal, because the foreign atom introduces nonuniformities in the electrical field within the crystal lattice. Therefore, the electrons encounter more deflections and reflections, with a consequent reduction in the length of the mean free path (Sections 5-4 and 5-7).

In a metal, electrons carry more than half the energy for thermal conduction. Thus there is a correspondence between the thermal and electrical conductivity. [Compare (e) and (f) of Figs. 6-1 and 6-2.]

6-3 Grain microstructures. Grains were described in Section 4-9 as individual crystals. Adjacent crystals have dissimilar orientations so that a grain boundary is present (Fig. 4-15). The microstructures of single-phase metals can be varied by changes in size, shape, and orientation of the grains (Fig. 6-3). These aspects are not wholly independent, because the shape and size of grains are both consequences of grain growth. Likewise, grain shape is usually dependent on the crystalline orientation of grains during growth.

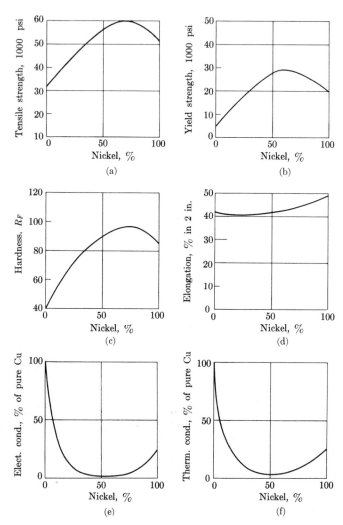

FIG. 6–2. Mechanical and physical properties of annealed copper-nickel alloys. (Adapted from ASM data.)

Grain growth. The average grain size of a single-phase metal increases with time if the temperature is such as to produce significant atom movements (Section 4–13). The driving force for grain growth is the energy released as an atom moves across the boundary from the convex to the concave surface, where the atom is coordinated with a larger number of neighbors at equilibrium interatomic spacings (Fig. 6–4). As a result, the boundary moves toward the center of curvature. Since small grains tend to have surfaces of sharper convexity than large grains,

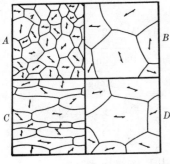

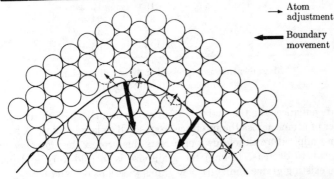

FIG. 6–3. Microstructural variables of single-phase metals. (*A* versus *B*) Grain size. (*A* versus *C*) Grain shape. (*B* versus *D*) Preferred orientation.

→ Atom adjustment

← Boundary movement

FIG. 6–4. Grain-boundary movement. The atoms move to the concave surface, where they are more stable. As a result the boundary is shifted toward the center of curvature.

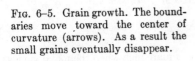

FIG. 6–5. Grain growth. The boundaries move toward the center of curvature (arrows). As a result the small grains eventually disappear.

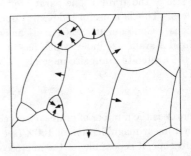

they disappear because they feed the larger grains (Fig. 6–5). The net effect is grain growth.

An interesting example of grain growth can be seen in the ice of a snow bank. Snowflakes start out as numerous small ice crystals, lose their identity with time, and are replaced by larger granular ice crystals. A few slightly larger crystals have grown at the expense of the many smaller crystals.

All crystalline materials, metals and nonmetals, exhibit this characteristic of grain growth. Its engineering importance will be treated in later sections, but the effect of temperature on grain growth must be considered first. An increase in

TABLE 6-1

GRAIN SIZE RANGES (ASTM); $N = 2^{n-1}$

Grain size number	Grains/in^2 at 100X (linear*)	
	Mean	Range
$n = 1$	$N = 1$	—
2	2	1.5–3
3	4	3–6
4	8	6–12
5	16	12–24
6	32	24–48
7	64	48–96
8	128	96–192

* Magnification is expressed in linear dimensions.
100 X linear = 10,000 X areal.

temperature enhances the thermal vibration of the atoms, which in turn facilitates the transfer of atoms across the interface from small to large grains. A subsequent decrease in temperature slows down or arrests this process, but *does not reverse it.* The only way to decrease (refine) the grain size is to cold-work and plastically deform the existing grains and start new grains (Sections 6–7 and 6–8).

Measurement of grain size. The effect of grain size on mechanical properties (Section 6–6) immediately interests the engineer in establishing parameters for the size of the grains. The parameter may be given as average diameter in millimeters. This is a useful index, but obtaining it under a microscope is somewhat tedious. Consequently, the American Society for Testing and Materials has standardized a grain size index which has been rather extensively adopted, particularly for the austenite grain size in steels. The *ASTM grain size number, n,* is obtained as follows:

$$N = 2^{n-1}, \tag{6-1}$$

where N is the number of grains observed per square inch when the metal is viewed with a linear magnification of 100X (see Table 6–1). With comparator nets in the microscope, it is possible for the microscopist to assign grain size values at a glance.

Example 6–1

A steel has an ASTM grain size No. 7. What would be the average area observed for each grain in a polished surface?

Answer:
$$N = 2^{7-1} = 64 \text{ grains/in}^2 \text{ at } 100X,$$

$$\frac{64}{(0.01)(0.01)} = 640,000 \text{ grains/in}^2 \text{ at } 1X.$$

$$\text{Area of 1 grain} = \frac{1}{640,000} \text{ in}^2.$$

Example 6–2

Assume that the grains in the previous calculation are cubic in shape.* What is the boundary area per cubic inch of steel?

Answer: From the previous example,

$$640{,}000 \text{ grains/in}^2 \text{ of surface } = 800 \text{ grains/inch of length}$$
$$= (800)^3, \quad \text{or } 5.12 \times 10^8 \text{ grains/in}^3 \text{ of volume.}$$

$$\text{Surface of each grain } = 6\left(\frac{1}{800}\right)^2 \text{in}^2.$$

Each boundary is composed of two grain surfaces, therefore

$$\text{Total boundary } = \frac{6}{2}\left(\frac{1}{800}\right)^2 \text{in}^2 \, (800)^3$$

$$= 2400 \text{ in}^2 \text{ boundary per cubic inch of steel.}$$

Grain shape. Although it is common to speak of grain size in terms of diameter, it is obvious that all grains of single-phase metals are not spherical. Rather, they must completely fill space and also maintain a minimum of total boundary area. This was shown in Figs. 4–16(a) and 6–3(a), where the term *equiaxed* is appropriate because the grains have approximately equal dimensions in the three coordinate directions.

Nonregular shapes of grains may include shapes that are platelike, columnar crystals, and dendritic (or treelike). No attempt will be made to systematize them in this book.

Grain orientation. The orientation of grains within a metal is typically quite random (Fig. 6-3a). However, there are exceptions, which can be important from the standpoint of engineering properties. For example, the [100] directions of iron have a higher magnetic permeability than other directions. Therefore, if the grains within a polycrystalline transformer sheet are not random, but have a *preferred orientation* so that the [100] direction is in the direction of the magnetic field, a significantly more efficient performance may be obtained from the transformer.

DEFORMATION OF METALS

6–4 Elastic deformation of metals. Elastic deformation precedes plastic deformation. When a small stress is placed on a piece of metal, or for that matter on any crystalline material, elastic deformation occurs (Section 1–2). When the load is applied in tension, the piece becomes slightly longer; removal of the load permits the specimen to return to its original dimension. Conversely, when a load

---

* Quite obviously, the above calculations give the order of magnitude only. As such, they are useful in determining reaction rates that depend on grain boundary area. This calculation assumes cubic shape and uniform size. In more accurate calculations, the boundary area would be slightly, but not significantly, smaller.

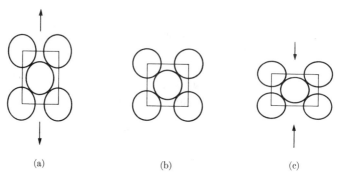

(a)   (b)   (c)

Fig. 6–6. Elastic normal strain (greatly exaggerated). Atoms are not permanently displaced from their original neighbors. (a) Tension. (b) No strain. (c) Compression.

is applied in compression, the piece becomes slightly shorter. Within the elastic range, the strain is a result of a slight elongation of the unit cell in the direction of the tensile load, or a slight contraction in the direction of the compressive load (Fig. 6–6).

When elastic deformation occurs, the strain is nearly proportional to the stress. This ratio between stress and strain is the *modulus of elasticity* (Young's modulus) and is a characteristic of the type of metal. The greater the forces of attraction between atoms in a metal, the higher the modulus of elasticity.

Any elongation or compression of the crystal structure in one direction, due to a uniaxial force, produces an adjustment in the dimensions at right angles to the force. In Fig. 6–6(a), for example, a small contraction is indicated at right angles to the tensile force. The negative ratio between the lateral strain ϵ_x and the direct tensile strains ϵ_y is called *Poisson's ratio* ν:

$$\nu = -\frac{\epsilon_x}{\epsilon_y}. \tag{6-2}$$

In engineering applications, *shear stresses* are also set up in crystal structures (Fig. 6–7). These produce a displacement of one plane of atoms relative to the

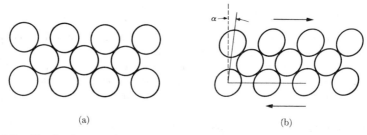

(a)   (b)

Fig. 6–7. Elastic shear strain. Shear couples produce a relative displacement of one plane of atoms past the next. This strain is elastic so long as atoms keep their original neighbors. (a) No strain. (b) Shear strain.

adjacent plane of atoms. The elastic shear strain γ is defined as the tangent of the shear angle α:

$$\gamma = \tan \alpha; \tag{6-3}$$

and the shear modulus G is the ratio of the shear stress τ to shear elastic strain γ:

$$G = \frac{\tau}{\gamma}. \tag{6-4}$$

This *shear modulus* (also called the modulus of rigidity) is different from the modulus of elasticity E; however, the two are related, a relationship which may be expressed by

$$E = 2G \, (1 + \nu). \tag{6-5}$$

Since Poisson's ratio ν is normally between 0.25 and 0.5, the value of G is approximately 35% of E.

A third elastic modulus, the *bulk modulus* K, is encountered in materials. It is the reciprocal of the compressibility β of the material, and is equal to the hydrostatic pressure σ_h per unit of volume compression, $\Delta V/V$:

$$K = \frac{\sigma_h V}{\Delta V} = \frac{1}{\beta}. \tag{6-6}$$

The bulk modulus is related to the modulus of elasticity as follows:

$$K = \frac{E}{3(1 - 2\nu)}. \tag{6-7}$$

Elastic moduli versus temperature. All elastic moduli decrease as temperature increases, as shown in Fig. 6-8 for four common metals. In terms of Fig. 2–18(a), a thermal expansion reduces the value of dF/da and thereby decreases the modulus of elasticity. The discontinuity in the curve for iron in Fig. 6-8 is due to the change from bcc iron to fcc iron at 910°C (1670°F).

Elastic moduli versus crystal direction. Elastic moduli are not isotropic within materials; that is, they vary with crystallographic orientation. As an example, iron has an average modulus of elasticity of about 30,000,000 psi; however, the actual modulus of a crystal of iron varies from 41,000,000 psi in the [111] direction

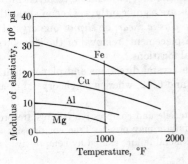

FIG. 6-8. Modulus of elasticity versus temperature. (Adapted from A. G. Guy, *Elements of Physical Metallurgy*, Reading, Mass.: Addison-Wesley, 1959.)

TABLE 6-2

MODULI OF ELASTICITY (YOUNG'S MODULUS)*

Metal	Maximum	Minimum	Random
Aluminum	11×10^6 psi	9×10^6 psi	10×10^6 psi
Gold	16	6	12
Copper	28	10	16
Iron (bcc)	41	18	30
Tungsten	57	57	57

* Adapted from E. Schmid and W. Boas, *Plasticity in Crystals*. English translation, London: Hughes and Co., 1950.

to only 18,000,000 psi in the [100] direction (Table 6-2). The consequence of any such anisotropy becomes significant in polycrystalline materials. Assume, for example, that Fig. 6-9(a) represents the cross section of a steel wire in which the average stress is 30,000 psi. If the grains are randomly oriented, the elastic strain will be 0.001 in./in., because the average modulus of elasticity is 30,000,000 psi. However, in reality, the stress will vary from 18,000 psi to 41,000 psi, as shown in Fig. 6-9(b), because grains have different orientations. Of course, this means that some grains will exceed their elastic limit before other grains reach their elastic limit.

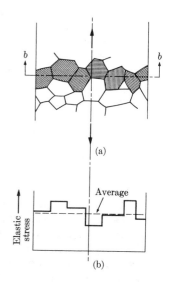

FIG. 6-9. Stress heterogeneities (schematic). Elastic stresses vary with grain orientation, because the moduli of elasticity are not isotropic.

6-5 Plastic deformation of metal crystals. Stresses may be applied by tension, compression, or shear forces. Since the first two can be resolved into shear forces (Fig. 6-10), and since most metals are significantly weaker in shear than in tension or compression, metals yield by *plastic shear*, or *slip* of one crystal plane over another. Slip causes permanent displacement; removal of the stress will not return the crystal planes to their original locations.*

Slip occurs more readily along certain crystal directions and planes than along others. This is illustrated in Figs. 6-11 and 6-12, where a single crystal of an hcp

* In ductile, nonporous materials, both tensile and compressive failures are preceded by slip. In brittle materials, true tensile failure may occur. True compressive failure does not occur in nonporous materials. All metal failure caused by compressive loads is a consequence of shear (Fig. 6-10b).

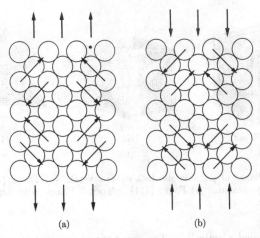

(a)   (b)

FIG. 6–10. Shear components of normal stresses. (a) Tension. (b) Compression.

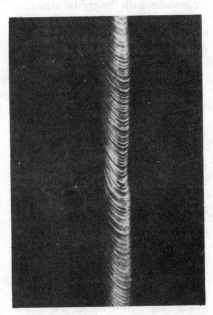

FIG. 6–11. Test bar of a single crystal of an hcp metal. Slip occurs parallel to the crystal plane of easiest slip. (Constance Elam, *The Distortion of Metal Crystals.* Oxford: Clarendon Press, 1935.)

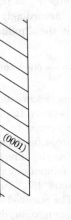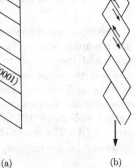

FIG. 6–12. Single crystal slip. (Compare with Fig. 6–11.) Slip is not restricted at the sides of the crystal.

(a)   (b)

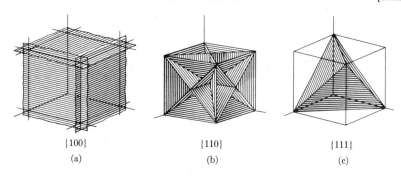

{100}   {110}   {111}
(a)   (b)   (c)

FIG. 6–13. Planes of possible slip in a cubic crystal. (a) Three {100} planes. (b) Six {110} planes. (c) Four {111} planes. Planes with higher indices are not shown.

metal was deformed plastically. The shear stress required to produce slip on a crystal plane is called the *critical shear stress.*

The number of planes on which slip can occur varies with the crystal structure. As shown in Fig. 6–12, only one plane accommodates slip with any facility in an hcp metal. Several planes are operative in most cubic metals (Fig. 6–13).

• *Resolved shear stresses.* The force required to produce slip is a function not only of the critical shear stress, but also depends on the angle between (1) the slip plane and the direction of force and (2) the slip direction and the direction of force. Consider Fig. 6–14, where A is the cross-sectional area perpendicular to the direction of force F, so that F/A is the axial stress. Accordingly, the *resolved shear stress* τ in the slip direction is

$$\tau = \frac{F}{A} \cos \lambda \cos \phi. \qquad (6\text{–}8)$$

In this equation, known as Schmid's law, ϕ is the angle between the direction of the force and the normal to the slip plane, and λ is the angle between the direction of force and the slip direction. Slip occurs with the minimum axial force when

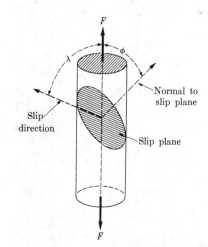

FIG. 6–14. Description of slip angles λ and ϕ used in determining the critical shear stress τ_s.

both λ and ϕ are 45°. Under these conditions τ_s is equal to one-half the axial stress F/A. The resolved shear stress is less in relation to the axial stress for any other crystal orientation, dropping to zero as either λ or ϕ approaches 90°.

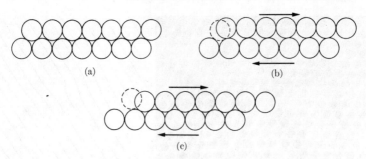

FIG. 6–15. An assumed mechanism of slip (simplified). Metals actually deform with less shear stress than this mechanism would require.

• **Example 6–3**

If the critical shear stress in the [1$\bar{1}$0] direction and on the (111) plane of a single crystal of *pure* copper is 0.10 kg/mm^2 (142 psi), what stress must be applied in the [100] direction to produce slip on the (111) plane?

Answer: From Fig. 3–24(c),

$$\cos \phi = \frac{\text{edge of unit cell}}{\text{long diagonal of unit cell}} = \frac{a}{\sqrt{3}\, a} = 0.577.$$

$$\cos \lambda = \frac{\text{edge of unit cell}}{\text{short diagonal of unit cell}} = \frac{a}{\sqrt{2}\, a} = 0.707.$$

$$F/A = \frac{142}{(0.577)(0.707)} = 350 \text{ psi.}$$

Mechanism of slip. Figure 6–15 shows a simplified mechanism of slip. If we attempted to calculate the strength of metals on this basis, the result would indicate that the strength of metals should be about $E/20$ psi, where E is the modulus of elasticity. Since metals are not that strong, it is apparent that another slip mechanism is operative. All experimental evidence supports a mechanism involving dislocation movements. If we use Fig. 6–16 as a model of a dislocation and place a shear stress along the horizontal direction, the dislocation can be moved (Fig. 6–17) with a shearing displacement within the crystal. (See also Fig. 4–13.) The shear stress required for this type of deformation is only a fraction of the previously cited value of $E/20$. In this respect it matches the shear strengths encountered in laboratory testing.

Since the mechanism of slip involves dislocation movements, the direction in which the critical shear stress is least is the direction with the shortest Burgers vector, i.e., the shortest displacement distance and the greatest atomic density (Fig. 4–11). In that direction, the energy required to move a dislocation is the least, because the energy E is a function of the product of the shear modulus G and the square of the Burgers vector b:

$$E = f(G, b^2). \tag{6–9}$$

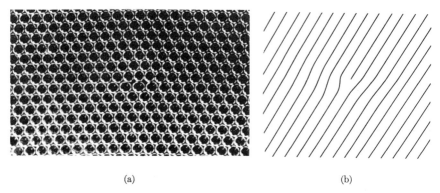

(a)   (b)

FIG. 6–16. Edge dislocation. (a) "Bubble-raft" model of an imperfection in a crystal structure. Note the extra row of atoms. (b) Schematic illustration of a dislocation. [Bragg and Nye, *Proc. Roy. Soc. (London)*, **A190,** 474, 1947.]

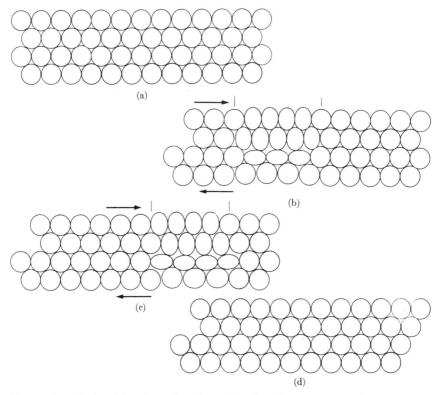

FIG. 6–17. Slip by dislocation. In this model only a few atoms at a time are moved from their low-energy positions. Less stress is therefore required to produce slip. Compare with the model of Fig. 6–15.

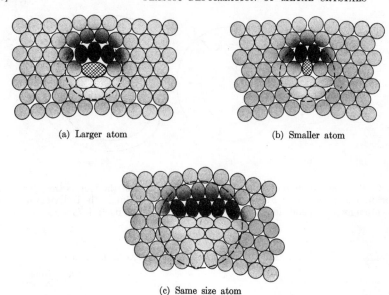

(a) Larger atom   (b) Smaller atom

(c) Same size atom

Fig. 6–18. Solid solution and dislocations. An odd-sized atom decreases the stress around a dislocation. As a result the dislocation is more stable and requires more stress to be moved. (Cf. Fig. 6–16a.)

Dislocation movements in solid solutions. The energy associated with an edge dislocation (Fig. 4–11) is the same, whether the dislocation is at point (b) or point (c) of Fig. 6–17. Therefore, no net energy is required for the movement between the two points.* Such is not the case when solute atoms are present. As shown in Fig. 6–18, when an impurity atom is present the energy associated with a dislocation is less than it is in a pure metal. Thus, when a dislocation encounters foreign atoms, its movement is restrained because energy must be supplied to release it for further slip. As a result, solid solution metals always have higher strengths than do pure metals.

• *Generation of dislocations.* A single dislocation produces a strain of only one Burgers vector. Therefore, it is obvious that many dislocations must be involved before any measurable plastic deformation can occur, and a dislocation source must be available to generate new dislocations. A source for dislocations frequently requires crystal boundaries or other imperfections that anchor the ends of a dislocation loop (Fig. 4–13c). For example, consider Fig. 6–19, which shows the full extension of the half loop in Fig. 4–13(c). As the shear is continued, the loop expands and eventually closes on itself, at which time a second loop is started.

---

* This statement does not apply if (1) the movement includes an increase in the length of the dislocation loop (Fig. 6–19), or (2) there is a pile-up of dislocations (Fig. 6–20). These situations will be considered later.

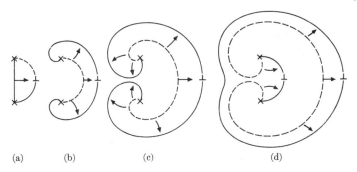

(a)   (b)   (c)   (d)

FIG. 6-19. Dislocation generation. (a) The dotted part of the loop is that part of the dislocation loop shown in Fig. 4-13(c). X = anchor points. (b-d) Extension of the dislocation loop with additional shear. As the loop closes on itself, it forms a second loop.

FIG. 6-20. Dislocation pile-up. A boundary or surface hinders continued dislocation movements. ⊥ = edge dislocation.

Thus, a continuous series of edge dislocations can be moved through a crystal along a specific crystal plane.

As the number of dislocations along the plane increases, more shear force is required. However, this is not significant unless there is interference by some other structural feature, such as a grain boundary. A pile-up of dislocations, as indicated in Fig. 6-20, is important because it increases the resistance of the metal to further slip.

• **Example 6-4**

Presumably two of the dislocations shown in Fig. 6-20 could condense into one double dislocation with two extra planes of atoms. How much more force would be required to move the double dislocation?

Answer: The value of Burgers vector b is doubled. Therefore, from Eq. (6-9), the shear force would need to be increased by a factor of four over that of one single dislocation, or a factor of two over two single dislocations.

6-6 Plastic deformation in polycrystalline metals. Grain boundaries interfere with slip because the planes on which dislocations move are not continued through the material. Figure 6-21 shows the effect of grain size on ductility and tensile strength in an annealed 70-30 brass (i.e., 70 w/o copper and 30 w/o zinc). The change in ductility and tensile strength is a direct reflection of the grain boundary area within the brass and the effect that the boundary has on slip.

Yield strength. The yield strength of polycrystalline metals has a complex origin. (1) As noted in Fig. 6–9, the various grains do not have the same elastic stresses when the metal is loaded. (2) The resolved shear stresses vary with grain orientation. (3) The critical shear stress which is required for slip depends on the crystal plane and crystal direction. (4) There are a number of possible slip planes within a crystal (Fig. 6–13). The above four factors* make it obvious that a polycrystalline metal does not have a unique elastic limit. Therefore, a gradual initiation of plastic deformation (Fig. 1–3) is to be expected, and it becomes desirable to define the yield strength as the stress for a finite amount of plastic deformation. Commonly, 0.2% is used (Fig. 1–5c).

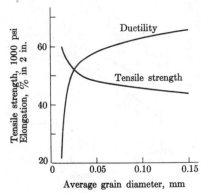

FIG. 6–21. Grain size versus strength or ductility (annealed 70–30 brass).

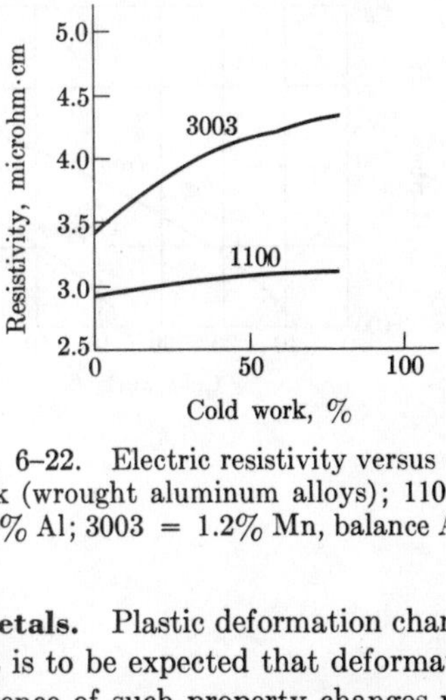

FIG. 6–22. Electric resistivity versus cold work (wrought aluminum alloys); 1100 = 99.9% Al; 3003 = 1.2% Mn, balance Al.

6–7 Properties of plastically deformed metals. Plastic deformation changes the internal structure of a metal; therefore, it is to be expected that deformation also changes the properties of a metal. Evidence of such property changes may be obtained through resistivity measurements. The distorted structure reduces the mean free path of electron movements (Sections 5–4 and 5–7), and therefore increases the resistivity (Fig. 6–22).

In the figure just cited, as well as in other cases, it is convenient to refer to the amount of *cold work* as an index of plastic deformation. Cold work is the amount of distortion resulting from a reduction in cross-sectional area during plastic deformation:

$$\mathrm{CW} = \left[\frac{A_o - A_f}{A_o}\right] 100, \qquad (6\text{–}10)$$

where A_o and A_f are the original and final areas respectively.

---

* A minor amount of deformation can also occur by twinning and kinking. However, we shall not consider these mechanisms here.

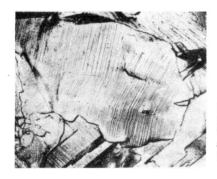

FIG. 6–23.   Plastically   deformed, polycrystalline copper (×25). The traces of the slip planes are revealed at the polished surface of the metal. (B. A. Rogers.)

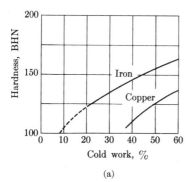

(a)

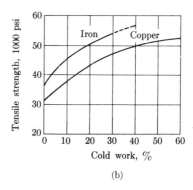

(b)

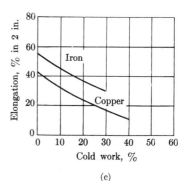

(c)

FIG. 6–24. Cold work versus mechanical properties (iron and copper).

Strain hardening. The traces of slip planes of cold-worked copper in Fig. 6–23 show that deformation has occurred. Dislocation movements along the slip planes and the distortion of the planes arising from restraint by adjacent grains have disordered the regular crystalline pattern which was initially present. Therefore, additional slip occurs less readily, and the hardness of the metal is increased (Figs. 6–24 and 6–25).

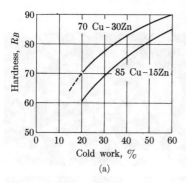

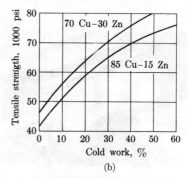

FIG. 6–25. Cold work versus mechanical properties (brasses).

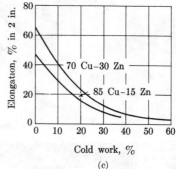

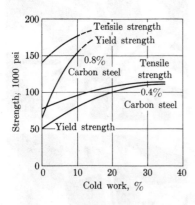

FIG. 6–26. Cold work versus strength of plain carbon steels.

The increase in hardness that results from plastic deformation is called *strain hardening*. Laboratory tests show that an increase in both tensile strength and yield strength accompanies this increase in hardness. On the other hand, strain hardening reduces ductility, because part of the "elongation" takes place during cold work, before the gage marks (Fig. 1–4) are placed on the test bar. Thus, less elongation is observed during testing. The process of strain hardening increases yield strength more than tensile strength (Fig. 6–26), and the two approach the true breaking strength (Fig. 1–5d) as the amount of cold work is increased.

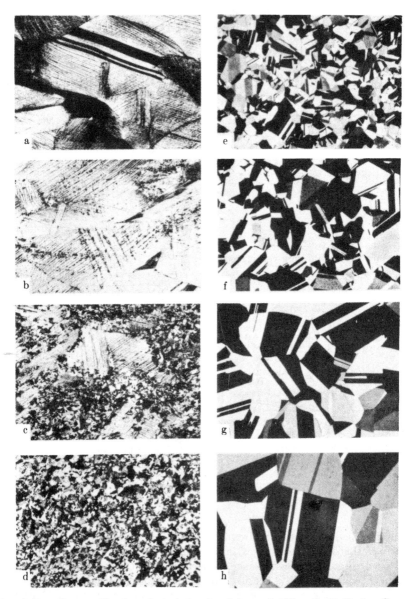

FIG. 6–27.   Recrystallization of strain-hardened brass (×40).   (J. E. Burke, General Electric Co., Schenectady, N.Y.)   Parts (a) through (h) show additional recrystallization and grain growth at elevated temperatures.

6–8 Recrystallization. Crystals which have been plastically deformed, like those in Fig. 6–23, have more energy than unstrained crystals because they are loaded with dislocations and other imperfections. Given a chance, the atoms will move to form a more perfect, unstrained array. Such an opportunity arises when the crystals are subjected to high temperatures, through the process called *annealing*. The greater thermal vibrations of the lattice at high temperatures permit a reordering of the atoms into less distorted grains. Figure 6–27 shows the progress of this *recrystallization*, including subsequent *grain growth*.

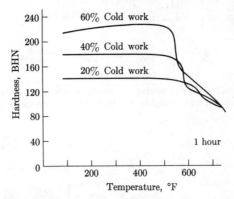

FIG. 6–28. Softening by recrystallization. The harder, more highly strained 65Cu-35Zn brass recrystallizes at lower temperatures with less thermal energy. (After ASM data.)

Recrystallization temperatures. Since recrystallization forms softer crystals, hardness values are good indexes of the occurrence of recrystallization. Figure 6–28 shows the variation with increased temperatures of hardness in strain-hardened 65Cu-35Zn brass. The temperature of marked softening is called the *recrystallization temperature.* As indicated in this figure, a highly strain-hardened metal is crystallographically more unstable than a metal with less cold work, because the metal with more cold work will soften at lower temperatures. Recrystallization temperature is also affected by length of time of heating. Since longer heating times give the atoms more opportunity to realign themselves, recrystallization occurs at lower temperatures.

Recrystallization requires realignment or diffusion of the atoms in a material; therefore, the temperature required for recrystallization depends on the forces holding the atoms together. This conclusion is consistent with the fact that the thermal energy required for melting is related to the forces holding the atoms together. Accordingly, it is natural to expect that there might be some correlation between the recrystallization and melting temperatures. Figure 6–29 compares these temperatures for a number of common metals. Although there are exceptions,

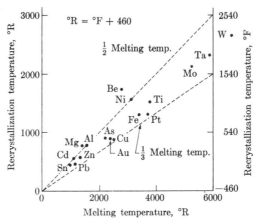

FIG. 6–29. Recrystallization temperature versus melting temperature. The average recrystallization temperature is roughly one-half the absolute melting temperature.

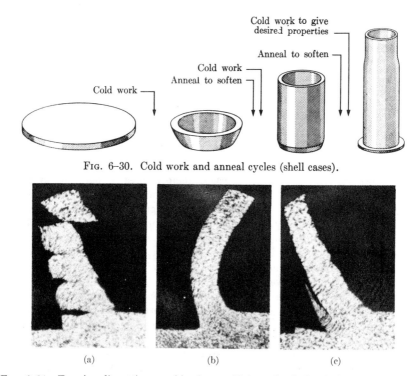

FIG. 6–30. Cold work and anneal cycles (shell cases).

(a)   (b)   (c)

FIG. 6–31. Forming discontinuous chips by machining. Strain-hardening facilitates the production of these chips because the ductility is decreased. (Hans Ernst, Cincinnati Milling Machine Co.)

the recrystallization temperature is between one-third and one-half of the (absolute*) melting temperature.

Hot-working versus cold-working of metals. In production operations, the distinction between *hot-working* and *cold-working* does not rest on temperature alone, but on the relationship of the processing temperature to the recrystallization temperature. Hot-working is performed above the recrystallization temperature; cold-working is performed below it. Thus the temperature for cold-working copper may be higher than that for hot-working lead.

The choice of the recrystallization temperature as the point for distinguishing between hot- and cold-working is quite logical from the production point of view. Below the recrystallization temperature, the metal becomes harder and less ductile with additional mechanical working. More power is required for deformation and there is a greater chance for cracking during the process. Above the recrystallization temperature, the metal will anneal itself during, or immediately after, the mechanical working. It remains soft and relatively ductile.

Engineering significance of cold-working and annealing. Cold work is of prime importance to the design engineer. It permits him to use smaller parts with greater strength. Of course, the product must not be used at temperatures which will anneal the metals.

Cold work limits the amount of plastic deformation which a metal can subsequently undergo during a shaping operation. The hardened, less ductile metal requires more power for working and is subject to cracking. Figure 6–30 shows a *cold-work-anneal cycle* which is used to assist production.

The loss of ductility during cold-working has a useful side effect in machining. With less ductility, the chips break more readily (Fig. 6–31) and facilitate the cutting operation.

Example 6–5

A 70-30 brass rod is required to have a diameter of 0.21 in., a tensile strength of more than 60,000 psi, and an elongation of more than 20%. The rod is to be drawn from a larger 0.35-in. rod. Specify the final processing steps for making the 0.21-in. rod.

Answer: From Fig. 6–25,

$$CW > 15\% \text{ for TS}, \quad CW < 23\% \text{ for El.}$$

Use 20% cold work as last drawing step. By Eq. (6–10),

$$0.20 = \frac{d^2\pi/4 - (0.21)^2\pi/4}{d^2\pi/4},$$

$$d = 0.235 \text{ in.}$$

Hot-work from 0.35 in. to 0.235 in. (or cold-work and anneal in one or more cycles). The rod should be annealed at 0.235 in. diameter. Cold-draw 20% to 0.21 in. diameter.

---

* °K = °C + 273, or °R = °F + 460.

FAILURE OF METALS

6–9 Introduction. Although most engineering designs call for metals which will not fail, it is desirable to know something about the failure of metals. An insight into the types of failure of metals will aid us in producing better designs, because we shall know the limitations which are to be encountered, including: (1) creep, (2) fracture, and (3) fatigue. Each will be considered in turn.

6–10 Creep. Strength and strain characteristics of materials are time-dependent, as is shown schematically in Fig. 6–32. When a metal is stressed, it undergoes immediate elastic elongation, and in the first short period of time makes additional plastic adjustments at points of stress along grain boundaries and at flaws. After these initial adjustments, a slow, nearly steady rate of strain, called *creep*, sets in and continues until sufficient strain has occurred so that a necking down and reduction of cross-sectional area occurs. After this and until *rupture*, the rate of elongation increases because there is less area to support the load. If the load were reduced so that the applied stress remained the same, the straight line of Stage 2 in the figure would continue until failure.*

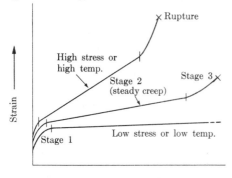

FIG. 6–32. Creep. The steady rate of creep in the second stage determines the useful life of the material.

Creep rate is defined as strain/time during the period of steady elongation. It is equal to the slope of the curves in Fig. 6–32 after the initial elastic and plastic adjustments have been made. The following relationships are shown schematically: (1) The steady creep rate increases with temperature. (2) The steady creep rate increases with stress. (3) The total elongation at rupture increases with stress. (4) The time before eventual failure by rupture is decreased as the temperature (and therefore the creep rate) is increased.

These relationships are corroborated by the data in Fig. 6–33. In Fig. 6–33(a), the creep rate is plotted against stress for different temperature parameters. Except for minor inflections which are associated with secondary structural changes in the alloy, a direct logarithmic relationship exists between the stress and the

---

* Accelerated deformation may also arise if a phase change or marked intergranular oxidation occurs during testing or service.

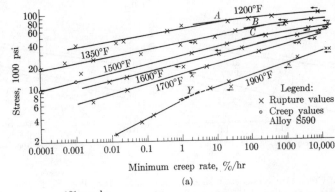

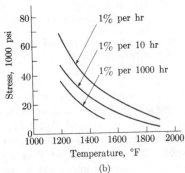

FIG. 6-33.   Creep rate versus stress versus temperature.   The minimum creep is the second-stage creep of Fig. 6-32.   (N. J. Grant, "Stress Rupture Testing," *High Temperature Properties of Metals.* Cleveland: American Society for Metals, 1951.)

creep rate. Part (b) of the figure plots the same data but with stress and temperature as the main variables and creep rate as the constant parameter.

• *Creep mechanisms.* The mechanism of creep is related to the movements of dislocations. At low temperatures strain is restricted because the dislocation movements are stopped by grain boundaries, or by impurity atoms.   However, at higher temperatures atomic movements permit the dislocations to *climb, jog,* or even be annihilated, as shown in Fig. 6-34. As vacancies and atoms move to and from the dislocation, the dislocation can climb out of the initial slip plane, thus permitting the continuation of incremental stress, or creep.

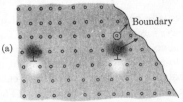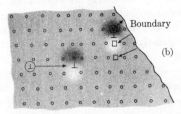

FIG. 6-34.   Dislocation climb.   At higher temperatures, the diffusion of vacancies (□) to edge dislocations (or of atoms away from the dislocations) permits dislocations to climb to another plane, thus relieving dislocation pile-ups and permitting the continuation of incremental strain, or creep, at low stresses.

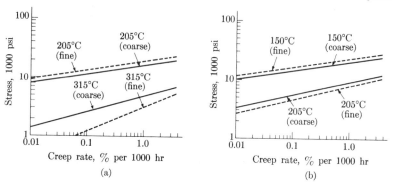

FIG. 6–35. Creep rate versus grain size. (a) 77Cu-22Zn-1Sn alloy; ECT, approx. 250°C. (b) 59Cu-40Zn-1Sn alloy; ECT, approx. 175°C. Above the equicohesive temperature, coarse-grained metals are stronger than fine-grained metals. The opposite is true at lower temperatures. (Adapted from C. L. Clark and A. E. White, "Influence of Recrystallization Temperature and Grain Size on the Creep Characteristics of Non-Ferrous Alloys," *Proceedings A.S.T.M.*, **32** (*II*), 42, 1932.)

Although at low temperatures grain boundaries provide interference to dislocation movements, they also provide sources (and sinks) of atoms, and vacancies which permit dislocation climbs during creep. Therefore, we find that as the temperature is increased the role of the grain boundary is reversed from one of resisting deformation to one of aiding deformation. The temperature of inversion is called the *equicohesive temperature* (ECT), and of course is important in the design of materials to be used at high temperatures (Fig. 6–35). In these two examples the equicohesive temperatures are 250°C and 175°C. The ECT increases with the melting temperatures of the alloy.

6–11 Fracture. Complete rupturing of a material may involve *ductile fracture* in which plastic deformation is continued to a 100% reduction of area [Eq. (1–2)]; or final rupture may result from a *brittle failure*, in which adjacent parts of the metal are separated by stresses normal to the fracture surface. Because brittle failure does not produce plastic deformation, it requires less energy than a ductile failure, where energy is introduced in the process of forming dislocations and other imperfections within the crystals.

Cleavage fracture. Fracture paths are usually between adjacent crystal planes, particularly between those planes with fewer interatomic bonds. We are familiar with cleavage fracture in mica and in diamond where the fracture surfaces are quite specific. Similar fracture paths are found in bcc and hcp metals, but not in fcc metals. A coarsely granular iron, for example, may be fractured to reveal small cleavage facets which formed as the crack propagated *transgranularly*.* (The lay-

---

* Some fcc materials fracture *intergranularly* if there has been a precipitation of a brittle phase along the grain boundaries; for example, an annealed alloy of Al and CuAl₂ (Fig. 11–17 D).

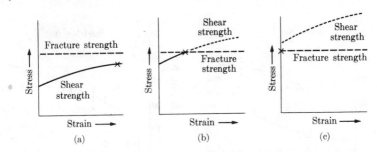

Fig. 6–36. Shear and fracture strengths. (a) Ductile failure. (b) Combined failure.
(c) Brittle failure. The cross indicates the point of failure.

man commonly considers that such a metal has been "crystallized," although, in
reality, all solid metals are crystalline.)

A schematic contrast between brittle fracture and ductile failure will be helpful to us. Figure 6–36 shows the relative stresses required for both types of failure.
In case (a), failure occurs ductilely before the level of fracture stress is reached.
This is the case for fcc metals. In case (c), fracture occurs before deformation can
occur by shear, e.g., glass, mica, or cast iron. In case (b), there is an overlap
which is typical of many metals such as iron. Plastic deformation starts, but
strain-hardening increases the tolerable stress until the fracture strength is exceeded. Thus, it is not uncommon to find metals undergoing some reduction in
area before a final brittle fracture.

Impact strength. Toughness was defined in Section 1–2 as the energy required
to fracture a material. These energy requirements are often more important in
engineering design than actual tensile strengths, particularly if the metal is used
in a dynamic application. The term *impact strength* is used to denote toughness,
and is commonly measured in foot-pounds. ("Impact strength" is a misnomer;
however, it has become well established, so no attempt will be made here to change
it to "impact energy.") Impact strength is sensitive to *rate of loading* and to
temperature, as well as to stress raisers.

Under impact loading, there is only
limited time available for uniform plastic
deformation. Hence deformation may
locally exceed the fracture stress at geometric irregularities, grain boundaries,
or other imperfections, so that a crack
is initiated. Once initiated, the crack itself causes a concentration of stresses; as
a result the crack is propagated to complete fracture. With slower loading rates
or at higher temperatures, the shear
strength curves are lowered (Fig. 6–37)
and the material becomes more ductile.

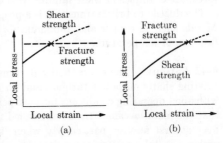

Fig. 6–37. Deformation prior to fracture.
(a) Low temperature or high rate of loading. (b) High temperature or slow loading.

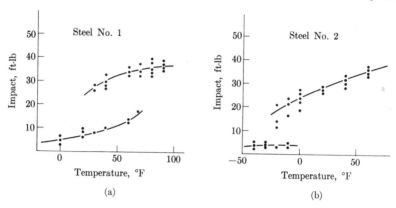

FIG. 6–38. Transition temperatures (ship plate steel). For each steel, there is a marked change in toughness at lower temperatures. The transition temperature is significantly lower for Steel No. 2 than for Steel No. 1. (Adapted from N. A. Kahn and E. A. Imbembo, "Reproducibility of the Single Blow Charpy Notch-Bar Test," *A.S.T.M. Bull.*, **146**, 66, 1947.)

Transition temperatures. When bcc metals are subjected to impact loads at comparatively low temperatures, a transition occurs from ductile fracture requiring high energies to nonductile fracture requiring lower energy. Figure 6–38 shows this transition for two different steels used for ship plates. Because the transition usually occurs over a range of temperatures, the *transition temperature* is often identified with a given impact energy level, for example 10 or 15 ft·lb.

This transition can become quite important to the engineer who is designing a structure which will be subject to impact stresses. When the transition temperature is below operating temperatures, brittle-type fractures will not occur. Thus, of the two steels whose transition temperatures are shown in Fig. 6–38, Steel No. 2 would be quite satisfactory for ship design because its transition temperature is below temperatures normally encountered by ships. Steel No. 1 could produce brittle fracture at ambient temperatures. There were a number of unfortunate examples of these failures with our Liberty ships during World War II.

The ductile-to-brittle transition is a property of bcc metals but not of fcc metals. Metals such as copper and aluminum do not change abruptly in toughness as a function of temperature.

6–12 Fatigue. There are many documented examples of eventual failure of rotating shafts on power turbines and on other mechanical equipment which had withstood operating conditions for long periods of time. The common explanation that the metal became "tired" and failed from *fatigue* is more appropriate than it may at first appear, particularly when it is known that the stresses developed within a metal are alternating stresses.

The stress a material can tolerate under cyclic loading is much less than it is under static loading. The yield strength, which is a measure of the static stress a

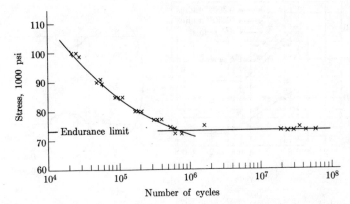

FIG. 6–39. S-N curve for 4340 steel, hot-worked bar stock. (S-N = permissible Stress versus the Number of cycles before failure.) Low stresses permit more cycles until, at the endurance limit, the number is nearly infinite. (Adapted from M. F. Garwood, H. H. Zurburg, and M. A. Erickson, "Correlation of Laboratory Tests and Service Performance," *Interpretation of Tests and Correlation with Service.* Cleveland: American Society for Metals, 1951.)

material will resist without permanent deformation, can be used as a guide only for structures that operate under static loading. Figure 6–39 shows the number of stress cycles before failure in a steel which has been repeatedly loaded. To increase the number of possible stress cycles in a machine, it is necessary to reduce the stress placed on the components. Fortunately, many materials have stress levels that permit an almost infinite number of cycles without failure. The level of maximum stress before failure, represented by the horizontal part of the curve in Fig. 6–39, is called the *endurance limit.*

Mechanism of fatigue. A decrease in usable strength under cyclic loading is directly attributable to the fact that the material is not an ideal homogeneous solid. In each half cycle, minute strains that are not completely reversible are produced. Close observation indicates that fatigue failure develops in the following pattern: (1) repeated cyclic stressing causes incremental slip and cold-working locally, (2) gradual reduction of ductility in the strain-hardened areas results in the formation of submicroscopic cracks, and (3) the notch effect of the submicroscopic cracks concentrates stresses until complete fracture occurs.

Fatigue failure is thus related to nonuniform plastic deformation (Sections 6–5 and 6–6), rather than to ideal reversible elastic behavior. These irreversible strains are localized along slip planes, at grain boundaries, and around surface irregularities of compositional or geometric defects. The influence of geometric irregularities (notches) is illustrated in Fig. 6–40 and Table 6–3. All three sets of data in Fig. 6–40 are for identical steels. The samples with a fillet of $\frac{1}{8}$-in. radius had an endurance limit only two-thirds as high as those with fillets of larger radii (Figs. 6–40 and 6–41).

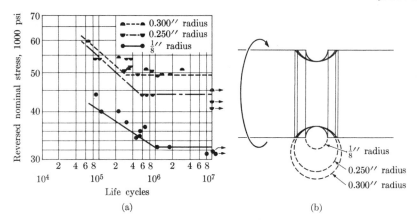

(a)   (b)

FIG. 6–40. S-N curves for filleted specimens (cf. Fig. 6–41). The smaller radii of curvatures permit higher stress concentrations and therefore lower endurance limits. (M. F. Garwood, H. H. Zurburg, and M. A. Erickson, "Correlation of Laboratory Tests and Service Performance," *Interpretation of Tests and Correlation with Service.* Cleveland: American Society for Metals, 1951.)

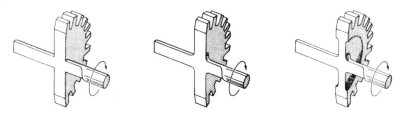

(a) Poor design   (b) Better design   (c) Better design

FIG. 6–41. Design of fillets. The use of generous fillets in mechanical design reduces the possibility of stress concentrations and fatigue in cyclically stressed parts. Surprisingly, a component with less material, (c) versus (a), may have lower stress concentrations if fillets are included.

Equally important is the nature of the *surface finish* of the part which is repeatedly stressed. Surface characteristics are of major importance, since the surface is usually more highly stressed than any other location. Table 6–3 shows the effect of surface finish on a 4063 steel which was quenched and tempered to R_C 44. Reduction of surface irregularities measurably increases the endurance limit, since macroscopic notches and microscopic surface irregularities concentrate stresses. These locations will undergo plastic deformation under loads which would not deform the bulk of the material, and therefore the design engineer will specify smoother surface finishes at points most subject to fatigue failure. However, it is poor economy to overspecify surface finish at locations which are not highly stressed.

TABLE 6-3

SURFACE FINISH VERSUS ENDURANCE LIMIT
(SAE 4063 steel, quenched and tempered to R_C 44)*

Type of finish	Surface roughness, micro-inches	Endurance limit, psi
Circumferential grind	16–25	91,300
Machine lapped	12–20	104,700
Longitudinal grind	8–12	112,000
Superfinished (polished)	3–6	114,000
Superfinished (polished)	0.5–2	116,750

* Adapted from M. F. Garwood, H. H. Zurburg, and M. A. Erickson, "Correlation of Laboratory Tests and Service Performance," *Interpretation of Tests and Correlation with Service.* Cleveland: American Society for Metals, 1951.

References for Further Reading

6-1. CLARK, D. S., and W. R. VARNEY, *Physical Metallurgy for Engineers*, second edition. New York: D. Van Nostrand, 1962. Chapters 4 and 5 discuss physical and mechanical properties of metals. Applications receive attention.

6-2. BIRCHENALL, C. E., *Physical Metallurgy*. New York: McGraw-Hill, 1959. Chapters 5–8 supply supplementary reading for this chapter.

6-3. DIETER, G. E., *Mechanical Metallurgy*. New York: McGraw-Hill, 1961. Complete presentation of mechanical behavior. Advanced undergraduate and instructor level.

6-4. DOLAN, T. J., "Basic Concepts of Fatigue Damage in Metals," *Fatigue*. Cleveland: American Society for Metals. Dolan's article elaborates on the nature of fatigue beyond the scope of this book. Recommended for the student as supplementary reading on fatigue.

6-5. GRANT, N. J., "Creep and Fracture at Elevated Temperatures," *Utilization of Heat Resistant Alloys*. Cleveland: American Society for Metals, 1954. For the advanced metallurgical student. A summary of the failure mechanism.

6-6. GUY, A. G., *Elements of Physical Metallurgy*. Reading, Mass.: Addison-Wesley, 1959. Chapter 9 on plasticity of metals. Chapter 12 on recovery, recrystallization, and grain growth. For the student who wants information in addition to that in this book.

6-7. GUY, A. G., *Physical Metallurgy for Engineers*. Reading, Mass.: Addison-Wesley, 1962. Chapters 6 and 7 present properties of metals at the introductory level.

6-8. KEYSER, C. A., *Basic Engineering Metallurgy*. Englewood Cliffs, N. J.: Prentice-Hall, 1959. Chapters 3, 6, 10, and 11 provide supplementary reading for this chapter. Introductory level.

6-9. LESSELS, J. M., *Strength and Resistance of Metals*. New York: John Wiley & Sons, 1954. Chapter 5 discusses impact fracture; Chapters 6, 7, and 8, fatigue; Chapter 9, strain hysteresis; and Chapter 10, mechanical wear. Each of these uses mathematics at the introductory mechanics level. Recommended for the advanced student.

6–10. MASON, C. W., *Introductory Physical Metallurgy.* Cleveland: American Society for Metals, 1947. Chapter 2 on alloys as solid solutions. Chapter 3 on working and annealing of metals. For the beginning student.

6–11. *Metals Handbook.* Cleveland: American Society for Metals, 1961. The encyclopedia of metals with particular reference to industrial requirements. For all engineers.

6–12. ROGERS, B. A., *The Nature of Metals.* Ames, Iowa: Iowa State University Press, and Cleveland: American Society for Metals, 1951. Chapter 1 on grains in metals. Chapter 10 on how metals are deformed. Chapter 11 on recrystallization. For the beginning student.

6–13. SINNOTT, M. J., *Solid State for Engineers.* New York: John Wiley & Sons, 1958. Chapters 10–14 and 16–18 present properties of metals on an advanced undergraduate level. Recommended for the instructor.

6–14. SMOLUCHOWSKI, R., "The Metallic State: Theory of Some Properties of Metals and Alloys," and "Dislocations in Solids," *The Science of Engineering Materials.* New York: John Wiley & Sons, 1957. Both these articles were written particularly for the instructor. However, they are readable by the advanced student.

6–15. SMITH, G. V., *Properties of Metals at Elevated Temperatures.* New York: McGraw-Hill, 1950. Chapter 4 discusses creep in polycrystalline metals. Recommended for the advanced student as supplementary reading.

Problems

6–1. Based on Fig. 6–1, what is the electrical resistivity of annealed 70-30 brass? *Answer:* 2.5 microhm·in.

6–2. A copper wire has a resistance of 0.5 ohm per 100 ft. Consideration is being given to the use of a 75-25 brass wire instead of copper. What would be the resistance, if the brass wire were the same size?

6–3. A brass alloy is to be used in an application which will have tensile strength of more than 40,000 psi and an electrical resistivity of less than 5×10^{-6} ohm·cm (resistivity of Cu = 1.7×10^{-6} ohm·cm). What percent zinc should the brass have? *Answer:* 14 to 27% zinc

6–4. A motorboat requires a seat brace. Iron is excluded because it rusts. Select the most appropriate alloy from Figs. 6–1 and 6–2. The requirements include: a tensile strength of at least 45,000 psi; a ductility of 45% elongation (in 2 in.); and low cost. [*Note:* Zinc is cheaper than copper.]

6–5. A brass wire must carry a load of 10 lb without deformation, and have a resistance of less than 0.01 ohm per foot. (a) What is the smallest wire that can be used if it is made of 60-40 brass? (b) 80-20 brass? (c) 100% Cu? *Answer:* (a) 0.07 in. dia. (b) 0.053 in. dia. (c) 0.057 in. dia.

6–6. A certain application requires a piece of metal having a yield strength greater than 15,000 psi and a thermal conductivity greater than 0.1 cal·cm/cm²·sec·°C. Specify either an annealed brass or an annealed Cu-Ni alloy that could be used.

6–7. The average grain dimension in a sample of copper is 1.0 mm. How many atoms are there per grain if we assume that the grains are spherical? *Answer:* 4.45×10^{19} atoms/grain

6-8. (a) How many grains of austenite per cubic inch exist in a steel with an ASTM grain size No. 2? (b) No. 8? (Assume cubes.)

6-9. Assuming that the grains are cubic in shape, (a) what is the grain boundary area in a steel with an ASTM austenite grain size No. 2? (b) No. 8?
Answer: (a) 425 in^2/in^3 (b) 3400 in^2/in^3

6-10. When iron is compressed hydrostatically with 30,000 psi, its volume is changed by 0.10%. How much will its volume change when it is stressed axially with 90,000 psi?

6-11. A test bar 0.5051 in. in dia. with 2-in. gage length is loaded elastically with 5,000 lb and is elongated 0.014 in. Its diameter is 0.5040 in. under load. (a) What is the bulk modulus of the bar? (b) the shear modulus?
Answer: (a) 22,000,000 psi (b) 9,500,000 psi

6-12. Assume that copper has a modulus of elasticity of 16,000,000 psi, a Poisson's ratio of 0.3, and is under a tensile stress of 12,000 psi. What would be the dimensions of the unit cell? (Stress is parallel to the axes.)

6-13. If copper has an axial stress of 14,000 psi, what will be the highest local stress within a polycrystalline copper bar?
Answer: 24,500 psi

• 6-14. An aluminum crystal slips on the (111) plane and in the [1$\overline{1}$0] direction with a 500-psi stress applied in the [1$\overline{1}$1] direction. What is the critical resolved shear stress?

• 6-15. (a) What is the normal stress perpendicular to the (110) plane in the above problem? (b) Perpendicular to the (001) plane?
Answer: (a) Zero (b) 167 psi

6-16. How much greater is the energy of a dislocation in tungsten with a [110] Burgers vector than one with (a) a [100] vector? (b) a [111] vector?

6-17. Show why slip occurs more readily on (110) planes of chromium than on (111) planes.
Answer: Cf. Burgers vectors

6-18. Show why slip occurs more readily on (111) planes of copper than on (110) planes.

6-19. A copper wire 0.10 in. in diameter was annealed before cold-drawing it through a die 0.08 in. in diameter. What tensile strength does the wire have after cold-drawing?
Answer: 48,000 psi

6-20. A pure iron sheet 0.10 in. thick is annealed before cold-rolling it to 0.08 in. (negligible change in width). (a) What would be the ductility of the iron after cold-rolling? (b) Estimate the approximate temperature of recrystallization for this iron. (c) Give two reasons why the recrystallization temperature of any metal is not fixed.

6-21. Copper is to be used in a form with at least 45,000 psi tensile strength and at least 18% elongation. How much cold work should the copper receive?
Answer: 25% cold work

6-22. Iron is to have a BHN of at least 125 and an elongation of at least 32%. How much cold work should the iron receive?

• Problems preceded by a bullet are based, in part, on optional sections.

6–23. A 70–30 brass (Fig. 6–25) wire with a tensile strength of more than 60,000 psi a hardness of less than R_B 75, and an elongation of more than 25% is to be made by cold drawing. The diameter as received is 0.25 in. The diameter of the final product is to be 0.10 in. Prescribe a procedure for obtaining these specifications.

Answer: 14 to 19% cold work; therefore it should be annealed when the diameter is 0.11 in. before the final 17% cold work.

6–24. A round bar of 85 Cu–15 Zn alloy 0.5 in. in diameter is to be cold-reduced to a bar 0.125 in. in dia. Suggest a procedure to be followed if a final tensile strength of 60,000 psi (or greater) is achieved along with a final ductility of at least 10% elongation (in 2-in. gage length).

6–25. A rolled 66 Cu–34 Zn brass plate 0.500 in. thick has a ductility of 2% elongation (in 2-in. gage length) when it is received from the supplier. This plate is to be rolled to a final thickness of 0.125 in. In this final form it is to have a tensile strength of at least 70,000 psi and a ductility of at least 7% elongation (in 2-in. gage length). Assuming that the rolling process which reduces a 0.500-in. plate to a 0.125-in. sheet does not change the width, specify *all steps* (including temperature, times, thickness, etc.) which are required.

6–26. A round bar of brass (85% Cu, 15% Zn) 0.20 in. in dia. is to be cold-drawn to wire that is 0.10 in. in dia. Specify a procedure for the drawing process such that the wire will have a hardness less than 72 R_B, a tensile strength greater than 60,000 psi, and a ductility of greater than 10% elongation.

6–27. The following data were obtained in creep-rupture test of Inconel "X" at 1500°F (a) 1% elongation after 10 hr, (b) 2% elongation after 200 hr, (c) 4% elongation after 2000 hr, (d) 6% elongation after 4000 hr, (e) "neck-down" started at 5000 hr and the rupture occurred at 5500 hr. What was the creep rate?

Answer: 0.001%/hr

6–28. Other things being equal, which will have the lowest creep rate: (a) steel in service with a high tensile stress and low temperature, (b) steel in service with a low tensile stress and high temperature, (c) steel in service with a high tensile stress and high temperature, (d) steel in service with a low tensile stress and low temperature? Why?

6–29. Look into the engine of an automobile. Name as many components as you can that would have to have endurance-limit specifications.

6–30. Make a two-page report on the failure of the British Comets. [T. Bishop, "Fatigue and the Comet Disasters," *Metal Progress*, **67**, 77–85 (May 1955).]

7

organic materials and their properties

7-1 Introduction. A second principal category of materials comprises the *organic materials*. Organic substances have served as engineering materials from the time of the first engineer. Wood has long been a common construction material, and such natural organic substances as leather for gaskets, felt for packings, cork for insulation, fibers for binding, oils for lubrication, and resins for protective coatings are extensively used by engineers.

Early in the history of the use of organic materials, attempts were made to improve their engineering properties. For example, the properties of wood are highly directional; the strength parallel to the grain is 50% greater than in the perpendicular direction. The development of plywood has helped to overcome this difficulty, and still better physical properties are obtained when the pores of the wood are impregnated with a thermosetting resin.

The ingenuity of technologists in working with organic materials has not been limited to improving natural organic materials; many synthetic substances have been developed as well. For example, the field of *plastics** has given the engineer an infinitely greater variety of materials for his applications. Great strides have been and continue to be made in the utilization of such materials (Fig. 7–1).

Whether the engineer is working with natural organic materials or with artificial ones, he is concerned primarily with the nature and characteristics of *large*

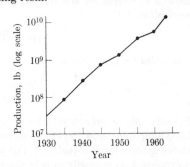

FIG. 7–1. Production of artificial resins (rubber is not included).

molecules. In natural materials, large molecules are "built in" by nature; in artificial materials, they are built by *deliberately joining small molecules.*

7-2 Molecular weights. We noted earlier that the melting temperature of a paraffin is related to the size of the molecule (Fig. 3–7). In general, those plastics made up of large molecules are stronger and more resistant to thermal and mechanical stresses than are those composed of small molecules (Fig. 7–2). Examples

---

* Strictly speaking, *plastic* is an adjective defining a permanently deformable material (Section 1–2), but by common usage "plastics" denotes organic materials which have been shaped by plastic deformation. This is the usage we shall follow here.

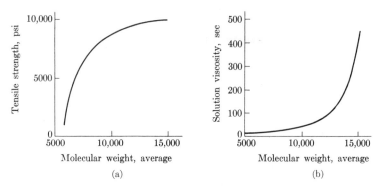

FIG. 7–2.   Polymer size versus polymer properties (copolymer of vinyl chloride and vinyl acetate). (a) Tensile strength. (b) Viscosity. Adapted from G. O. Crume and S. D. Douglas, *Ind. Eng. Chem.* **28,** 1123, 1936.

of this type of relationship between molecule size and properties exist for such artificial organic plastics as polyvinyl chloride, nylon, saran, etc., and such natural substances as cellulose, rubber, waxes, and shellac.

Degree of polymerization. The size of a molecule is determined by dividing the molecular weight by the mer weight. This number is called the *degree of polymerization, DP:*

$$DP = \frac{molecular\ weight}{mer\ weight}. \qquad (7\text{--}1)$$

The units for this expression are

$$\frac{gm/gm\text{-}mole}{gm/gm\text{-}mer} = \frac{mers}{mole}.$$

For example, a polyvinyl chloride molecule (Fig. 3–9) containing 1000 carbons, 1500 hydrogens, and 500 chlorines contains 500 mers, each with 2, 3, and 1 of the above atoms; for this molecule DP = 500. In commercial plastics the degree of polymerization normally falls in the range of 75 to 750 mers per molecule.

The molecule described above has a molecular weight of more than 31,200. Such a value differs by a major order of magnitude from that of other molecules. However, as large as the polymer molecule appears to be by weight, it is still smaller than the resolving power of an optical microscope, and only under certain circumstances can it be resolved even by an electron microscope. Consequently, molecular weight determinations are usually made indirectly by such physical means as measurement of viscosity, osmotic pressure, or light scattering, all of which are affected by the number, size, or shape of molecules in a suspension or in a solution (Fig. 7–2b).

Average molecular weights. When a material like polyethylene or polyvinyl chloride is formed from small molecules, not all the resulting large molecules are identical in size. As might be expected, some grow larger than others. As a result, plastics contain a range of molecular sizes, somewhat analogous to the mixture of ropane, hexane, octane, and other paraffin hydrocarbons in crude oils. Hence it necessary to calculate the *average* degree of polymerization if a single index is esired.

One procedure for determining average molecular weights (Fig. 7–3) utilizes the eight fraction of the polymer that is in each of several size fractions. The *"weight-erage" molecular weight* $\overline{M}_w$ is calculated as follows:

$$\overline{M}_w = \frac{\sum [(W_i)(MW)_i]}{\sum W_i}, \qquad (7\text{–}2)$$

here W_i is the weight fraction of each size fraction and $(MW)_i$ is the mean molec-lar weight of the size fraction. The "weight-average" molecular weight is par-cularly significant in the analysis of properties such as viscosity, where the eight of the molecules is important.

xample 7–1

It has been determined that a polyvinyl acetate (see Appendix F) has the molecular ze distribution shown in Fig. 7–3. What is the "weight-average" molecular weight and e average degree of polymerization?

Answer: On the basis of weight fraction of polyvinyl acetate,

Range of molecular weights, gm/mol wt	$(MW)_i$, gm/mol wt	W_i, fraction	$(W_i)(MW)_i$, gm/mol wt
5,000–10,000	7,500	0.12	900
10,000–15,000	12,500	0.18	2,250
15,000–20,000	17,500	0.26	4,550
20,000–25,000	22,500	0.21	4,725
25,000–30,000	27,500	0.14	3,850
30,000–35,000	32,500	0.09	2,925
$\sum$		1.00	19,200

$$\overline{M}_w = \frac{\sum [(W_i)(MW)_i]}{\sum W_i}$$

$$= 19,200 \frac{gm}{ave \ mol \ wt}.$$

ler weight of vinyl acetate (Appendix F):

$$C_4H_6O_2 = 48 + 6 + 32 = 86 \frac{gm}{mer \ wt}.$$

$$DP = \frac{19,200}{86} = 224.$$

Units: $\dfrac{gm/ave \ mol \ wt}{gm/mer \ wt} = \dfrac{mers}{ave \ mol \ wt}.$

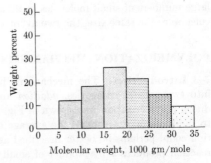

FIG. 7–3. Polymer size distribution (see Example 7–1).

Properties such as strength (Fig. 7–2a) are more sensitive to the numbers of molecules in each weight fraction than to the actual weight. Hence, a *"number average" molecular weight* $\overline{M}_n$ has some significance:

$$\overline{M}_n = \frac{\sum [(X_i)(MW)_i]}{\sum X_i}. \tag{7-3}$$

The value X_i is the number of molecules in each size fraction, and is calculated as shown in Example 7–2.

Example 7–2

Determine the "number-average" molecular weight for the polymer of Example 7–1.

Answer: On the basis of 100 gm polyvinyl acetate.

Range of molecular weights, gm/mol wt	X_i, molecules	$(X_i)(MW)_i$
5,000–10,000	(12)(AN)*/7,500	(12)(AN)
10,000–15,000	(18)(AN)/12,500	(18)(AN)
15,000–20,000	(26)(AN)/17,500	(26)(AN)
20,000–25,000	(21)(AN)/22,500	(21)(AN)
25,000–30,000	(14)(AN)/27,500	(14)(AN)
30,000–35,000	(9)(AN)/32,500	(9)(AN)
$\sum$	(0.00624)(AN)	(100)(AN)

$$\overline{M}_n = \frac{100(AN)}{(0.00624)(AN)} = 16,010 \text{ gm/mole}$$

* AN = Avogadro's number.

Whenever there is a distribution in sizes, the "number-average" molecular weight will be less than the "weight-average" molecular weight, because of the large numbers of small molecules in the smaller weight fractions. If all the molecules were the same size, the two averages would be identical.

POLYMERIZATION MECHANISMS

7–3 Introduction. The mechanisms by which polymerization takes place fall into two general categories, *addition* and *condensation*. The prototype for addition polymerization was shown in Fig. 3–8, in which succeeding mers are added to the molecule to increase the average molecule size. Condensation polymerization could perhaps be better described as by-product polymerization, because the reaction produces a by-product of small molecules, such as H_2O, along with the growing polymer molecule. This mechanism will be discussed in Section 7–5.

Functionality. Since a monomer, or other small molecule, must be grafted onto growing molecule in order to produce polymeric molecules, each monomer must ave *two or more* reaction sites at which junctions may be made. Consider the reviously cited ethylene (Fig. 3–8); when the double bond is broken, two single onds become available for connections:

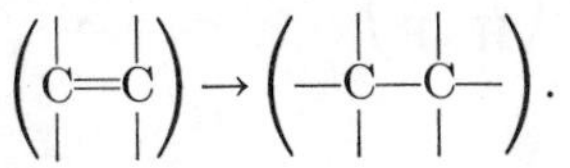

$$\left(\begin{array}{c} | \quad | \\ C = C \\ | \quad | \end{array}\right) \rightarrow \left(\begin{array}{c} | \quad | \\ -C-C- \\ | \quad | \end{array}\right). \tag{7-4}$$

hus, ethylene is considered to be *bifunctional.* Other molecules with three or our reaction sites are called tri- and tetrafunctional, respectively. Still higher unctionality, although theoretically possible, is not encountered in monomers or ther small molecules because of space limitations. For example, a phenol mole- ule (Appendix F) is only trifunctional in a condensation polymer, because it is geometrically impossible for it to utilize more reaction sites, though in theory it ould use as many as six.

'-4 Addition polymerization. In this type of polymerization, the molecule btains its reaction bonds by breaking double bonds and forming two single bonds Eq. (7–4)]; it therefore may occur without the formation of a by-product. Many f our commonly encountered addition polymers are of the ethylene type (Table '–1); therefore their polymerization reactions are identical to that of Eq. (7–4).

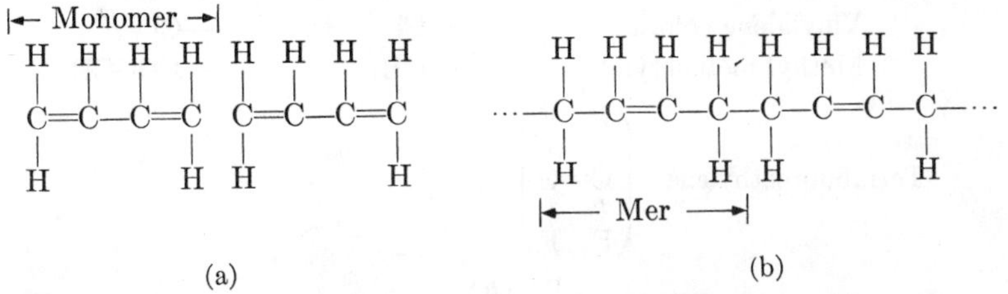

FIG. 7–4. Butadiene polymerization into unvulcanized rubber. The presence of two double bonds in each monomer only slightly alters the polymerization process from that used in making polyethylene.

A slightly different addition reaction occurs in the polymerization of *butadiene,* which is one of the main constituents of artificial rubber. Figure 7–4 illustrates the necessary bond changes. In the molecule of butadiene there are two double bonds, but since only one is necessary for the addition reaction, the other must shift its position to maintain four covalent bonds around each carbon. This second double bond, however, as will be explained later, is necessary for the vulcanization of rubber. The general rule for addition polymerization is that at least one double bond must exist in the monomer.

TABLE 7-1

ETHYLENE-TYPE MOLECULES (See Appendix F)

Vinyl compounds $\begin{pmatrix} H & H \\ | & | \\ C=C \\ | & | \\ H & R \end{pmatrix}$

	R
Ethylene	—H
Vinyl chloride	—Cl
Vinyl alcohol	—OH
Propylene	—CH₃
Vinyl acetate	—OCOCH₃
Acrylonitrile	—C≡N
Styrene (vinyl benzene)	— ⬡

Vinylidene compounds $\begin{pmatrix} H & R'' \\ | & | \\ C=C \\ | & | \\ H & R' \end{pmatrix}$

	R'	R''
Isobutylene	—CH₃	—CH₃
Vinylidene chloride	—Cl	—Cl
Methyl methacrylate	—CH₃	—COOCH₃

Tetrafluoroethylene $\begin{pmatrix} F & F \\ | & | \\ C=C \\ | & | \\ F & F \end{pmatrix}$

Trifluorochloroethylene $\begin{pmatrix} F & Cl \\ | & | \\ C=C \\ | & | \\ F & F \end{pmatrix}$

Simply placing monomers close to one another does not automatically produce an addition polymerization reaction. The addition reaction usually must be instigated by the application of heat, light, pressure, or a catalyst, in the following manner:

$$n(C_2H_4) \xrightarrow[\text{light, or catalyst}]{\text{heat, pressure,}} \begin{pmatrix} H & H \\ | & | \\ -C-C- \\ | & | \\ H & H \end{pmatrix}_n . \qquad (7\text{-}5)$$

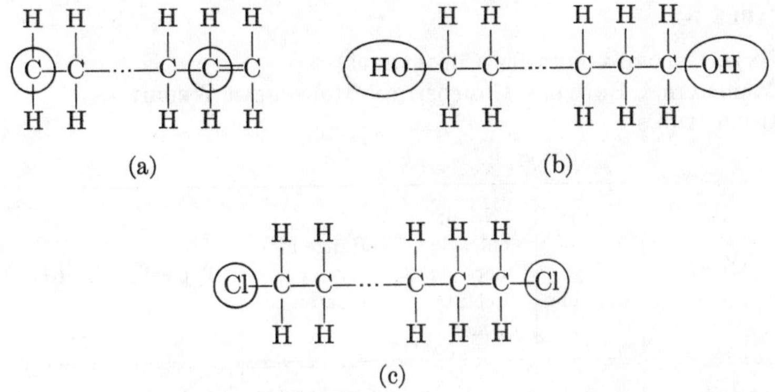

FIG. 7-5. (a) This arrangement of an addition polymer would be impossible. There would be one carbon with three bonds and one with five. (b) H_2O_2 initiators and (c) Cl_2 initiators permit all carbons to have four bonds.

The need for help in starting the process of polymerization arises in part from the necessity for breaking the double bonds of monomers. As indicated in Table 3-1, the energy required to break each $C=C$ bond is equal to $146,000 \text{ cal}/6.02 \times 10^{23}$ bonds. Although the number of bonds is large, the required energy per bond compares in magnitude with the energy released per bond in burning coal. Were it not for the fact that this energy, and more too, is recovered in the polymerization process it would be almost impossible to supply enough energy to proceed with the reaction. Since two new single $C-C$ bonds are formed from each former double bond, $2(83,000)/(6.02 \times 10^{23})$ cal of energy are released.

We may now ask why the polymerization process does not continue indefinitely, once it has been initiated. Theoretically it would be possible to link all the monomers in a plastic into one long continuous chain. One reason why this does not take place is that the molecules must be available in the immediate locality at the ends of the chains, and if they are not there, it is necessary to diffuse them to the ends of the chains. Diffusion is a relatively simple process until polymerization becomes sufficiently extensive so that the movement of the individual molecules is progressively restricted.

As shown in Fig. 7-5(a), both ends of a polymer molecule which was grown simply from the original mers would be unstable because the carbons do not have four covalent bonds. Terminal radicals or atoms are necessary to produce stability (Figs. 7-5b and 7-5c). Since the addition chain cannot start to grow until one of the ends is stabilized, such an end unit is called an *initiator*. H_2O_2, which dissociates to 2(OH), is commonly used, although other compounds are possible. Excessive additions must be avoided, inasmuch as these initiators may terminate a growing chain.

Copolymerization. In each of the polymers considered so far, only one kind of mer was used in the addition process. A marked advance in the technology of producing plastics occurred when it was learned that addition polymers contain-

TABLE 7-2

VINYL CHLORIDE-ACETATE COPOLYMERS.
CORRELATION BETWEEN COMPOSITION MOLECULAR WEIGHT AND
APPLICATIONS*

Item	w/o of vinyl chloride	No. of chloride mers per acetate mer	Range of average mol. wts.	Typical applications
Straight polyvinyl acetate	0	0	4,800–15,000	Limited chiefly to adhesives.
Chloride-acetate copolymers	85–87	8–9	8,500– 9,500	Lacquer for lining food cans; sufficiently soluble in ketone solvents for surface-coating purposes.
	85–87	8–9	9,500–10,500	Plastics of good strength and solvent resistance; molded by injection.
	88–90	10–13	16,000–23,000	Synthetic fibers made by dry spinning; excellent solvent and salt resistance.
	95	26	20,000–22,000	Substitute rubber for electrical-wire coating; must be externally plasticized; extrusion-molded.
Straight polyvinyl chloride	100	—	—	Limited, if any, commercial applications *per se;* nonflammable substitute for rubber when externally plasticized.

* A. Schmidt and C. A. Marlies, *Principles of High Polymer Theory and Practice.* New York: McGraw-Hill, 1948.

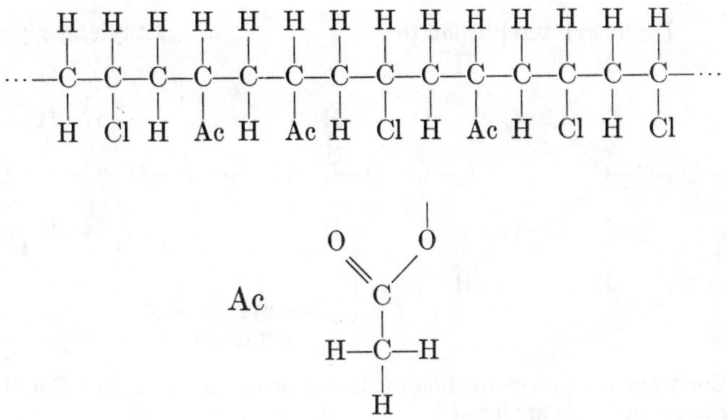

FIG. 7–6. Copolymerization of vinyl chloride and vinyl acetate. This is comparable to a solid solution in metallic and ceramic crystals.

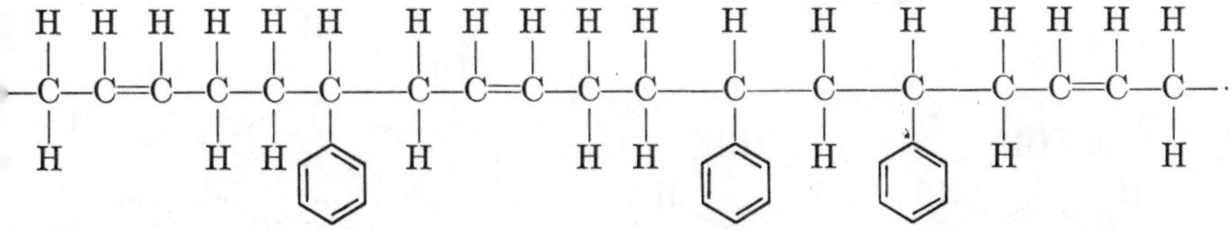

FIG. 7–7. Copolymerization of butadiene and styrene. This is the basis for many of our artificial rubbers. (Hydrogens are not shown on the benzene ring.)

ing mixtures of two or more different mers frequently have more desirable physical and mechanical properties.

It is possible, for example, to have a polymer chain composed of mers of vinyl chloride and vinyl acetate (Fig. 7–6). The resulting structure, called a *copolymer*, is comparable to a solid solution in crystals (Section 4–5). A copolymer may have properties quite different from those of either component member. Table 7–2 shows the variety of properties and applications of vinyl chloride-vinyl acetate mixtures with different degrees of copolymerization. The range is striking. It means that the engineer may tailor-make his plastics to a wide variety of requirements.

Copolymerization has been applied extensively in the field of artificial rubbers. For example, the *buna-S* rubbers which gained widespread importance during and after World War II are copolymers of butadiene and styrene (Fig. 7–7).

7–5 Condensation polymerization. In contrast to addition reactions, which are primarily a summation of individual molecules into a polymer, *condensation reactions* form a second, nonpolymerizable molecule as a by-product. Usually the by-product is water or some other simple molecule such as HCl or CH_3OH. A familiar example of a condensation polymer is dacron, which is formed as indicated

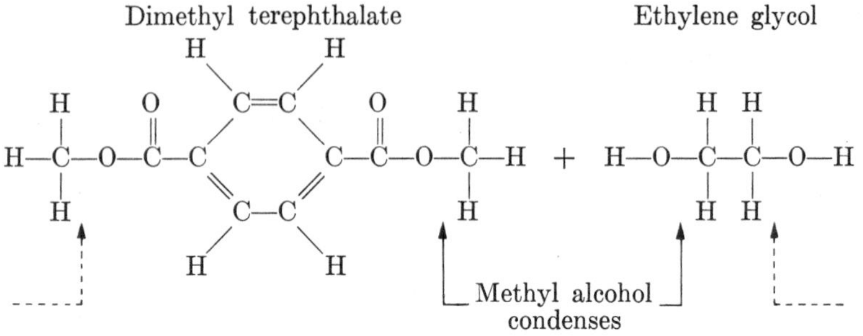

Fig. 7-8. Condensation polymerization of dacron or mylar. A small CH_3OH molecule and a larger linear molecule are formed.

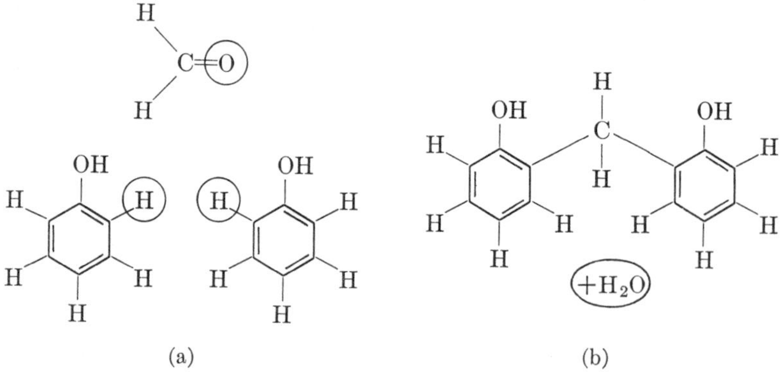

Fig. 7-9. Condensation polymerization. In contrast to addition polymerization, condensation polymerization has a small molecular by-product. Phenol = C_6H_5OH; formaldehyde = CH_2O.

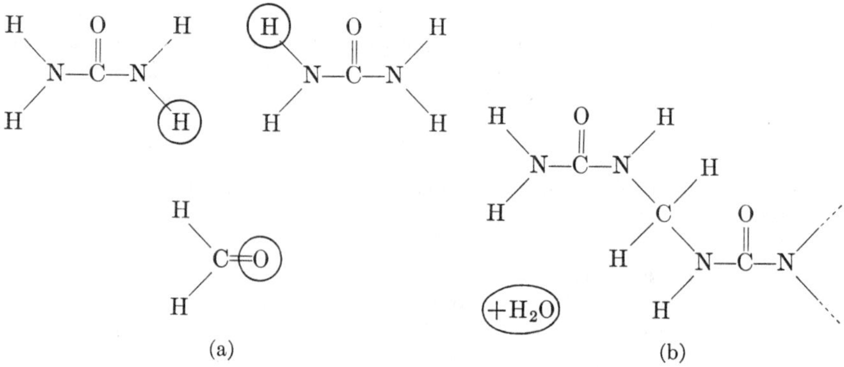

Fig. 7-10. Urea and formaldehyde polymerization. Urea is tetrafunctional.

in Fig. 7-8. With dacron, as with polyethylene, a linear-type polymer is formed because the contributing molecules are bifunctional. The atomic arrangement in a complicated polymer such as that in Fig. 7-8 need not be memorized, but it should be remembered that a by-product is formed through a reaction which breaks bonds on each of the two contributing molecules. In this case, the (CH_3) end of one molecule and the (OH) end of the other combine to form methyl alcohol (CH_3OH) as a small by-product, and the polymer is developed by joining at the exposed bonds.

Another familiar condensation polymer, which goes by various trade names (Appendix G), is formed from formaldehyde (CH_2O) and phenol (C_6H_5OH). The atom arrangements within these molecules are shown in Fig. 7-9(a). At room temperature formaldehyde is a gas; phenol is a low-melting solid. The polymerization which results from the interaction of these two compounds is shown in Fig. 7-9(b). The formaldehyde has supplied a CH_2 unit which serves as a bridge between the benzene rings in two phenols. Stripping two hydrogens from the benzene rings and one oxygen from the formaldehyde (to permit the connection) forms water, which can volatilize and leave the system. The reaction of Fig. 7-9 can occur at several points around the phenol molecule. As a result of this polyfunctionality, a molecular network is formed, rather than a simple linear chain.

Example 7-3

A common polymer is formed from urea and formaldehyde by condensation. These two compounds have the structures shown in Appendix F. Show how these could be polymerized.

Answer: See Fig. 7-10 for the reaction. There is one H_2O molecule formed and re-
$$\text{H}$$
moved for each —C— bridge which develops between urea molecules.
$$\text{H}$$

The following differences between addition and condensation polymers produce important differences in the thermal properties of these two types of plastics (see Sections 7-14 and 7-15).

(1) *Addition polymers* require unsaturated monomers and utilize all the reactant(s) in the final product:

$$nA \longrightarrow (-A-)_n, \qquad (7\text{-}6a)$$

or

$$nA + mB \rightarrow (-A_n B_m-). \qquad (7\text{-}6b)$$

(2) *Condensation polymers* always have a reaction by-product and may (Fig. 7-8) or may not (Fig. 7-9) be linear in character:

$$pC + pD \rightarrow (-E-) + pH_2O \text{ (or similar molecule)}. \qquad (7\text{-}7a)$$

7–6 Degradation or depolymerization.   During polymerization, conditions are carefully controlled so that the reaction proceeds in only one direction. A change in environment may cause a reversal of the reaction, or *depolymerization*. For example, such degradation may occur with the urea-formaldehyde plastic shown in Fig. 7–10 if it is used for extended periods of time with steam:

$$p\mathrm{C} + p\mathrm{D} \leftarrow (\mathrm{-E-}) + p\mathrm{H_2O}. \qquad (7\text{–}7\mathrm{b})$$

Degradation may also occur in any plastic being formed at high temperatures, since thermal vibrations may disrupt the bonds within the molecules:

$$n\mathrm{A} \leftarrow (\mathrm{-A-})_n \qquad (7\text{–}6\mathrm{c})$$

Degradation processes are not always harmful. For example, the above reaction is commercially used for cracking petroleum into more combustible, light molecules. Other familiar examples of degradation are the charring of carbohydrates (toast) and of cellulose (charcoal). In the latter two examples the molecular structure is more completely disrupted than is the case with a simple depolymerization reaction. After disruption, the degradation products are no longer monomers, but are entirely new molecules.

POLYMER STRUCTURES

7–7 Introduction.   The structure of the polymer affects the behavior of a plastic in a number of ways. We have already noted that bifunctional monomers produce linear polymers (Fig. 7–11), whereas trifunctional and tetrafunctional monomers form network or framework polymers (Fig. 7–12). We shall observe later that this contrast plays an important role in the deformation and strength of plastics. However, before considering such behaviors, we should consider various types of polymer structures.

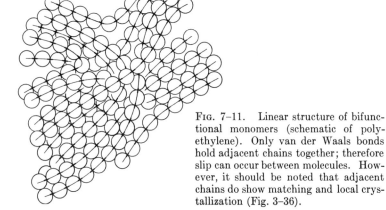

Fig. 7–11.   Linear structure of bifunctional monomers (schematic of polyethylene). Only van der Waals bonds hold adjacent chains together; therefore slip can occur between molecules. However, it should be noted that adjacent chains do show matching and local crystallization (Fig. 3–36).

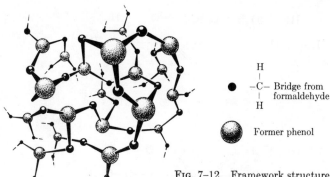

- $-\overset{\overset{\displaystyle H}{|}}{\underset{\underset{\displaystyle H}{|}}{C}}-$ Bridge from formaldehyde

⬤ Former phenol

FIG. 7–12. Framework structure of polyfunctional units. Slip does not occur as readily as in linear polymers.

7–8 Polymer shape. Polyethylene molecules are relatively simple and uniform (Fig. 7–13a). A polyvinyl chloride molecule, on the other hand, has large "lumps" periodically along its chain (Fig. 7–13b), with the result that (1) movement between molecules is much more restricted, and (2) there are stronger van der Waals attractive forces as a result of polarization within the molecule (Section 2–11). Consequently polyvinyl chloride is a tougher and stronger plastic than polyethylene and, were it not for other adjustments, it would not be possible to use it in applications that require flexible films. The effect of structure becomes even more significant in polystyrene (Fig. 7–13c).

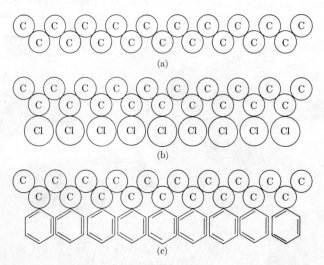

FIG. 7–13. Molecular chains. Schematic representation of (a) polyethylene, (b) polyvinyl chloride, (c) polystyrene. The shape affects properties. (The small hydrogen atoms are not shown.)

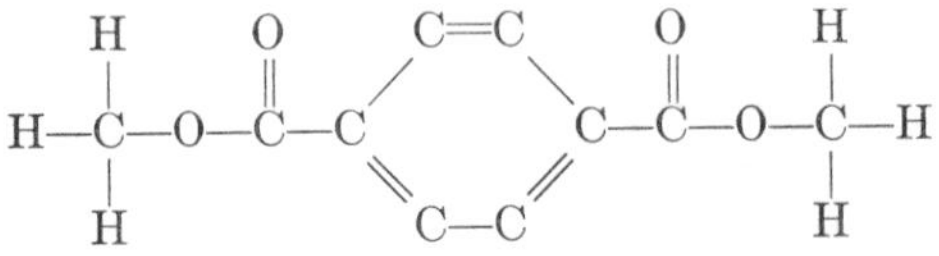

$$\text{H—C—O—C—C} \quad \text{C—C—O—C—H}$$

(a)

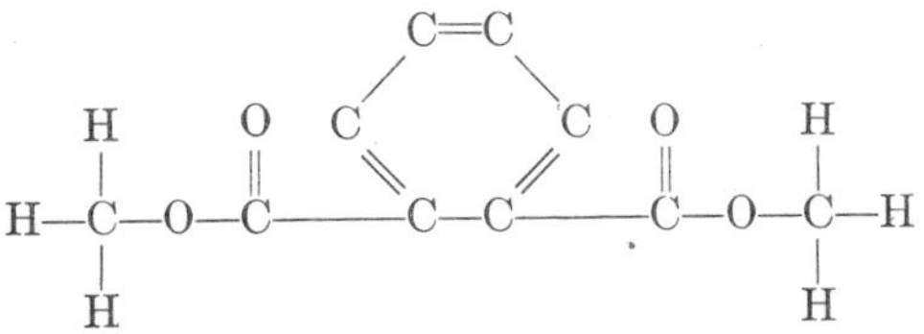

(b)

FIG. 7–14. Isomers of dimethyl phthalate: (a) terephthalate, (b) orthophthalate. (Hydrogens are not shown with the benzene ring.)

The examples just cited involve a change in polymer composition to effect a change in polymer shape. Similar results may be obtained by changes in intramolecular arrangements. Figure 7–14 shows two isomers of dimethyl phthalate which differ in the symmetry of their structures across the benzene ring in their respective molecules. When these two isomers are polymerized by condensation with ethylene glycol, they form identical compositions but different structures. The symmetric terephthalate structure is the linear polymer known commonly as dacron (a fiber) or mylar (a film) (Figs. 7–8 and 7–15), which are strong but

FIG. 7–15. Use of mylar film in insulation. This polymer has the same structure as that shown in Fig. 7–8. (Du Pont.)

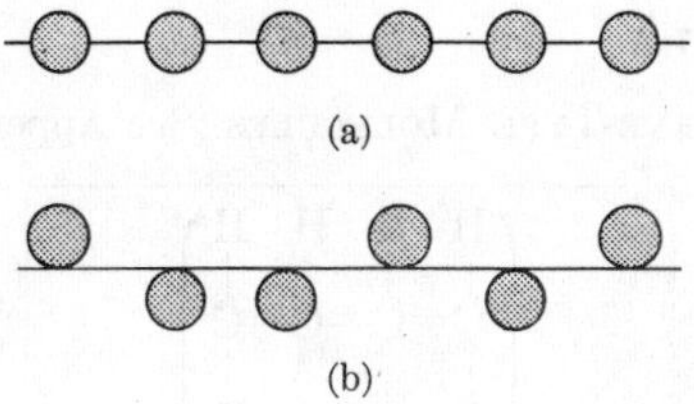

(a)

(b)

Fig. 7–16. Polymer symmetry (dacron and glyptol). The symmetric molecule is much more flexible because it does not have the highly polarized side groups which are attracted to adjacent chains. (Compare with Fig. 7–14.)

flexible plastics. The asymmetric orthophthalate isomer produces a hard, horny resin with comparatively little flexibility. It is an important constituent in some protective coatings such as glyptol. The contrast between these two structures is shown schematically in Fig. 7–16.

7–9 Stereoisomerism. The molecular chains of Fig. 7–17(a) show a high degree of regularity along the polymer. Not only is there an additional sequence of monomers which form a linear polymer, but there is also identical ordering of the propylene mers so that the radicals are always at the corresponding position within the mer. Such an ordering is called *isotactic*, as contrasted to the *atactic* arrangement in Fig. 7–17(b), and the *syndiotactic* arrangement in Fig. 7–17(c).

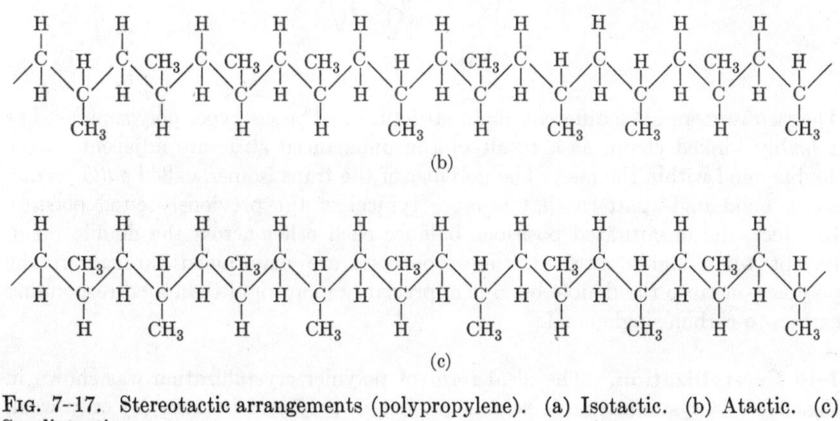

(a)

(b)

(c)

Fig. 7–17. Stereotactic arrangements (polypropylene). (a) Isotactic. (b) Atactic. (c) Syndiotactic.

TABLE 7-3

BUTADIENE-TYPE MOLECULES (See Appendix F)

$$\begin{pmatrix} \overset{\displaystyle H}{\underset{\displaystyle H}{\overset{|}{\underset{|}{C}}}} = \overset{\displaystyle R}{\overset{|}{C}} - \overset{\displaystyle H}{\overset{|}{C}} = \overset{\displaystyle H}{\underset{\displaystyle H}{\overset{|}{\underset{|}{C}}}} \end{pmatrix}$$

	R
Butadiene	—H
Chloroprene	—Cl
Isoprene	—CH$_3$

A second example of polymer arrangement is found in rubbers which are made of butadiene-type molecules (Table 7-3). Natural rubber is polymerized isoprene with

$$\begin{matrix} CH_3 & H \\ \diagdown & \diagup \\ C = C \end{matrix} \tag{7-8}$$

as a mer. In the resulting polymer, the unsaturated positions (Section 3-7) are on the same side of the chain. This positioning is called *cis* (same side), and has important consequences in the chain behavior. Another modification, which is called *trans*, has the unsaturated positions on opposite sides of the chain:

$$\begin{matrix} CH_3 & H \\ | & | \\ C & C \\ \diagup \diagdown & \diagup \diagdown \\ C & C & H \\ | & | \\ H & H \end{matrix} \tag{7-9}$$

The two isomers have different chain structures. The cis type, polyisoprene, has a highly kinked chain, as a result of the unbalanced structure adjacent to the double bond within the mer. The polymer of the trans isomer, called *gutta percha*, has a bond-angle pattern that is more typical of the previously cited plastics. In effect, the unsaturated positions balance each other across the double bond. Except when highly stressed, these contrasts are maintained throughout the polymer, because the double bond is appreciably more rigid than a corresponding carbon-to-carbon single bond.

7–10 Crystallization. The ideal form of polymer crystallization was shown in Fig. 3-36. Crystallization is seldom perfect in polymers because (1) only weak van der Waals forces are available for aligning the molecules, and (2) a very large number of atoms must be maneuvered into position. In reality, crystallization is quite imperfect at best,* and often is completely lacking.

Several structural factors favor crystallization. (1) A linear polymer has a higher degree of crystallinity than a network polymer because adjustments may be made in the positioning of the weak van der Waals bonds. (2) Isotactic polymers crystallize more readily than atactic polymers because a matching repetition is possible along adjacent chains in isotactic polymers. (3) Crystallization is better in trans than in cis polymers because the latter tend to kink and produce disorder between adjacent chains.

7–11 Cross-linking. A common variation of polymer growth, called *cross-linking*, ties the chains of molecules together (Fig. 7–18). The effect of cross-linking is immediately apparent; it greatly restricts movement between adjacent chains and therefore markedly alters mechanical properties.

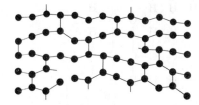

FIG. 7–18. Cross-linking (schematic). Adjacent chains are anchored together; therefore less movement is possible between molecules.

For cross-linking to be extensive, there must be a number of unsaturated carbon atoms within the chain in its normal polymerized condition, since it is through these connecting points that linkage takes place. Figure 7–19 shows the mechanism for the cross-linking of two butadiene molecules with oxygen atoms. This particular example is typical of the effect of aging on rubber. Long periods of time in air or similar oxidizing environments permit extensive cross-linking by oxygen, until the rubber molecules are well anchored to one another and obvious elastic strain becomes impossible.

Cross-linking is not always undesirable. To recognize its value in certain circumstances, consider the characteristics of discrete rubber molecules. Polymerized isoprene latex (natural rubber) is weak at normal temperatures; that is, while the individual molecules are capable of elastic extension, they slide by one another rather than deforming elastically. However, a minimum amount of anchoring prevents intermolecular movement and makes possible elastic strain under stress. Such anchors (fix points) may be established by a variety of means. The most common method is vulcanizing with sulfur. Figure 7–20 is a structural diagram of the results achieved by Mr. Goodyear, early in our technical history. Table 7–4 shows the resulting change in physical properties.

---

* It has been suggested that a crystallized linear polymer may be compared with a bowl of spaghetti in which each string of spaghetti is a molecular chain. Any one chain is commonly in close alignment with adjacent chains; however, because the chain is not straight, the neighbors change along the chain's length. (See Fig. 7–11.)

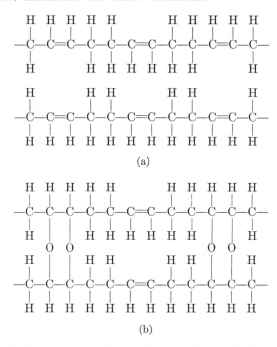

Fig. 7-19. Oxidation of polybutadiene. Through this cross-linking, the elasticity of rubber is reduced.

Obviously there is a limit to the elasticity gained in rubbers by cross-linking. In an ordinary automobile tire sufficient sulfur is added to form anchorages at a number of fix points, but not enough to restrict elastic movement entirely. In hard rubber, which is used for such things as battery cases, a much greater degree of vulcanization is necessary. A tire tread may contain 3% to 5% sulfur, but a battery case may contain as much as 40%.

Example 7-4

How many pounds of sulfur are required per 100 lb of final rubber product to completely cross-link butadiene (C_4H_6) rubber?

Answer: 1 atomic wt of sulfur (32) is required per 1 mer wt of butadiene:

$$(4)(12) + (6)(1) = 54.$$

$$\text{Fraction sulfur} = \frac{32}{32 + 54} = 0.37 \qquad \text{or 37 lb S/100 lb product.}$$

Example 7-5

What fraction of butadiene (C_4H_6) is cross-linked if the product contains 18.5% sulfur? (Assume all the sulfur is utilized in cross-linking.)

TABLE 7–4

PROPERTIES OF NONVULCANIZED AND VULCANIZED NATURAL RUBBER*

Property	Nonvulcanized	Vulcanized
Tensile strength, psi	300	3,000
Elongation at break, %	1,200	800
Permanent set	Large	Small
Rapidity of retraction (snap)	Good	Very good
Hysteresis loop in load-elongation curve	Large	Small
Water absorption	Large	Small
Swelling in hydrocarbon solvents	Infinite (soluble)	Large, but limited
Tackiness	Marked	Slight
Useful temperature range	10 to 60°C	−40 to +100°C

* A. Schmidt and C. A. Marlies, *Principles of High Polymer Theory and Practice.* New York: McGraw-Hill, 1948.

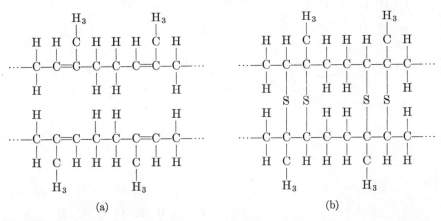

(a)   (b)

FIG. 7–20. Vulcanization of natural rubber with sulfur. The sulfur content must be controlled to give the desired number of anchor points. Hard rubber has a high sulfur content.

Answer: Based on the fact that 1 mer wt of butadiene [= $(4)(12) + (6)(1) = 54$] requires 1 atomic wt of sulfur (= 32). Therefore

$$\frac{54}{1 - 0.185} = \frac{x}{0.185},$$

$x = 12.25$ = amount of sulfur present per mer wt of butadiene;

$$\frac{12.25}{32} = \text{fraction of cross-links} = 0.383.$$

[*Note:* The answer can*not* be obtained from Example 7–4 as 18.5/37.]

FIG. 7–21. Branching (schematic). Side chains permit greater interlocking of the structure. As a result, deformation is more difficult.

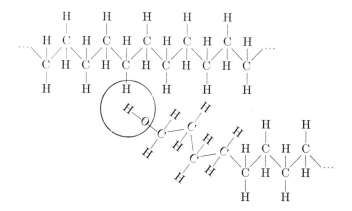

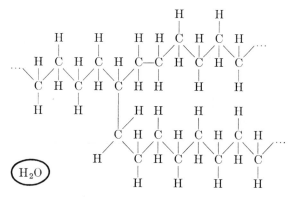

FIG. 7–22. Branching mechanism (simplified). Energy must be supplied to open up a connection point on the main chain. (Compare with Fig. 12–39.)

7–12 Branching. In addition to cross-linking, it is also possible under certain conditions to develop another form of three-dimensional molecules from chain polymers by the method called branching (Fig. 7–21), in which the main chain is bifurcated into two chains. The *controlled branching* of linear molecules is a relatively new and important achievement in the production of plastics. Its importance lies in the fact that if branching is extensive it will effectively restrict movement between adjacent molecules by the simple mechanism of intertangling.

Branching of linear molecules is not a spontaneous reaction, since it results in an increase in net energy. In effect, branching is achieved by removing a side atom from the main chain and introducing another C—C bond (Fig. 7–22). Although not spontaneous, this reaction occurs somewhat more readily than the cross-linking reaction discussed above, since taking one side atom from the main chain is easier than simultaneously removing two atoms from adjacent locations on two chains.

DEFORMATION OF POLYMERS

7–13 Elastic deformation of polymers. The elastic (Young's) moduli of metals generally exceed 10^7 psi. Exceptions to this figure are the softer, low-melting metals, such as lead (Appendix E-1). In contrast, the same moduli for plastics are generally below 10^6 psi, and in some cases as low as 10^4 psi (Appendix E–3). One of several reasons for this contrast is demonstrated in Fig. 7–23, where it is evident that stresses can produce bond-straightening as well as bond-lengthening, thus producing appreciably more strain.

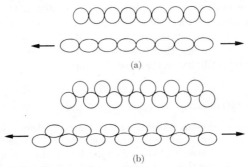

(a)

(b)

Fig. 7–23. Elastic strains (a) by bond lengthening, (b) by bond straightening. (Exaggerated.)

A comparison of the moduli data in Appendix E–3 reveals some contrasts. Organic materials containing polyfunctional units have the higher moduli, e.g., urea-formaldehyde and melamine-formaldehyde. Nonvulcanized rubbers have the lowest modulus of elasticity, i.e., the greatest strain per unit of stress. The above contrasts may be accounted for on the basis of structure. The polyfunctional polymers form a network structure (Fig. 7–12) which is appreciably more rigid

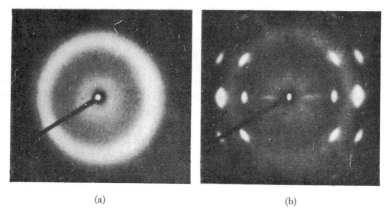

(a)   (b)

FIG. 7–24. Deformation crystallization of natural rubber (polyisoprene) revealed by x-ray diffraction. (a) Unstretched. (b) Stretched. (S. D. Gehman, *Chem. Revs.* **26**, 203, 1940.)

than a linear structure. Rubbers generally contain a cis-type structure with an extensive amount of chain-kinking. As stress is applied, the chains are first un-kinked (in nonvulcanized rubbers) before bond-straightening and eventual bond-lengthening. Because an extraordinary amount of strain arises, the term *elastomer* has been applied to such polymers.

Deformation crystallization. Crystallization is favored by the application of stresses, because the molecules are pulled into closer alignment. This is most evident with the elastomers, or rubbers, because in the unstretched condition they are essentially lacking in crystallinity (Fig. 7–24a). However, as the molecules are straightened by a stress, they become aligned and crystalline (Fig. 7–24b). The rubber loses its crystallinity as the stress is reduced.

• **Example 7–6**

Detect evidence of crystallization of a rubber by a temperature change.

Answer: This is a simple experiment using a heavy but easily deformable rubber band. Your lip can serve as a sensitive detector of temperature changes. Place the band in con-tact with your lower lip. Stretch it rapidly, then quickly (without snapping) return it to its original length, repeating this cycle several times. A little care will permit one to detect a temperature increase on stretching and a temperature decrease on release. These temperature changes occur because energy is released from the rubber band to your lip during crystallization. Energy is absorbed (as entropy) during decrystallization when the stress is removed.

7–14 Plastic deformation of polymers. Plastics acquired their name by virtue of the fact that they are subject to plastic deformation. Their plastic behavior is of great use during processing, because a product may be shaped into a desired contour. Of course it is desirable that the "set" be permanent and that further plastic deformation not occur during use.

Permanent deformation occurs as "slip" between adjacent molecules, because the attractive forces are weaker between than within molecules. This type of deformation is simplest for the special case in which all the linear molecules are aligned. The situation for randomly oriented molecules is analogous, so long as the molecules are bonded only by van der Waals forces. Deformation occurs by slippage at the weaker points between the molecules rather than by the breaking of intramolecular bonds.

Thermoplastic resins. Resins (plastics) with the characteristics just described deform easily under pressure. This is especially true at high temperatures, since then the weak van der Waals forces are easily overcome. Thus when a heated resin of this type is injected into a mold under pressure, it readily takes on the shape of the mold. When the molded shape cools, it again becomes rigid. Such a polymerized material is called a *thermoplastic* resin because its plasticity increases with temperature. Thermoplastic resins are used extensively in such articles as plastic wall and floor tile (polyvinyl chloride and polystyrene), fluorescent light reflectors (polystyrene), and plastic lenses (polymethyl methacrylate), to name but a few.

Thermosetting resins. Figure 7–12 showed the structure of a phenol-formaldehyde resin schematically in three dimensions. Recall that in Fig. 7–11 each polymerized molecule was distinct, and deformation occurred as slip between the molecules. Here, however, polymerization has developed a *continuous framework structure*, in which slip between molecules cannot occur. In effect, the whole structure is one large molecule, since primary covalent bonds are present throughout. Such polymers do not increase in plasticity with increased temperatures. In fact, if polymerization is not complete, higher temperatures accelerate the reactions and provide a permanent "set"; hence the term *thermosetting resins* is widely used.

In general, thermosetting plastics are stronger than thermoplastic resins. Furthermore, they are more usable in processes requiring high temperatures. Thermosetting resins are used, for example, for telephone receivers, electrical outlets, and appliance handles, whose processing makes use of the electrical or thermal insulating properties of the covalently bonded organic materials.

By implication, it may appear that thermosetting resins are to be preferred to thermoplastic resins, but this is not always true. If thermal or mechanical properties are secondary to formability in production, thermoplastic resins have a marked advantage, since they can fill an intricate mold more readily than a thermosetting plastic does. Furthermore, because scrap resin may frequently be recycled, thermoplastic resins are economically advantageous.

BEHAVIOR OF POLYMERS

7–15 Thermal behavior. Thermoplastic (linear) polymers differ from thermosetting (framework) polymers in that the thermoplastic type have their intermolecular forces overcome at high temperatures. Furthermore, thermosetting plastics, after the completion of polymerization, can eventually lose strength if they are exposed to high temperatures, because degradation occurs (Section 7–6).

The most critical effect of increased temperature is an increased rate of chemical reaction, which will be described in Section 7–18. The temperature at which polymers become highly susceptible to chemical reaction corresponds closely to the temperature at which mechanical strength drops off. This is below the melting temperature in linear polymers, and corresponds to the start of degradation in framework polymers.

7–16 Mechanical behavior. A molten polymer is amorphous and possesses random chain orientation. If the molecules are linear, their structure may be compared with that of a ball of cotton. This structure of the molecules at higher temperatures can be preserved at lower temperatures through a quench (Fig. 7–25a). Tension on such a mass produces most of the initial deformation and improves the alignment of the molecules. As a result, the stress-strain relationships are not like those of metals, because the modulus of elasticity is increased when the stress is applied directly against the polymer chain after alignment has occurred (Fig. 7–25, curve II–IV).

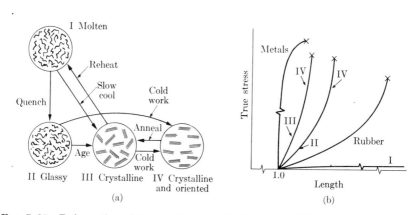

FIG. 7–25. Deformation of linear polymers. (a) Thermal and deformation treatments. (b) Comparative stress-strain relationships. [The numbers in (b) correspond to the structures in (a).]

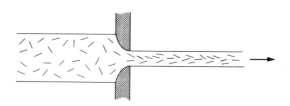

FIG. 7–26. Molecular orientation by extrusion. Greater longitudinal tensile strength exists after orientation because the strong intramolecular bonds must be ruptured before failure.

The stress-strain behaviors shown in Fig. 7-25 suggest means whereby polymers may have their properties enhanced. For example, the drawing process which is used in making artificial fibers (Fig. 7-26) provides an added benefit of increased strength through molecular orientation (and crystallization). An extension of our previous analogy would liken this to the production of a cotton cord from a ball of cotton. Of course, the strength at right angles to the axis of the drawn fiber would be exceptionally weak in the absence of cross-linking, because only van der Waals bonds are operative. Fortunately, we never load a fiber in that direction; however, the problem is real in a plastic film or sheet. The production of plastic film requires the simultaneous drawing of the product in two directions at the same time.* This is achieved through blowing procedures or through rolling operations which increase the width as the length is increased.

Rate of deformation. We observed in Section 6-10 that metals can creep when they are exposed to stresses below their yield strength for extended periods of time. Atoms are moved locally at points of stress concentration. Both time and temperature are factors in determining whether only elastic deformation occurs, or whether both elastic and plastic deformation develop. More time or higher temperatures provide more opportunity for the atoms to establish new positions under applied stresses.

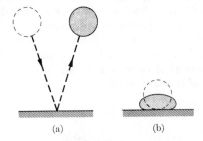

(a)   (b)

FIG. 7-27. Time versus flow of asphalt. (a) A ball of asphalt behaves elastically with fast loading. (b) Under prolonged stressing (from its own weight), it deforms plastically, since there is time for the molecules to rearrange themselves and adjust to the stresses.

Polymers are subject to the same time-dependent phenomena as metals are, and although molecular movements are more complicated than atom movements, simply because of size, the bonding forces are generally weaker so that high creep rates are developed. The significance of time in this respect is illustrated schematically in Fig. 7-27, for asphalt. Instantaneous stressing reveals only elastic responses, while prolonged exposure to even weak stresses allows plastic deformation to occur.

---

* It may be assumed that the cross-sectional strength of a film is low.

TABLE 7-5

RATE OF STRAIN VERSUS STRENGTH OF RAW RUBBER
(AT 20°C)*

Rate of elongation, %/sec	Time to break, sec	Tensile strength, psi	Elastic elongation, %
50+	20	450	1,250
3+	300	145	1,020
0.02	14,400	31	300

* After V. P. Rosbaud and E. Schmid, *Z. tech. Physik*, **9,** 98 (1928).

More quantitative data are presented in Fig. 7–28 and Table 7–5, for raw rubber. There is a decrease in strength if there is opportunity for atoms to adjust to applied stresses.

• *Stress relaxation.* With time, stresses are relaxed in those applications where they are initially developed from elastic elongation. The reader has undoubtedly observed such a phenomenon if he has removed a stretched rubber band from a book or bundle of papers after a period of time. The rubber band does not return to its original length, indicating that some of the stress has disappeared.

The time required for the adjustment of stresses is called the *relaxation time.* Since the relaxation of stresses is a continuous phenomenon, the relaxation time is defined mathematically as the time it takes for the stress to be reduced to $1/e$ (that is, $1/2.718$) of its original value (Fig. 7–29). This is a convenient definition, since under conditions of constant strain

$$d\sigma/dt = -\sigma/\lambda, \tag{7-10a}$$

or

$$\sigma = \sigma_0 e^{-t/\lambda} \tag{7-10b}$$

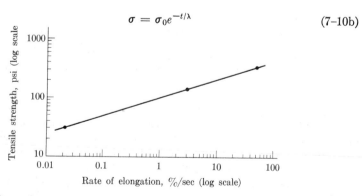

FIG. 7–28. Strength versus strain rate (raw rubber). Slow deformation rates permit more time for plastic adjustment to applied stress, and therefore less resistance to deformation. (Adapted from V. P. Rosbaud and E. Schmid, *Z. tech. Physik*, **9,** 98, 1928.)

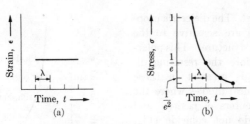

FIG. 7–29. Relaxation time. Under constant strain (a), the stresses decrease with time (b). The relaxation time, λ, is the time required to decrease the stresses to $1/e$ of the original value ($e = 2.718 \ldots$).

where σ_0 is the original stress and λ is the relaxation time. Thus, when $t = \lambda$, $\sigma = \sigma_0(1/e)$.

Since stress relaxation depends on movements of atoms or molecules, we find that relaxation time has a reciprocal exponential relationship to temperature, and an equation such as

$$1/\lambda = f\left(e^{-Q/RT}\right) \tag{7–11}$$

is appropriate. In effect, relaxation time is a function of the same factors as diffusion [Eq. (4–9)].

• **Example 7–7**

A stress of 1200 psi is required to stretch a 4-in. rubber band to 5.6 in. After 42 days in the same stretched position, the band exerts a force of only 600 psi. (a) What is the relaxation time? (b) What stress would be exerted by the band in the same stretched position after 90 days?

Answer:

$$\text{(a)} \quad \ln \frac{600}{1200} = -\frac{42}{\lambda}, \quad \lambda = 61 \text{ days.}$$

$$\text{(b)} \quad \sigma_{90} = 1200 \, e^{-90/61} = 274 \text{ psi.}$$

Alternative answer for (b), with 48 additional days:

$$\sigma_{48} = 600 \, e^{-48/61} = 274 \text{ psi.}$$

7–17 Electrical characteristics of organic materials. There is considerable use of plastics in electrical insulation. Plastics have obvious advantages, such as their ability, when they are applied on wire as unpolymerized or partially polymerized liquid, to form a uniform coating which can then be polymerized in place. Some plastics lend themselves to film formation; these are particularly useful as electrical materials (Fig. 7–15). A wide choice of flexible or rigid plastics is available. Of primary importance is the fact that the predominantly covalent bonds of all polymers limit electrical conduction.

Dielectric constant. The dielectric properties of polymers are sensitive to the polarization of the structure. This polarization, and therefore the resulting dielectric constant, is greatest in those polymers with natural dipoles where the positions of the centers of positive and negative charges do not coincide (Fig. 2–14). At low frequencies the dipoles respond to changes in the electric field. However, as the frequency is increased it eventually becomes impossible for the polar groups of the molecules to respond, and only electronic polarization (Fig. 2–15) occurs. The frequency limit of response varies with the size of the dipoles and with the temperature (Fig. 7–30). Temperature becomes important because thermal energy supplements the force of the electric field in displacing atoms.

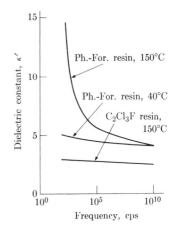

FIG. 7–30. Dielectric constant versus frequency. Generally speaking, higher frequencies and lower temperatures reduce the dielectric constant, because there is less time for dipole alignment.

Example 7–8

The capacitance of a parallel-plate capacitor can be calculated from Eq. (1–9). The dielectric constants for polyvinyl chloride (pvc) and polytetrafluoroethylene (ptfe) are as follows:

Frequency, cycles/sec	pvc	ptfe
10^2	6.5	2.1
10^3	5.6	2.1
10^4	4.7	2.1
10^5	3.9	2.1
10^6	3.3	2.1
10^7	2.9	2.1
10^8	2.8	2.1
10^9	2.6	2.1
10^{10}	2.6	2.1

(a) Plot the capacitance versus frequency curves for three capacitors with $1'' \times 50''$ effective area separated by 1 mil of (1) vacuum, (2) pvc, and (3) ptfe. (b) Account for the decrease in the dielectric constant of pvc with increased frequency, and the constancy in the dielectric constant of ptfe.

Answer: (a) Sample calculations at 10^2 cycles per second:

$$C_{vac} = \frac{(1)(50)(1)}{(4.452 \times 10^6)(0.001)} = 0.0112 \ \mu f, \qquad C_{pvc} = \frac{(6.5)(50)(1)}{(4.452 \times 10^6)(0.001)} = 0.073 \ \mu f.$$

See Fig. 7–31(a) for the remainder of the results.

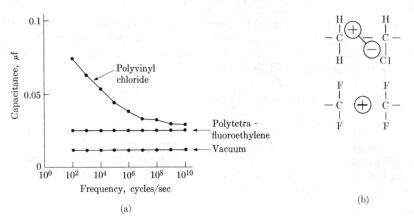

Fig. 7–31. Capacitance versus frequency. (a) See Example 7–8. (b) Symmetry of polyvinyl chloride and polytetrafluoroethylene mers.

(b) The dielectric constant of pvc is high at low frequencies because the molecular polarization of pvc is in an asymmetric mer (Fig. 7–31b). At high frequencies the resulting large dipole cannot maintain alignment with the alternating field. On the other hand, ptfe has a symmetric mer, and therefore its polarization is only electronic and atomic. Although the dipoles in ptfe are weaker, they can be oscillated at the indicated frequencies.

• *Conduction.* Although polymers are inherently insulators, their compositions can be adjusted to permit some conductivity. Conductivity is achieved in specialized rubbers through the addition of finely powdered graphite, which provides a path for electron movements. Thus the conductivity does not arise from the polymer *per se*, but results from the inclusion of a second, conducting phase. The polymer itself can achieve conductivity through one of several procedures. The first of these is to "mistreat" polymers by gamma-ray irradiation or by partial thermal degradation. Either treatment will partially destroy the structure and thus expose bond and chain irregularities that contain donor and/or acceptor sites (Section 5–9). Resistivities as low as 10^2 ohm·cm are reported, which can be compared to similar resistivities for germanium, and to values of greater than 10^{10} ohm·cm for normal polymers (Fig. 5–1).

A second method of attaining conductivity is to produce a polymer which has radicals along the chain. These radicals provide either donor or acceptor sites. Resistivities as low as 10 ohm·cm have been realized, with some lower values possible if crystallization can be improved.

7–18 Chemical reactions in organic materials. During chemical reactions, there is a breaking and recombination of bonds. Although chemical reactions are necessary for the polymerization process itself, subsequent reactions are generally considered to be undesirable (Section 7–6). Some special cases of chemical reaction of organic materials will be discussed in this section.

Combustion. It is common to associate organic substances with flammable materials. Many of our fuels are hydrocarbons similar to polyethylene, but with smaller molecules. With complete combustion, hydrocarbons dissociate and react with oxygen to give CO_2 and H_2O:

$$C_xH_y + \left(x + \frac{y}{4}\right) O_2 \rightarrow xCO_2 + \frac{y}{2} H_2O. \tag{7-12}$$

Each gram-mole of CO_2 produced from carbon and oxygen provides 94,600 cal of heat, and each gram-mole of steam produced from hydrogen and oxygen provides 68,180 cal of heat. Although energy is released by the formation of CO_2 and H_2O from their component elements, energy is also required to dissociate the fuel into its elements. A calculation will be illustrative.

Example 7-9

Twenty-five pounds of benzene, C_6H_6, are burned with an appropriate quantity of air. How many Btu's are released? The heats of formation are:

C_6H_6 (liquid) 20,400 Btu/lb-mole,

CO_2 170,000 Btu/lb-mole,

H_2O (liquid) 123,000 Btu/lb-mole.

Answer:

$C_6H_6 + 7\frac{1}{2} O_2 \rightarrow 6CO_2 + 3H_2O.$

Calculation basis: $= \dfrac{25}{78}$ or 0.32 lb-mole.

Heat required to dissociate C_6H_6 to C and H_2 = (1)(20,400)(0.32).

Heat released in formation of CO_2 from C and O_2 = $-(6)(170,000)(0.32)$.

Heat released in formation of H_2O from H_2 and O_2 = $-(3)(123,000)(0.32)$.

Net energy change = $-437,500$ Btu.

It is assumed that combustion products and the reactants are both at ambient temperatures.

The benzene of the above calculation develops significantly more heat upon burning than most organic materials, which is, of course, the reason it is used as a fuel (Table 7-6). In addition, many organic materials used for fuel have a high vapor pressure, which provides volatility and permits ready mixing with the oxygen of the air for fast burning. If a fuel lacks volatility, it must either be atomized (e.g., in a carburetor) or powdered (e.g., coal in a steam boiler) to facilitate mixing for increased burning rate.

Organic materials used by the engineer for components of his designs ordinarily do not have the fuel characteristics just described, partly by coincidence and partly by intent. For example, because the polyethylene molecule is extremely large and has negligible vapor pressure, polyethylene is less combustible than paraffin or gasoline, even though the heat developed is of the same order of magni-

TABLE 7-6

HEATS OF COMBUSTION FOR COMMON FUELS
(Products at Room Temperature) 378 ft^3/lb·mole

		Btu/lb	Btu/ft^3
Hydrogen	H_2	61,000	324
Carbon monoxide	CO	4,350	323
Methane	CH_4	24,000	1016
Propane	C_3H_8	21,400	2500
Benzene	C_6H_6	18,000	—
Methanol	CH_3OH	10,200	—
Natural gas		—	~1000
Producer gas		—	125
Coal gas		—	550
Carbon		14,500	—
Wood		~ 7,500	—
Coal		~15,000	—

tude per pound. Polyethylene does not volatilize easily, and consequently its reaction with the oxygen of the air is very slow.

Substitution of other elements for hydrogen in the chain structure also serves to reduce combustibility. For example, polyvinyl chloride has a lower heat of combustion than polyethylene because (roughly) each chlorine atom (1) is itself noncombustible and (2) prevents a hydrogen from combining with oxygen:

$$C_2H_3Cl + 2\tfrac{1}{2}O_2 \rightarrow 2CO_2 + H_2O + HCl. \qquad (7-13)$$

Vinylidene chloride (saran) and tetrafluoroethylene (teflon) (Appendix F) produce polymers which are still less combustible because the available hydrogen is further reduced. For either of these to support combustion, the temperature must be sufficient to dissociate the polymer, remove the resulting gases (HCl and F_2) from the surface, and admit oxygen to the nonvolatile carbon.

Explosives. Explosive materials, of course, require very little if any net energy for dissociation, and have sufficient oxygen within their structures to produce the "products of combustion." The structures of cellulose nitrate and nitroglycerine, shown in Fig. 7-32, will serve as illustrations. They contain sufficient oxygen so that no external source of air is required. A mechanical detonation can supply the activating energy to dissociate either into gaseous molecules:

$$C_6H_7(ONO_2)_3O_2 \rightarrow CO, CO_2 \ H_2O, NO, \qquad (7-14)$$

$$C_3H_5(ONO_2)_3 \rightarrow CO, CO_2, H_2O, NO. \qquad (7-15)$$

Polyelectrolytes. So far, organic materials have been considered to be primarily covalent-bonded (and to have van der Waals attractions between molecules), but

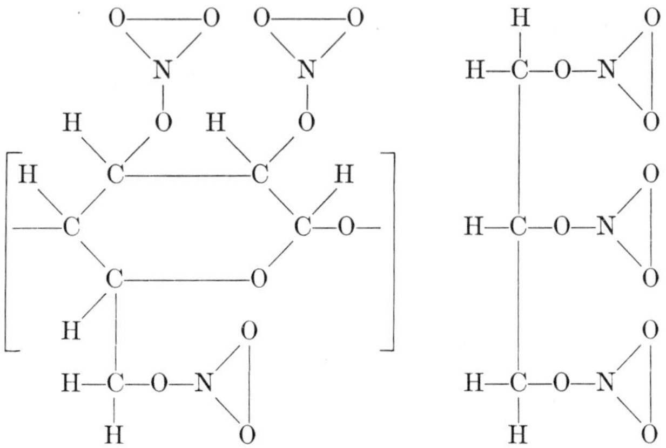

FIG. 7-32. Structures of explosives. (a) Cellulose nitrate, and (b) nitroglycerine. See Eqs. (7–14) and (7–15).

it is possible to ionize certain organic compounds to a limited extent. For example, organic acids such as acetic acid will produce some hydrogen ions and negative acetate radicals:

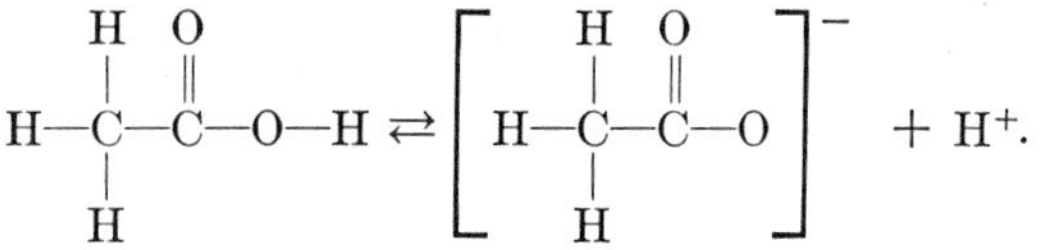

$$ (7\text{-}16) $$

The reaction tends to go to the left, producing a weak acid. However, such ionization does provide the opportunity to form organic salts. Calcium stearate, shown in Fig. 7–33 as an example, is the scum we find after using soap in hard water; it has precipitated from an aqueous solution.

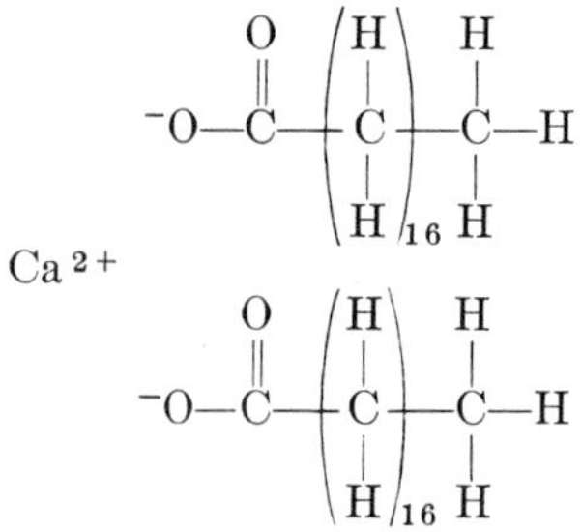

FIG. 7-33. Structure of calcium stearate. Most of the structure is covalently bonded; the calcium ion is an exception.

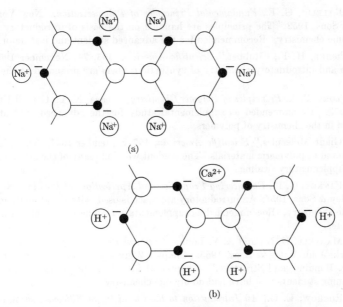

FIG. 7–34. Ion exchange resins (schematic). Both covalent and ionic bonds are present. Some of the ions may be exchanged without affecting the basic covalent structure.

There may also be some ionization present in polymeric solids. Figure 7–34 illustrates one of these *polyelectrolytes*, whose characteristics are very similar to many of the ceramic materials which possess combinations of covalent and ionic bonds. The polyelectrolytes are ionic conductors of electricity, but conduction is limited to slow ion diffusion rates. Because it is possible to interchange ions, these organic compounds are commonly used in such applications as ion exchange for water softening.

References for Further Reading

7–1. BARRON, H., *Modern Plastics*. London: Chapman and Hall, 1949. Written in a manner that the layman can understand. Indicates the versatility of polymeric materials.

7–2. BATTISTA, O. A., *Fundamentals of High Polymers*. New York: Reinhold, 1958. Written for the nonspecialist who wants a basic knowledge of the field of polymers.

7–3. BILLMEYER, F. W., JR., *Textbook of Polymer Chemistry*. New York: Interscience, 1957. Introduction to polymers at the advanced undergraduate level. Assumes a familiarity with organic nomenclature.

7–4. BILLMEYER, F. W., JR., *Textbook of Polymer Science*. New York: Interscience, 1962. Pays more attention to applications than the author's other book (Reference 7–3).

7–5. COUZENS, E. G., and V. E. YARSLEY, *Plastics in the Service of Man*. Baltimore: Penguin, 1956. Paperback. Written for the layman. Also serves as an introduction to plastics for the student.

7-6. D'ALELIO, G. F., *Fundamental Principles of Polymerization.* New York: John Wiley & Sons, 1952. The principles are handled on the basis of introductory physical and organic chemistry. Recommended for the advanced student and instructor.

7-7. FISHER, H. F., "Rubber," *Scientific American,* **195,** 74, November 1956. The structure and introductory chemistry of synthetic rubbers are presented at the student level.

7-8. FLORY, P. J., *Principles of Polymer Chemistry.* Ithaca, N. Y.: Cornell University Press, 1953. Recommended as supplemental study for the advanced student who is interested in the chemistry of polymers.

7-9. "Giant Molecules," *Scientific American,* **197,** September 1957. This is a special issue devoted to polymeric materials. The student will find many of the articles interesting for supplementary reading.

7-10. KINNEY, G. F., *Engineering Properties and Applications of Plastics.* New York: John Wiley & Sons, 1957. An introductory approach is used, with the absolute minimum of organic chemistry. Recommended as supplementary reading to the subject matter in this chapter.

7-11. MARVELL, E. N., and A. V. LOGAN, *Chemical Properties of Organic Compounds.* New York: John Wiley & Sons, 1955. Chapter 2 gives an elementary explanation of "Valence, Bonding, and Structure." Chapter 21 introduces polymers. Recommended for beginning students who have had no organic chemistry.

7-12. ROCHOW, E. G., *An Introduction to the Chemistry of Silicones,* second edition. New York: John Wiley & Sons, 1951. For the student who has a special interest in polymeric-ceramic materials. Requires organic chemistry background.

7-13. SCHMIDT, A. X., and C. A. MARLIES, *Principles of High Polymer Theory and Practice.* New York: McGraw-Hill, 1948. Chapters 1 and 2 contain subject matter similar to that in Chapter 7 of this book. Chapter 3 elaborates on the effects of polymer structures on their properties.

7-14. WINDING, C. C., and G. D. HIATT, *Polymeric Materials.* New York: McGraw-Hill, 1961. Polymeric principles and production of plastics. Requires a minimum knowledge of organic nomenclature.

Problems

7-1. Equation (3–2) is sometimes given for the determination of the freezing points of the paraffin series. What melting point would polyethylene with (a) a DP of 10 have? (b) a DP of 100? (c) a DP of 1000? [*Note:* Mer = C_2H_4.]

Answer: (a) 35°C (b) 130°C (c) 142°C

7-2. The following data were obtained in a determination of the average molecular weight of a polymer:

Molecular weight	Weight
gm/gm mol wt	gm
30,000	3.0
20,000	5.0
10,000	2.5

Compute the "weight-average" molecular weight of this polymer.

7-3. (a) How many molecules per gram are there in the polymer of Problem 7-2? (b) What is the "number-average" molecular weight of this polymer?

Answer: (a) 3.42×10^{19} molecules/gm (b) 17,500 gm/MW

7-4. Two-tenths of one percent by weight of H_2O_2 was added to ethylene prior to polymerization. What would the average DP be if all the H_2O_2 were used as terminals for the molecules? (Mer = C_2H_4.)

7-5. If HCl is used as an initiator in polyvinyl chloride, how much would have to be added to produce an average molecular weight of 6300 gm/gm·mole? (Assume 30% efficiency of the HCl.)

Answer: 2% HCl

7-6. H_2O_2 is added to 280 lb of ethylene prior to polymerization. The average degree of polymerization obtained is 1000. Assuming all the H_2O_2 was used to form terminal groups for polymer molecules, how many pounds of H_2O_2 were added? (Mer = C_2H_4.)

7-7. Show how a polymer could be made from (a) propylene, (b) isobutylene, (c) acrylonitrile (Appendix F).

7-8. Nylon is a condensation polymer of molecules, such as adipic acid [OH·CO·$(CH_2)_4$CO·OH] and hexamethylene amine [NH_2·$(CH_2)_6$·NH_2]. (a) Sketch the structure of these two molecules. (b) Show how polymerization can occur. (c) What is the condensation by-product?

7-9. (a) Show how a melamine-formaldehyde "plastic" may be formed. (See Appendix F for melamine.) Predict the characteristics of this plastic under conditions (b) of high temperature, (c) of stress.

7-10. Show how a silicone can be polymerized out of dimethyl-silanediol (Appendix F).

7-11. What percent sulfur would be present if it were used as a cross-link at every possible point (a) in polyisoprene? (b) in polychloroprene?

Answer: (a) 32% S (b) 26.5% S

7-12. A rubber contains 91% polymerized chloroprene and 9% sulfur. What fraction of the possible cross links are joined in vulcanization? (Assume that all the sulfur is used for cross links.)

7-13. A rubber contains 54% butadiene, 34% isoprene, 9% sulfur, and 3% carbon black. What fraction of the possible cross links are joined by vulcanization, assuming that all the sulfur is used in cross-linking?

Answer: 0.188

7-14. Divinyl benzene has the structure shown in Appendix F. In making polystyrene plastics, 2-3% of divinyl benzene may be added. In what ways may this change the structure and properties of the polymer?

7-15. (a) A butadiene rubber becomes harder simply by exposing it to air. An analysis shows that some of the rubber has oxidized. Account for the change in properties. (b) Additional exposure indicates that the rubber loses weight and becomes friable. Account for the change in properties.

7-16. Select the thermosetting resins listed in Appendix G.

7-17. Select the thermoplastic resins listed in Appendix G.

7-18. Scrap bakelite is worthless. Scrap polyvinyl chloride may be reused. Why?

• 7–19. The relaxation time for a plastic is known to be 45 days and the modulus of elasticity is 10^4 psi (both at 100°C). The plastic is compressed 0.05 in./in. and held at 100°C. What is the stress (a) initially? (b) after 1 day? (c) after 1 month? (d) after 1 year?

Answer: (a) 500 psi   (b) 490 psi   (c) 260 psi   (d) 0.15 psi

• 7–20. An initial stress of 1500 psi is required to strain a piece of rubber 0.5 in./in. After the strain has been maintained constant for 40 days, the stress required is only 750 psi. What would be the stress required to maintain the strain after 80 days?

7–21. How many cubic feet of ethylene gas (60°F) would be needed to make 100 in³ of polyethylene for which the average degree of polymerization is 10,000. (The specific gravity of polyethylene is 0.95.)

Answer: 46 ft³

7–22. Gasoline has approximately the following composition: 85% C, 14% H, 1% O. How many gallons of water (assuming it could be condensed) would come out of an exhaust pipe of an automobile per gallon of gasoline burned? (Specific gravity of gasoline = 0.7.)

7–23. Propane (C_3H_8) produces 21,400 Btu per pound when burned. (a) Compare this value with the value that would be obtained if carbon produced 14,500 Btu per pound and hydrogen produced 60,800 Btu per pound when burned. (b) Account for any difference.

Answer: (a) 22,900 Btu/lb. (b) Energy must be used to dissociate C_3H_8.

7–24. A fuel gas mixture containing 30% CO, 15% H_2, 5% CO_2, and 50% N_2 by volume is burned with 10% excess air (air contains 20.9% O_2 and 79.1% N_2 by volume). (a) Compute the volume of air required per 100 ft³ of fuel gas mixture burned. (b) Compute the analysis of the gas mixture (volume percent) that would exit from the chimney stack, assuming that all the water formed in the combustion process is condensed in the chimney. (c) Compute the volume of the dry-stack gas formed per 100 ft³ of fuel gas burned, assuming that fuel gas and stack gas are both measured at the same pressure and temperature (1 lb molecular weight of gas occupies 378 ft³ at 1 atmosphere pressure and 60°F).

7–25. The basic reaction for making ethylene is $C_2H_2 + H_2 \rightarrow C_2H_4$. Predict the process for making (a) vinyl chloride, (b) vinylidene chloride, (c) styrene (Appendix F).

Answer: (a) $C_2H_2 + HCl \rightarrow C_2H_3Cl$

7–26. Select the resins in Appendix G which are more inflammable than polyethylene.

7–27. Other things being equal, which will have the *greatest toughness:* (a) rubber subjected to low temperatures and a fast rate of impact, (b) rubber subjected to high temperatures and a fast rate of impact, (c) rubber subjected to high temperatures and a slow rate of impact, (d) rubber subjected to low temperatures and a slow rate of impact? Why?

• Problems preceded by a bullet are based, in part, on optional sections.

8

ceramic phases
and their properties

8–1 Introduction. *Ceramic materials* contain phases which are *compounds of metallic and nonmetallic elements.* We recall from Section 2–7 that the few valence electrons of a metallic atom can be removed and given to nonmetallic atoms or groups of atoms which have outer shells that are nearly complete, and that nonmetallic atoms may also share electrons covalently.

There are many ceramic phases because (1) there are many possible combinations of metallic and nonmetallic atoms, and (2) there may be several structural arrangements of each combination. In general, ceramic phases have properties which are different from those of metallic materials (Chapter 6) or polymeric materials (Chapter 7). However, there is considerable overlap among metallic, ceramic, and polymeric materials, particularly when their phases contain semimetallic elements.

CERAMIC PHASES

8–2 Examples of ceramic materials. The term *ceramic* is most familiar as an adjective describing artware. For the engineer, however, ceramics include a wide variety of substances such as glass, brick, stone, concrete, abrasives, porcelain enamels, dielectric insulators (Fig. 8–1); nonmetallic magnetic materials, high-temperature refractories, and many óthers. The characteristic feature all these

(a)

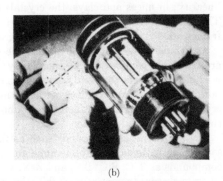

(b)

FIG. 8–1. Ceramics for engineering applications. (a) Glass heat exchangers for cooling corrosive fluids (Corning Glass Works). (b) Electron tubes (*Ceramic Industry*).

materials have in common is that they are compounds of metals and nonmetals. The compound MgO is representative of a simple ceramic material; it is used extensively as a refractory because it can withstand exceedingly high temperatures (3000 to 4500°F) without dissociation or melting. Clay is also a common ceramic material but is more complex than MgO. The simplest clay is $Al_2Si_2O_5(OH)_4$. It forms a crystalline structure of the four different units: Al, Si, O, and the (OH) radical. Although ceramic materials are not as simple as metals, they may be classified and understood in terms of their internal structures.

8–3 Comparison of ceramic and nonceramic phases. Most ceramic minerals (phases), like metals, have crystal structures. Unlike metals, however, these structures do not contain large numbers of free electrons. Either the electrons are shared covalently with adjacent atoms, or they are transferred from one atom to another to produce an ionic bond, in which case the atoms become ionized and carry a charge.

Ionic bonds give ceramic materials relatively high stability. As a class, they have a much higher melting temperature, on the average, than do metals or organic materials. Generally speaking, they are also harder and more resistant to chemical alteration. Like the organic materials, solid ceramic minerals are usually insulators. At elevated temperatures, with more thermal energy, they do conduct electricity, but poorly as compared with metals. Due to the absence of free electrons, most ceramic materials are transparent, at least in thin sections, and are poor thermal conductors.

Crystalline characteristics may be observed in many ceramic materials. Mica, for example, has cleavage planes which permit easy splitting. In some of the simpler crystals, such as MgO, plastic slip, similar to metallic slip, may occur. Crystal outlines can form during growth, as exemplified by the cubic outline of ordinary table salt. In asbestos, the crystals have a marked tendency toward linearity; in micas and clays, the crystals form two-dimensional sheet structures. The stronger, more stable ceramic materials commonly possess three-dimensional framework structures with equally strong bonding in all three directions.

As compared with those of metals, the crystal structures of ceramic materials are relatively complex. This complexity and the greater strength of the bonds holding the atoms together make ceramic reactions sluggish. For example, at normal cooling rates glass does not have time to rearrange itself into a complicated crystalline structure, and therefore at room temperature it remains as a super-cooled liquid for a long time.

The properties of compounds such as the refractory carbides and nitrides fall somewhere between those of ceramic and metallic materials. These include such compounds as TiC, SiC, BN, and ZrN, which contain semimetallic elements and whose structures comprise a combination of metallic and covalent bonds. Ferromagnetic spinels are another example. Because they lack free electrons, they are not good conductors of electricity; however, the atoms can be oriented within the crystal structure so as to possess the magnetic properties normally associated with iron and related metals (Chapter 5).

Between ceramic materials and organic materials there are also classes of materials intermediate in structure, like the silicone group. Later in this chapter, analogies will be drawn between the crystallization of silicates and the polymerization of organic materials.

CRYSTAL STRUCTURE OF CERAMIC PHASES

8–4 Introduction. Inasmuch as each ceramic phase is composed of more than one type of atom, the crystal structure of each phase must accommodate the different kinds of atoms. Figure 3–10 shows the structure of NaCl, which consists of the metal sodium and the nonmetal chlorine; and Figs. 2–22(a) and 8–2 show the identical structure for MgO. In both NaCl and MgO, the structure is such that the ion size and the electron number requirements are met.

Other ceramic compounds may include several or many types of atoms; however, in every case the stringent requirement of charge balance is necessary. Furthermore, atomic coordination requirements are present which involve both atom packing and covalent considerations (Section 2–15).

Example 8–1

The three-dimensional structure of the MgO unit cell is shown in Fig. 8–2 as a plan view. The third dimension is indicated by fractions that show the depth locations of the atoms in the unit cell.

A similar sketch is shown in Fig. 8–3 for the unit cell of fluorite (CaF_2). (a) How many atoms are there per unit cell? (b) What is the weight of a unit cell?

Answer: (a) Calcium: $\frac{8}{8} + \frac{6}{2} = 4/uc$. Fluorine: (all within the cell) $= 8/uc$.

(b) $$\frac{(8)(19.00) + (4)(40.08)}{6.02 \times 10^{23}} = 5.2 \times 10^{-22} \text{ gm.}$$

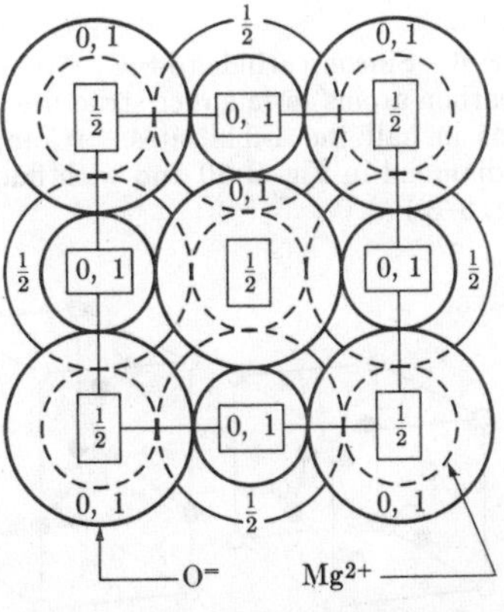

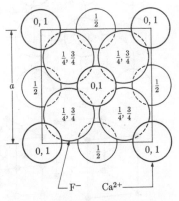

FIG. 8–2. Structure of MgO, three-dimensional. The numbers show the depth locations of the atoms in the unit cell. (0 = top surface, $\frac{1}{2}$ = midcell position, 1 = bottom side.) Compare with Fig. 3–10 for NaCl.

FIG. 8–3. Fluorite (CaF_2) structure. (Cf. Fig. 8–2.)

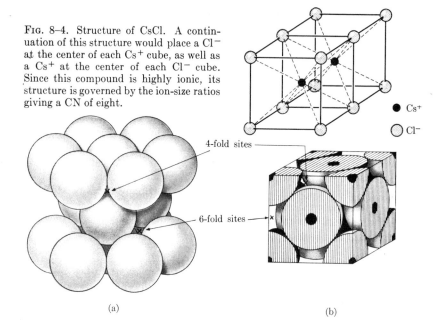

FIG. 8–4. Structure of CsCl. A continuation of this structure would place a Cl⁻ at the center of each Cs⁺ cube, as well as a Cs⁺ at the center of each Cl⁻ cube. Since this compound is highly ionic, its structure is governed by the ion-size ratios giving a CN of eight.

$\bullet$ Cs⁺

$\bigcirc$ Cl⁻

4-fold sites

6-fold sites

(a)   (b)

FIG. 8–5. Interstitial sites in (a) hcp and (b) fcc structures. There are twice as many 4-fold sites as 6-fold sites (i.e., holes with four and six neighboring atoms).

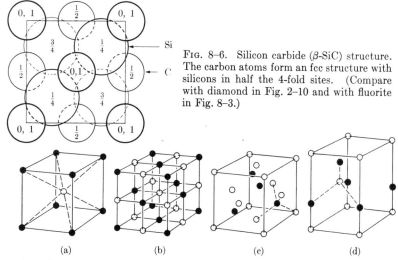

FIG. 8–6. Silicon carbide (β-SiC) structure. The carbon atoms form an fcc structure with silicons in half the 4-fold sites. (Compare with diamond in Fig. 2–10 and with fluorite in Fig. 8–3.)

(a)   (b)   (c)   (d)

FIG. 8–7. AX-type compounds. (a) CsCl has a CN of 8 for both anions and cations. (b) In NaCl or MgO the CN's are 6. (c) Cubic ZnS (sphalerite). (d) Hexagonal ZnS (wurtzite). In both the ZnS polymorphs, the CN's are 4.

8-5 Close-packed compounds. *AX-compounds.* Recall that simple cubic structures are not found among metals because the sc packing factor is relatively low; a denser packing produces a more stable metallic structure (Section 3–11). It is possible, however, for compounds to have simple cubic structures. For example, if a small atom is placed in the center of a simple cube among eight larger atoms, a relatively efficient packing is developed. Such a structure must be a compound because atoms of two different sizes are necessary. Cesium chloride is the prototype for this case (Fig. 8–4). The size ratio of its ions is 1.65/1.81, or approximately 0.9, which favors the coordination number of eight.* Also there is one smaller cation, A, and one larger anion, X, per unit cell to give the necessary ion ratio for an AX-type compound.

A second type of AX-compound is typified by NaCl and MgO (Figs. 3–10 and 8–2). With MgO, which is called periclase, the ion-size ratio is 0.78/1.32, or approximately 0.6. Thus we find an fcc structure of anions favored with cations in interstitial sites with six anion neighbors, i.e., 6-fold sites. This structure has four anion and four cation positions per unit cell. In addition to MgO, a number of other simple compounds possess this structure; for example, LiF, MnS, CaO, and AgCl.

We recall that an hcp arrangement of atoms has the same atomic packing factor (0.74) and the same coordination number (12) as an fcc structure; the only difference is the stacking sequence (Section 3–17). Therefore, the interstitial sites are the same, and for each equivalent position of the unit cell there is one 6-fold site in the two structures. Iron sulfide (FeS) typifies a structure where the anions form an hcp pattern and the cations fill all 6-fold sites.

Face-centered-cubic and hcp structures have small 4-fold sites, as well as 6-fold sites (Fig. 8–5). Since there are twice as many of these 4-fold sites per unit cell as there are 6-fold sites, only half of them are filled in an AX-compound. Two of the more common cubic ceramic compounds which contain atoms in the 4-fold sites are ZnS (sphalerite) and β-SiC. The latter is shown in Fig. 8–6 where four observations may be made: (1) Each type of atom forms an fcc pattern of its own. (You may need to extend the structure to visualize this pattern for the Si atoms.) (2) Only half the 4-fold sites are filled. (3) A maximum coordination number does not exist because there is some covalent bonding present which gives a preference for four neighbors. (4) The structure is the same as the diamond cubic (Fig. 2–10), except that alternate atoms are of different elements. Comparable hcp structures of AX-compounds with atoms in the 4-fold sites include BeO, a second ZnS poylmorph (wurtzite), and ZnO (zincite). Although strongly ionic, BeO has a cation coordination number of only four because of its small ion ratio, 0.34/1.32. In contrast, the two zinc compounds maintain a CN of four because there is some covalency in their bonding; their size ratios would permit a CN of six.

The foregoing AX-compounds are summarized in Fig. 8–7 and in Table 8–1.

---

* The structure of Fig. 8–4 is *not* body-centered cubic, inasmuch as the center and the corner of the cube contain different types of atoms and therefore are not equivalent positions.

TABLE 8-1

PACKING OF SELECTED A_mX_n COMPOUNDS*

Structure	Anion arrangement	Cation interstitial location	Locations filled	Other examples
CsCl	sc	8-fold	All	
NaCl	fcc	6-fold	All	MgO, MnS, LiF
NiAs	hcp	6-fold	All	FeS
Zincblende (ZnS)	fcc	4-fold	$\frac{1}{2}$	β-SiC, CdS, AlP
Wurtzite (ZnS)	hcp	4-fold	$\frac{1}{2}$	BeO, ZnO, AlN
Corundum (Al$_2$O$_3$)	hcp	6-fold	$\frac{2}{3}$	Cr$_2$O$_3$, Fe$_2$O$_3$, MgTiO$_3$
γ-Al$_2$O$_3$	fcc	6-fold	$\frac{2}{3}$	γ-Fe$_2$O$_3$
Fluorite (CaF$_2$)	sc	8-fold	$\frac{1}{2}$	(See below)

Structure	Cation arrangement	Anion location	Locations filled	Other examples
Fluorite (CaF$_2$)	fcc	4-fold	All	ZrO$_2$, UO$_2$

* Van Vlack, L. H., *Physical Ceramics for Engineers*. Reading, Mass.: Addison-Wesley, 1964.

Example 8-2

MnS normally forms the same structure as MgO and NaCl (Fig. 8-7b); however, under favorable conditions of formation, it may form the same structure as cubic ZnS (Fig. 8-7c). Calculate the density of MnS in each case. [Assume that the atom sizes are only 0.94 as large when the CN is four as when it is six (Section 2-14).]

Answer: (a) MnS with the MgO-type structure:

$$\text{(From Appendix D)}, \quad r + R = 0.91 + 1.74 = 2.65 \text{ A.}$$

$$\text{Density} = \frac{[4(54.9) + 4(32.1)]/(0.602 \times 10^{24})}{[2(2.65 \times 10^{-8})]^3}$$

$$= \frac{(4)(87.0)}{(149)(0.602)} = 3.88 \text{ gm/cm}^3.$$

(b) MnS with the cubic ZnS structure:

$$r + R = (0.94)(0.91 + 1.74)$$
$$= 2.50 \text{ A.}$$

In the cubic ZnS structure, a sulfur atom is at 0, 0, 0, and a metal atom is at $\frac{1}{4}, \frac{1}{4}, \frac{1}{4}$.

$$\text{Density} = \frac{[4(54.9) + 4(32.1)]/(0.602 \times 10^{24})}{[4(2.50 \times 10^{-8})/\sqrt{3}]^3}$$

$$= \frac{(4)(87.0)}{(191)(0.602)} = 3.03 \text{ gm/cm}^3.$$

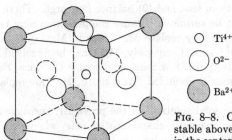

○ Ti⁴⁺

○ O²⁻

◉ Ba²⁺

Fig. 8–8. Cubic BaTiO₃. This structure is stable above 120°C, where it has a Ti⁴⁺ ion in the center of the cube, Ba²⁺ ions at the corners, and O²⁻ ions at the center of each face.

A_mX_n *compounds.* The simplest compound with $m \neq n$ is CaF_2 (fluorite), which has the structure shown in Fig. 8–3. This is also the basic structure of UO_2, which is used in nuclear fuel elements, and of one of the forms of ZrO_2, which is a useful high-temperature oxide. This structure has an fcc arrangement of cations with anions in all 4-fold positions, giving a cation CN of eight and an anion CN of four. Also, it may be suggested that there is a simple cubic arrangement of anions with cations in half the 8-fold positions. Although this description is useful, it is not fully satisfactory, because it leaves us with two types of simple cubic cells, with and without center cations.

Other types of A_mX_n compounds may be described on the basis of their packing arrangements (Table 8–1). Corundum (Al_2O_3) is probably the most important among these. It has an hcp arrangement of O^{2-} ions with Al^{3+} in two out of every three 6-fold sites, thus giving the necessary 2-to-3 cation/anion ratio.* One is not surprised to find a cubic polymorph of alumina, called γ-Al_2O_3, which has an fcc arrangement of O^{2-} ions also with two out of every three 6-fold sites filled with Al^{3+} cations.

AB_mX_n-*type compounds.* Although the presence of three types of atoms lends additional complexity, several AB_mX_n compounds are of sufficient interest for our attention. First among these is $BaTiO_3$, the prototype for the ceramic materials used in applications such as cartridges for record players. Above 120°C, $BaTiO_3$ has a cubic unit cell with Ba^{2+} ions at the corners, O^{2-} ions at the center of the faces, and a Ti^{4+} ion at the center of the cell (Fig. 8–8).

Nonmetallic magnets are also AB_mX_n compounds, the most common being a ferrospinel (often called a ferrite) with the composition of MFe_2O_4, where the M are divalent cations with radii of 0.85 ± 0.1 A. These spinel structures have a close-packed (fcc) structure of O^{2-} ions with cations selectively positioned in the 6-fold and 4-fold interstitial sites. The ferromagnetic characteristics of these structures are influenced by the cation locations.

Solid solutions. Brief attention was given in Section 4–4 to solid solutions in ionic compounds. Two chief requirements were cited as necessary for solid solu-

---

* The Al_2O_3 structure is not truly hcp, because one out of the three cation sites is empty.

tions to occur: (1) compatibility in size, and (2) balance in charge. These limitations are not as rigid as might be surmised, because compensation may be made in charge. For example, Li^+ ions may replace Mg^{2+} ions in MgO *if* F^- is simultaneously present to replace O^{2-} ions. Conversely, MgO may be dissolved in LiF. We may also find Mg^{2+} dissolved in LiF without comparable O^{2-} ions; however, in this case cation vacancies must be included. As a result, $2Li^+$ are replaced by $(Mg^{2+} + \square)$.

Ceramists depend heavily on solid solutions in the previously mentioned magnetic spinels, because optimum magnetic characteristics exist when part of the divalent ions are zinc ($r = 0.83$ A) and the balance of the divalent ions are ferromagnetic; for example, Ni^{2+} ($r = 0.78$). In this case it is a simple matter of direct substitution; however, for certain applications it is desirable to replace $2M^{2+}$ with an Li^+Fe^{3+} pair, or to replace $2Fe^{3+}$ with an $Mg^{2+}Ti^{4+}$ pair.

Example 8–3

A ferrospinel has a lattice of 32 oxygen ions, 16 ferric ions, and 8 divalent ions. (The unit cell contains 8 times as many oxygen ions as MgO does, so that the repeating pattern can be developed.) If the divalent ions are Zn^{2+} and Ni^{2+} in a 3:5 ratio, what weight fraction of ZnO, NiO_2, and Fe_2O_3 must be mixed for processing?

Answer: Basis: 8 mol wt of Fe_2O_3.

$$5\,NiO + 3\,ZnO + 8\,Fe_2O_3 \longrightarrow (Zn_3, Ni_5)Fe_{16}O_{32}.$$

				Wt fraction
5 NiO	$= 5(58.71 + 16.00)$	$=$	373.5	$= 0.197$
3 ZnO	$= 3(65.37 + 16.00)$	$=$	244.1	$= 0.129$
8 Fe_2O_3	$= 8[2(55.85) + 3(16.00)]$	$=$	1277.6	$= 0.673$
			1895.2	0.999

● **8–6 Silicate structures.** Many ceramic materials contain *silicates*, partly because silicates are plentiful and cheap and partly because they have certain distinct properties which are useful in engineering applications. Probably the most widely known silicate is portland cement, which has the very definite advantage of being able to form a hydraulic bond for rock aggregates. Many other construction materials, such as brick, tile, glass, and vitreous enamel, are also made of silicates. Other engineering applications of silicates include electrical insulators, chemical ware, and reinforcing glass fibers.

Silicate tetrahedral units. The primary structural unit of silicates is the "SiO_4" *tetrahedron* (Fig. 8–9), in which one silicon atom fits interstitially among four oxygen atoms. The forces holding these tetrahedra together alternate between ionic and covalent bonds; consequently the tetrahedra are tightly bonded. However, with either the ionic or covalent bonding mechanism, each oxygen has only seven electrons rather than the eight available to its outer shell.

Two methods are available to overcome this deficiency of electrons for the oxygen ions: (1) An electron may be obtained from other metal atoms. In this

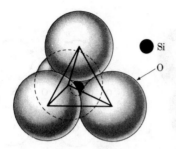

FIG. 8–9. Tetrahedral arrangement of SiO_4^{4-}. Compare with Fig. 2–22(b). The SiO_4^{4-} ions must obtain four electrons from other sources.

case SiO_4^{4-} ions and Metal$^+$ ions are developed. (2) Each oxygen may share an electron pair with a second silicon. In this case multiple 4-fold coordination groups are formed.

SiO_4^{4-} silicate structures. The simplest example of minerals containing SiO_4^{4-} ions is forsterite (Mg_2SiO_4), a mineral frequently used as a high-temperature refractory, since its melting point is 3430°F. In Mg_2SiO_4, the SiO_4^{4-} ion has received four electrons from four adjacent magnesium atoms. Each magnesium atom provides a second electron to other SiO_4 units. Consequently, a strong structure is formed in which Mg^{2+} ions serve as connecting links between SiO_4^{4-} ions. Since the SiO_4^{4-} tetrahedral groups are separated from one another, they have received the name "island" structures. When forsterite eventually melts, the melt contains Mg^{2+} and SiO_4^{4-} ions which possess some mobility and therefore ionic conductivity. It should be noted that Mg_2SiO_4 is not a molecule in the structural sense (Section 3–1), because all units are held by primary ionic and by covalent bonds. Secondary, van der Waals forces are not apparent. Also the resulting structure has a pattern of oxygen ions rather closely packed with silicon atoms in part of the 4-fold interstitial sites and magnesium ions in part of the 6-fold sites.

• **Example 8–4**

If the close-packed arrangement of oxygens in forsterite (Mg_2SiO_4) has the same number of 4-fold and 6-fold sites as does MgO (Fig. 8–2), what fraction of these sites is occupied?

Answer: Basis: 100 oxygen atoms = 100 6-fold sites = 200 4-fold sites. In Mg_2SiO_4,

$$100 \text{ oxygen atoms} = 50 \text{ } Mg^{2+} \text{ ions} = 0.50 \text{ of 6-fold sites;}$$
$$100 \text{ oxygen atoms} = 25 \text{ Si atoms} = 0.125 \text{ of 4-fold sites.}$$

Double tetrahedral units. The second of the two methods available to overcome the deficiency of electrons produces a double tetrahedral unit. One of the oxygens is a member of two units (Fig. 8–10a). The consequent composition of the double unit is Si_2O_7, which produces an $Si_2O_7^{6-}$ ion when electrons are obtained from adjacent metal atoms (Fig. 8–10b).

As in crystal bonding in NaCl (Fig. 3–10), both the SiO_4^{4-} and the $Si_2O_7^{6-}$ units may be held rigidly in a solid by mutual attraction with positive metal ions.

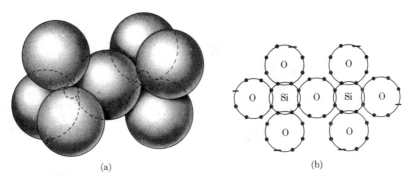

FIG. 8–10. Double tetrahedral silicates, $Si_2O_7^{6-}$. The center oxygen receives an electron from each adjacent silicon.

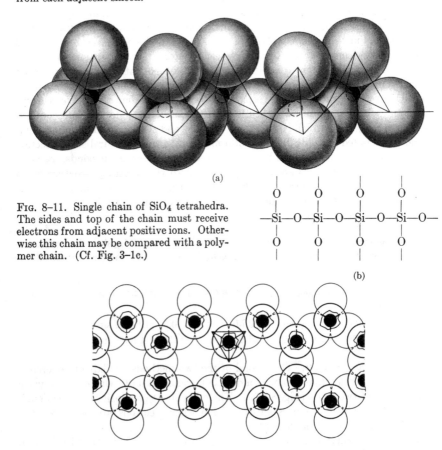

FIG. 8–11. Single chain of SiO_4 tetrahedra. The sides and top of the chain must receive electrons from adjacent positive ions. Otherwise this chain may be compared with a polymer chain. (Cf. Fig. 3–1c.)

FIG. 8–12. Double chain of SiO_4 tetrahedra.

$$
\begin{array}{cccccccc}
O^- & O^- & O^- & O^- & O^- & O^- & O^- & O^- \\
| & | & | & | & | & | & | & | \\
-Si-O-Si-O-Si-O-Si-O-Si-O-Si-O-Si-O-Si-O- \\
| & | & | & | & | & | & | & | \\
O^- & O^- & O^- & O^- & O^- & O^- & O^- & O^-
\end{array}
$$

$$
\underline{Mg^{2+}} \ \underline{Mg^{2+}} \ \underline{Mg^{2+}} Na^+ Na^+ \ \underline{Mg^{2+}} \ \underline{Mg^{2+}} Na^+ Na^+ Na^+ Na^+
$$

$$
\begin{array}{cccccccc}
O^- & O^- & O^- & O^- & O^- & O^- & O^- & O^- \\
| & | & | & | & | & | & | & | \\
-Si-O-Si-O-Si-O-Si-O-Si-O-Si-O-Si-O-Si- \\
| & | & | & | & | & | & | & | \\
O^- & O^- & O^- & O^- & O^- & O^- & O^- & O^-
\end{array}
$$

Fig. 8–13. Ionic bonding between chains. The slightly weaker ionic bonds provide a location for cleavage in these crystals.

Chain structures. It immediately becomes apparent that if one of the oxygens can be shared by two adjacent tetrahedra, similar sharing of oxygens on the other corners of the tetrahedra is possible. Figures 8–11 and 8–12 show examples in which silica tetrahedra have been built into single and double chains. These *chain structures,* theoretically, can be almost infinite in length and may be compared quite directly with polymerization in organic materials (Section 7–4) except for one major difference. In organic materials the adjacent chains are usually held together by weak van der Waals forces, but in ceramics the chains are commonly held together by ionic bonds, as shown schematically in Fig. 8–13. Since the ionic bonds between the chains are not quite as strong as the partially covalent Si–O bonds within the chain, fracture, or *cleavage,* occurs parallel to the chain. The rock minerals pyroxene and amphibole show examples of this parting. Also, the fibrous characteristics of *asbestos* are associated with the lower strength between the silicate chains rather than within them.

• Example 8–5

Calculate the number of ionic bonds per micron of length between adjacent chains in Fig 8–13.

Answer: The distance between adjacent silicons is approximately 3 A. The angle is approximately 120° (Fig. 8–14). The distance a in Fig. 8–14 is $(\sqrt{3}/2)(3 \text{ A}) = 2.6 \text{ A}$.

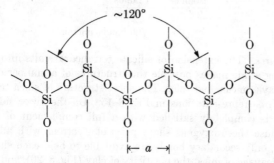

Fig. 8–14. Ionic bond calculation (see Example 8–5).

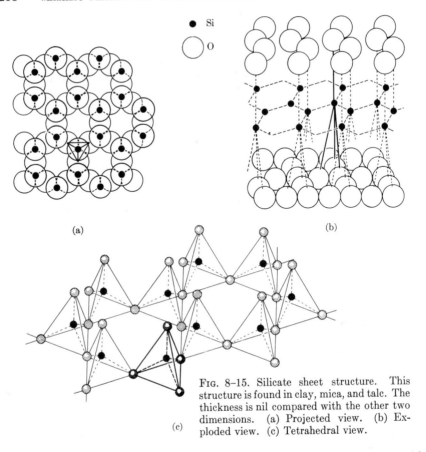

FIG. 8–15. Silicate sheet structure. This structure is found in clay, mica, and talc. The thickness is nil compared with the other two dimensions. (a) Projected view. (b) Exploded view. (c) Tetrahedral view.

There are two ionic bonds per silicon as a result of the two unsatisfied oxygens with each silicon:

$$\frac{2 \text{ bonds}}{2.6 \text{ A}} = \frac{x \text{ bonds}}{1 \text{ micron}},$$

$$x = 7700 \text{ bonds/micron}.$$

Sheet structures. The extension of silicate tetrahedral units into a plane rather than just along a line makes possible the structures of a number of such ceramic minerals as clays, micas, and talc. The sheet structure of silica tetrahedral units is shown in three representations in Fig. 8–15. On the lower side of the sheet, every oxygen is completely satisfied with a full complement of eight available electrons because these oxygens share pairs of electrons with adjacent silicons. Consequently, only secondary bonds are available to hold each sheet to adjacent sheets. The cleavage of mica, the plasticity of clay (Fig. 8–20), and the lubricating characteristic of talc are all consequences of this structural arrangement.

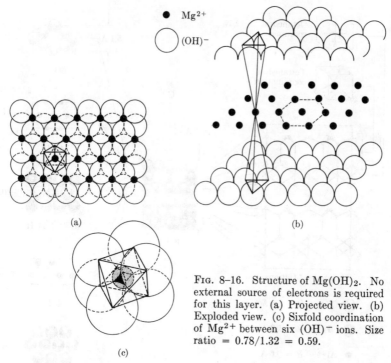

(a)

(b)

(c)

Fig. 8–16. Structure of $Mg(OH)_2$. No external source of electrons is required for this layer. (a) Projected view. (b) Exploded view. (c) Sixfold coordination of Mg^{2+} between six $(OH)^-$ ions. Size ratio = $0.78/1.32 = 0.59$.

Sheet structures are also developed with atom combinations other than those of silicon and oxygen. Figure 8–16 shows the structure of *magnesium hydroxide*. Since neither side of the sheet can form additional primary bonds, a crystal of $Mg(OH)_2$ is essentially two-dimensional, with a hexagonal pattern. Each magnesium ion is surrounded octahedrally by six $(OH)^-$ ions (Fig. 8–16b). This arrangement, made possible by the size ratios, provides two $(OH)^-$ ions for each Mg^{2+} ion.*

$Al(OH)_3$ (Fig. 8–17) has a structure very similar to $Mg(OH)_2$ but with one main difference: each aluminum ion gives up three electrons. Hence there must

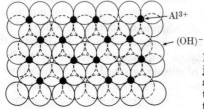

Fig. 8–17. Structure of $Al(OH)_3$ (projected view). The structure is the same as for $Mg(OH)_2$ except that only two-thirds of the positive ion positions are filled.

─────────

* The unit cell outlined has three Mg^{2+} ions and six $(OH)^-$ ions. These $(OH)^-$ ions are drawn as spheres, since the hydrogen is very small and lies close to the oxygen atom.

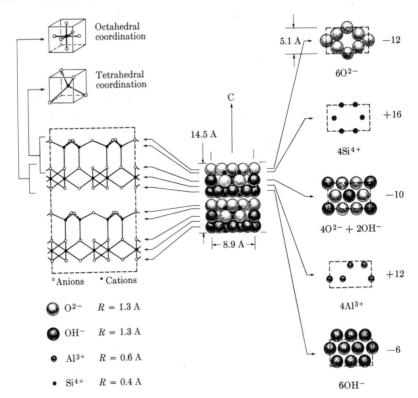

Fig. 8–18. Structure of kaolinite. The structure of this clay is a combination of those shown in Figs. 8–15 and 8–17. (F. H. Norton, *Elements of Ceramics.* Reading, Mass.: Addison-Wesley, 1952.)

be one Al^{3+} for every three $(OH)^-$ ions and only two-thirds of the interstitial locations are filled. (Cf. Fig. 8–16a.)

The simplest clay, *kaolinite*, has a double layer in which each of the upper, unsatisfied oxygens shown in Fig. 8–15(b) replaces one of the $(OH)^-$ ions in $Al(OH)_3$ (Fig. 8–17). In this position, the oxygens have obtained their full complement of eight electrons by accepting one from the aluminum atom (Fig. 8–18). The resulting structure of clay is essentially two-dimensional (Fig. 8–19). Because there are no primary bonds between adjacent layers,* slippage is less restricted (Fig. 8–20).

Framework structures. An extension of silicate tetrahedral units into three dimensions produces a framework structure. In these structures each of the oxygens of any particular unit is jointly shared with an adjacent unit, and of course each silicon is among four oxygens. The simplest framework structure is that of cristo-

---

* The structure shown in Fig. 8–18 is considered to be the *crystal layer* because the thickness is negligible compared with the other two dimensions.

FIG. 8–19. Electron micrographs of kaolinite crystals (×33,000). (W. H. EAST, "Fundamental Studies of Clay: X," *Journal American Ceramic Society* **33**, 211, 1950.)

balite, one of the SiO_2 polymorphs (Fig. 8–21a). This structure is interesting because it may be compared directly with metallic silicon, which has the diamond-cubic structure (Fig. 2–10). For example, silicon would result if the oxygen atoms of Fig. 8–21(a) were removed and silicon atoms could be collapsed into contact, but maintain their same relative positions. A second comparison is useful as a means of relating structures; viz., if every zinc *and* sulfur atom of cubic ZnS (Fig. 8–7c) were replaced with a silicon atom and then intervening oxygens were introduced, the resulting structure would be the cristobalite of Fig. 8–21(a).

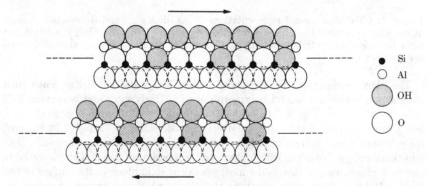

FIG. 8–20. Plasticity of clay (schematic). The plasticity is the result of the easy sliding of clay. There are strong intralayer attractions but weak interlayer attractions; therefore one layer will slide over another.

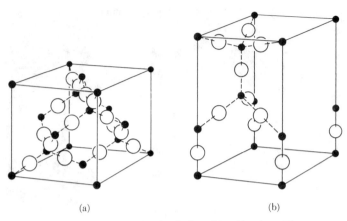

(a)   (b)

Fig. 8–21. Framework structures: (a) cristobalite, (b) tridymite. These structures may be compared to the two polymorphs of ZnS [Fig. 8–7(c) and (d)].

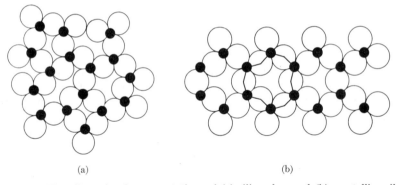

(a)   (b)

Fig. 8–22. Two-dimensional representations of (a) silica glass and (b) crystalline silica at room temperature. Each has a short-range framework structure. Only the crystalline silica has a long-range framework order. (The fourth oxygen above or below the silicon is not shown.)

The above comparison between cristobalite (SiO_2) and cubic ZnS leads to a comparison between a second polymorph of SiO_2 (tridymite) and hexagonal ZnS (Fig. 8–21b versus Fig. 8–7d). The framework structures of Fig. 8–21 have low atomic packing factors and relatively low densities (2.32 and 2.28 gm/cm^3 for cristobalite and tridymite, respectively). It is not surprising, therefore, that additional SiO_2 polymorphs with higher packing factors are found. Quartz (SiO_2) is one such phase, and, in fact, is the most prevalent solid phase in the surface of the earth. It has a framework structure of SiO_4 tetrahedra; however, they are arranged in a more complex pattern than those of Fig. 8–21. We shall not examine this structure in more detail, except to note that the density of quartz is 2.65 gm/cm^3.

Other silicate phases form framework structures. One of the feldspars, for example, is $KAlSi_3O_8$, which may be compared with Si_4O_8 (or $4\ SiO_2$). However, one of the Si^{4+} ions has been replaced by an Al^{3+}; this necessitates an additional K^+ ion, which is accommodated at specific open sites within the framework structure. The structure of $KAlSi_3O_8$ is distinct from those of Fig. 8–21; therefore, solid solution is not involved.

• **Example 8–6**

Compare the atomic packing factors of cristobalite ($\rho = 2.32$) and quartz ($\rho = 2.65$). Both are SiO_2. (Assume spherical atoms and ionic radii.)

Answer: Basis: 1 cm³ of each.

$$\text{Cristobalite:}\quad 2.32\ \text{gm/cm}^3 = \frac{2.32(6.02 \times 10^{23})}{[28.1 + 32.0]}\ SiO_2/\text{cm}^3$$
$$= 2.31 \times 10^{22}\ SiO_2/\text{cm}^3.$$

$$APF = \frac{(2.31 \times 10^{22})(4\pi/3)[(0.39 \times 10^{-8})^3 + 2(1.32 \times 10^{-8})^3]}{1.0} = 0.455.$$

$$\text{Quartz:}\quad 2.65\ \text{gm/cm}^3 = \frac{2.65(6.02 \times 10^{23})}{60.1}\ SiO_2/\text{cm}^3$$
$$= 2.64 \times 10^{22}\ SiO_2/\text{cm}^3.$$

$$APF = \frac{(2.64 \times 10^{22})(4\pi/3)[(0.39 \times 10^{-8})^3 + 2(1.32 \times 10^{-8})^3]}{1.0} = 0.52.$$

Vitreous structures. Glass is a *vitreous silicate*. Like liquid, glass is an amorphous material (Section 3–23), but unlike many of the more common liquids, glass has a three-dimensional framework structure containing covalent bonds. Consequently it is more rigid (viscous) than most liquids.

A pure *silica glass* is composed of SiO_4 units in which each oxygen is part of two adjacent tetrahedra (Fig. 8–22a). Its *short-range*, atom-to-atom arrangement is

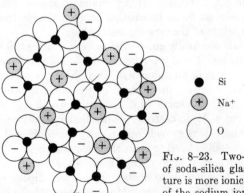

Si ●
Na⁺ ⊕
O ○

Fıɢ. 8–23. Two-dimensional representation of soda-silica glass. This framework structure is more ionic than silica glass, as a result of the sodium ions that give an electron to the partially connected oxygens.

identical to that of crystalline silica (Fig. 8–22b). For this reason silica glass is often called fused or vitreous quartz. However, although silica glass has the same short-range, atom-to-atom order that crystalline silica has, it does not have the *long-range*, repetitious crystalline pattern of crystalline silica. Silica glass may be compared directly with a framework polymer (Fig. 7–12), because both are bonded with primary bonds and neither has crystallinity.

The noncrystalline structure of glass can readily adjust itself to the presence of other atoms. Figure 8–23 shows a simple soda-silica glass. Each sodium atom has supplied one electron to an oxygen atom, which now needs to belong to only one tetrahedron. Consequently there is greater ionic bonding in this glass than in pure silica glass, and there are fewer rigidly held Si-O bonds. Therefore, such glasses are less viscous than pure SiO_2 glasses, so that they may be shaped into products at lower temperatures. Also, since the alkali-containing glasses are partially de-polymerized, crystallization can proceed more readily with the sodium ions present.

EFFECT OF STRUCTURE ON THE BEHAVIOR OF CERAMIC PHASES

8–7 Introduction. The properties of ceramic materials, as of other materials, depend on their structures. Foremost among these properties are the low electrical conductivities which result from the immobile electrons of the covalent and ionic bonds. Because ceramic materials are generally used as insulators, their dielectric properties become important. These properties are closely associated with the structure of the crystals. Likewise, magnetic properties of ceramic materials depend on the arrangement of the cations and of their subvalence electrons. Mechanical properties result from the various combinations of covalent, ionic, and van der Waals bonds that exist within the structures.

8–8 Dielectric ceramics. Ceramic materials are used both as electrical insulators and as functional parts of an electric circuit. When they are used as insulators, ceramic materials are simply required to be electrically inert and to isolate two conductors of different potentials. When ceramic materials are used as functional components, there must be an interaction between the electric field and the charges within the structure of the ceramic material.

Electrical insulators. Materials commonly considered to be insulators can break down under high electrical voltages. Usually the breakdown is a *surface* phenomenon. For example, the spark plugs of an automobile may short out on a damp morning because condensed moisture on the surface of the ceramic insulators permits the current to short-circuit the spark gap. Insulators are designed with lengthened surface paths (see Fig. 8–24) to decrease the possibility of surface shorting, and since internal pores and cracks provide opportunity for additional "surface" failure, the insulators are usually glazed to make them nonabsorbent. *Volume breakdown* occurs only when extremely high voltage gradients are encountered. A very strong electric field can be sufficient to disrupt the induced dipoles in the insulator, and when the strength of the field exceeds the strength of the dipole, rupture may occur.

FIG. 8–24. Surface breakdown. Adsorbed moisture and contaminants provide a surface path for electrical shorting. (R. Russell, *Brick and Clay Record*, page 52, 1957.)

Electrical insulators have *relative dielectric constants* which are significantly above unity. Recall that Fig. 4–19 showed ion displacement within an electric field, the positive ions moving toward the negative electrode and the negative ions moving toward the positive electrode. Such displacements can occur at frequencies up to 10^{13} cps if only single atoms are involved. However, most displacements involve groups or clusters of atoms within a material. Therefore, there is a limit in response and a reduction in the dielectric constant beyond about 10^5 cps (Fig. 8–25).

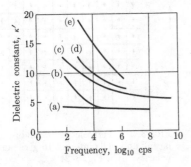

FIG. 8–25. Dielectric constant versus frequency. The higher dielectric constant at lower frequencies is a consequence of ion displacements within the electric field. (a) Fused silica, 100°C; (b) fused silica, 400°C; (c) AlSiMag A-35, 150°C; (d) ZrO_2 porcelain; (e) Al_2O_3.

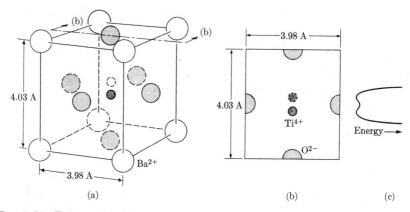

Fig. 8–26. Tetragonal BaTiO₃. Below 120°C (248°F), where the thermal vibrations are less vigorous, the Ti^{4+} ion settles into one of the two low-energy positions.

• *Ferroelectric ceramics.* All the ion displacements shown in Fig. 4–19 and discussed in the previous paragraph are reversible because after the electric field has been removed the ions return to vibrate around their original positions. This is not the case for all materials. Consider, for example, $BaTiO_3$ at room temperature. Below 120°C, $BaTiO_3$ changes from a cubic structure (Fig. 8–8) to one with a tetragonal unit cell (Fig. 8–26) in which the Ti^{4+} ion has a choice of two locations. Since neither location is at the center of the unit cell, the centers of positive and negative charges are not coincidental and an electrical dipole exists. Although the displacement is a small fraction of an angstrom, it is much greater than ionic displacements in most solids. This, coupled with the $4+$ charge on the ion, gives an exceedingly large dipole moment to the unit cell, and a relatively high dielectric constant to $BaTiO_3$, one that exceeds 1000!

The energy barrier between the two possible Ti^{4+} sites is low enough for this ion to be moved from one site to the other by an electric field. The electric field need not be an external field, but may be the field from the dipoles in the next unit cell. Thus it is common to find adjacent unit cells spontaneously developing parallel electrical polarity. Furthermore, the polarity of a group of unit cells, called a *domain* (Fig. 8–27), can be maintained for a period of time because energy is required to move the Ti^{4+} ion out of the low-energy position (Fig. 8–26c). This property of cooperative alignment of electrical dipoles is called *ferroelectricity*.

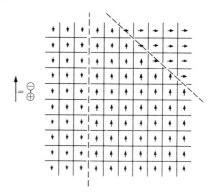

Fig. 8–27. Ferroelectric domains. Adjacent unit cells interact to give similar polarity. (Cf. Fig. 5–24.)

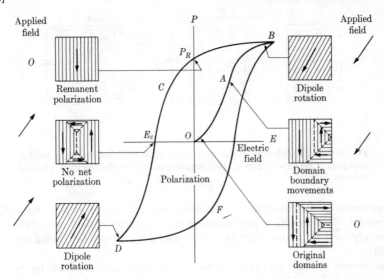

FIG. 8–28. Ferroelectric hysteresis. The above behavior is called ferroelectric because of its similarity to ferromagnetic behavior. (See the text for an explanation. Also compare with Fig. 5–29.)

Consider a ferroelectric material containing many domains of many different alignments, so that none is generally preferred. If an external electric field is applied, the boundaries between the domains will move in such a way that the more favorably oriented domains expand and the less favorably oriented domains contract in volume. This gives a net polarization which increases rapidly, as shown in the O-to-A part of the curve in the P-E diagram of Fig. 8–28. Eventually, alignment approaches a maximum and a further increase in the electric field makes only slight increases in preferential polarization, as in the A-to-B part of the curve in Fig. 8–28. A removal of that external electric field does not remove the preferential polarization, so that some remanent polarization, P_r, is maintained; not until a coercive field, E_c, of opposite polarity is applied does the material lose its net polarization. Cyclic fields produce a *hysteresis loop*, as indicated by the completed $BCDFB$ path of the P-E curves.

A *ferroelectric Curie point* exists at 120°C in $BaTiO_3$ because the spontaneous polarization of adjacent unit cells is lost when the crystal changes to a cubic structure (Fig. 8–8). Although new domains form spontaneously as $BaTiO_3$ is cooled below 120°C, these do not have any preferred alignment until a new external field is applied.

• *Piezoelectric ceramics.* Ferroelectrics are among the ceramic materials which do not have identical centers of positive and of negative charges. This type of material, e.g., quartz, either elongates or contracts in an electric field because the dipole lengths are changed with voltage gradients (Fig. 8–29). This provides a means of changing electrical energy into mechanical energy because the crystal

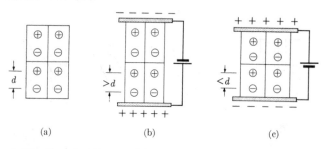

FIG. 8–29. Piezoelectric material. An electric field induces dimensional changes. Conversely, strain from pressure induces a change in end-to-end voltage.

vibrates with the frequency of an alternating field and in proportion to the voltage differential. The resulting mechanical-electrical devices, called *transducers*, are commonly used to produce high-frequency sound waves and for tuning electrical circuits.

The reverse process, that is, conversion of mechanical to electrical energy, can be accomplished by placing a crystal of the type just described under pressure. The electrical dipoles are then displaced from their equilibrium position and the charge differential across the crystal is altered. Vibrations, sound waves, and other mechanical movements may thus be transformed into electric potentials. Furthermore, since the amount of charge developed is dependent on the extent of crystal distortion, it is possible to construct pressure-sensing devices which may be read by means of a low-range voltmeter.

The above reversible mechanical-electrical interchanges are called *piezoelectric* effects (literally, pressure electric). The more commonly used piezoelectric ceramics include $BaTiO_3$, SiO_2, and $PbZrO_3$.

• 8–9 Ceramic semiconductors. Although ceramic compounds are nominally insulators, they may become semiconductors if they contain multivalent transition elements. This was illustrated in Fig. 5–11, where electron holes carry charges by moving from one iron ion to another. Magnetite (Fe_3O_4 or $Fe^{2+}Fe_2^{3+}O_4$) is a ceramic semiconductor with a resistivity of 10^{-2} ohm·cm, which is comparable to graphite and gray tin (Fig. 5–1). The origin of the conductivity is identical to that of FeO in Fig. 5–11; however, the number of electron holes for carrying the charge is much higher because the fraction of Fe^{3+} ions is greater.

The resistivity can be increased by solid solutions which replace the multivalent iron ions with other ions. This is shown in Table 8–2 for solid solutions of $MgCr_2O_4$ and $FeFe_2O_4$. Neither Mg^{2+} nor Cr^{3+} ions can react with the electrons or electron holes. Thus the resistivity can be adjusted to selected levels. The temperature coefficient of resistivity of these semiconductors is equally interesting to the engineer. As noted in Table 8–2, the resistance change is more than 1%/°C, and in other solid solutions may be as high as 4%/°C. This sensitivity is sufficient for accurate temperature measurement and has led to devices called *thermistors*

TABLE 8-2

RESISTIVITIES OF CERAMIC SEMICONDUCTORS*

Composition, mole percent		Resistivity, ohm·cm		$\Delta\rho/\Delta T$,
$FeFe_2O_4$	$MgCr_2O_4$	25°C	60°C	%/°C
100	0	0.005	0.0045	−0.3
75	25	0.7	0.45	−1.0
50	50	1.8×10^2	75.0	−1.6
25	75	4.0×10^4	1.2×10^4	−2.0
0	100	$>10^{12}$	$>10^{12}$	—

* Adapted from E. J. Verwey, P. W. Haayman, and F. C. Romeijn, *J. Chem. Phys.*, "Physical Properties and Cation Arrangement of Oxides with Spinel Structures: II. Electronic Conductivity," **15** (4), 181.

which are used for thermometric purposes. Because thermistors usually have a negative temperature coefficient of resistivity, they may also be used to compensate for positive resistance changes in the metallic components of a circuit.

8-10 Magnetic ceramics. Ceramic compounds which contain iron, cobalt, or nickel can be magnetic if their structures are such that the above ions can have their magnetic moments spontaneously aligned (cf. Section 5–11.) The *spinel* structure is one which may be magnetic and is therefore widely used.

Spinels are $[AB_2X_4]$ compounds (Section 8–5) which have an fcc arrangement of oxygen ions and cations in specific 4-fold and 6-fold sites. The A cations are divalent and the B cations are trivalent, thus giving electrical balance. Since the spinel unit cell contains 32 O^{2-} ions (and therefore has a lattice constant which is approximately twice that in MgO or FeO), there are 32 6-fold sites and 64 4-fold sites. In those spinels which are magnetic, eight of the 64 4-fold sites are occupied by Fe^{3+} ions; and 16 of the 32 6-fold sites are occupied by the remainder of the Fe^{3+} ions plus the divalent ions which may be Fe^{2+}, Mn^{2+}, Ni^{2+}, Zn^{2+}, or others of similar size.

The surroundings of the 4-fold sites and the 6-fold sites of spinels differ; therefore it is not surprising to find that the spontaneous alignment of the magnetic ions does not orient all the magnetic moments in the same direction. Specifically, the magnetic atoms in the 4-fold sites are oriented in one direction and the magnetic atoms in the 6-fold sites in the opposite direction. This is illustrated schematically in Fig. 8–30 for $[NiFe_2O_4]_8$; the effect is called *ferrimagnetism*. Although there is partial cancellation of magnetic moments, ferrimagnetic materials have wide use because they are better electrical insulators than comparable metallic magnets, and because they can have hysteresis-loop characteristics which are favorable for various applications.

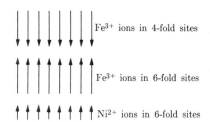

Fe³⁺ ions in 4-fold sites

Fe³⁺ ions in 6-fold sites

Ni²⁺ ions in 6-fold sites

FIG. 8–30. Ferrimagnetism. In $[NiFe_2O_4]_8$, the magnetic ions are oriented in two directions. The net effect is called *ferrimagnetism*. The term *antiferromagnetic* is used for those materials which have equal opposing magnetic moments (such as $MgFe_2O_4$).

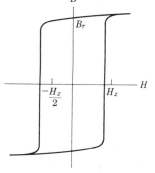

FIG. 8–31. Square-loop hysteresis. Small ceramic rings ($\sim$1 mm) with the adjacent hysteresis loop can be used as memory units. (See text.)

• *Square-loop magnets.* One of several useful hysteresis loops available in ceramic magnets is the "square loop" shown in Fig. 8–31. A field H_x can magnetize a small magnetic ring or film in one direction. This magnetization is stable until an opposite field of greater than $-H_x/2$ is applied. Thus, the magnetization can give "yes-no" binary switching for memory units of computers and not be sensitive to the small ($<H_x/2$) fields that accompany the reading-out operation.

8–11 Mechanical behavior of ceramic materials. With the exception of a few materials such as clay, ceramic materials are characterized by their high shear strengths and low fracture strengths (cf. Fig. 6–36). Therefore, they commonly fail nonductilely.

Nonductile fracture. The contrast between slip in pure metallic phases and in ceramic phases is illustrated in Fig. 8–32. The coordination arrangement in metals is the same after a one-step slip as it was before. A similar one-step slip in a biatomic crystal would produce new neighbors with different attraction-repulsion forces, and this new arrangement would have to be achieved by breaking strong positive-to-negative bonds of the Mg^{2+} and O^{2-} ions. The double step of slip required to rematch the original structure would have to proceed over a high-energy negative-versus-negative and positive-versus-positive position. In most ceramics these requirements restrict the mechanism of slip.

The restricted slip of most ceramic materials has several consequences: (1) these ceramic materials are nonductile, (2) true compressive strengths may be very high, provided no porosity is present (see footnote in Section 6–5), and (3) there is a theoretical possibility that the tensile strength can be high. In practice, the

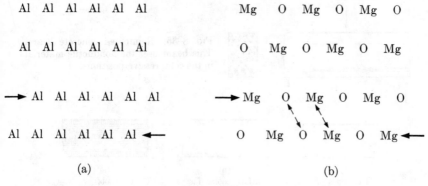

Fig. 8-32. Comparison of slip processes (schematic). (a) Monatomic metals. (b) Biatomic ceramics. More force is required to displace the atoms in MgO because strong repulsive forces become significant.

tensile strength frequently is not high. Any kind of irregularity produces stress concentrations in a material (Fig. 8-33); such an irregularity may be a crack, a grain boundary, a pore, or even an internal corner of the engineering part. In ductile materials, these stress concentrations may be relieved by plastic deformation (Fig. 8-34). However, in a nonductile material this relief is not possible; instead, fracture will occur if the stress concentration exceeds the strength of the material. Once started, the fracture propagates readily under tension because the stress concentration is intensified as the crack proceeds. Conversely, under compression a crack type of defect will not be self-propagating; the loads may be transferred across the crack and not accentuate the stresses at its root.

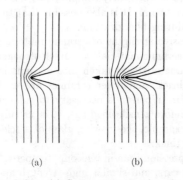

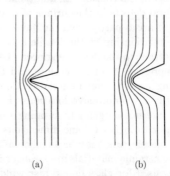

Fig. 8-33. (a) Stress concentrations in a nonductile material. A nonductile material will not adjust to these stresses. Therefore, while the average stress may be low, the tensile strength may be exceeded locally to start a crack. Such a crack propagates easily (b).

Fig. 8-34. Stress concentrations in a ductile material. Strains permit adjustments to localized stress concentrations with a reduction of the stress concentration.

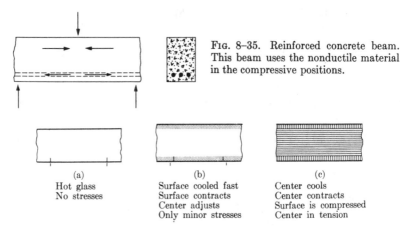

FIG. 8-35. Reinforced concrete beam. This beam uses the nonductile material in the compressive positions.

(a)
Hot glass
No stresses

(b)
Surface cooled fast
Surface contracts
Center adjusts
Only minor stresses

(c)
Center cools
Center contracts
Surface is compressed
Center in tension

FIG. 8-36. Dimensional changes in "tempered" glass.

FIG. 8-37. Surface compression of "tempered" glass. These compressive stresses must be overcome before the surface can be broken in tension.

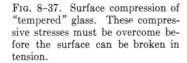

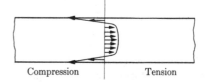

Compression   Tension

Glass fibers may have tensile strengths approaching 1,000,000 psi. This marked advantage over metals is partly a consequence of the fact that slip cannot occur. Some ceramists consider an additional factor to be the nearly complete absence of structural defects in the surface of drawn glass fibers. It is also possible that the strength arises partly from the quick cooling during fiber drawing.

The relationship of the tensile and compressive strengths of ceramic materials is important to the design engineer. Usually, ceramic materials are much stronger in compression than in tension, and this characteristic is taken into account in selecting construction materials. Concrete, brick, and other ceramics are used primarily in compressive locations (Fig. 8-35). When it is necessary to subject such materials as glass to bending (and therefore tensile loading), it is usually necessary to increase some dimensions. For example, the viewing glass of a television picture tube may be as much as $\frac{3}{4}$-inch thick.

Since ceramic materials are stronger in compression than in tension, "tempered" glass is used for glass doors, rear windows of cars, and similar high-strength applications. To produce tempered glass, the glass plate is heated to a temperature high enough to permit adjustments to stresses among the atoms, and is then quickly cooled by an air blast or oil quench (Fig. 8-36). The surface contracts because of the drop in temperature and becomes rigid, while the center is still hot and can adjust its dimensions to the surface contractions. When the center cools and contracts slightly later, compressive stresses are produced at the surface

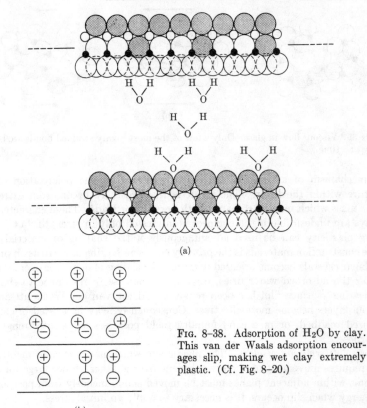

FIG. 8-38. Adsorption of H₂O by clay. This van der Waals adsorption encourages slip, making wet clay extremely plastic. (Cf. Fig. 8-20.)

(and tensile stresses in the center). The stresses which remain in the cross section of the glass are diagrammed in Fig. 8-37. A considerable load must be applied to the glass before tensile stresses can be developed in the surface of the glass where cracks start.* In effect, since the compressive stresses must be overcome first, the over-all strength of the glass is greatly enhanced.

• *Plastic deformation of layered structures.* Clays and other layered structures were specifically excluded from the generalization that ceramic materials have greater resistance to slip than do metals. It was pointed out in Section 8-6 that crystal layers of clay, mica, and similar minerals are strongly bonded within layers, but only lightly bonded between layers. Thus slip can occur quite readily between the crystal layers if the shear stresses are appropriately aligned.

The slip along crystal planes may be accentuated by the adsorption of water (or some other small molecule) onto the surface of the crystal layer (Fig. 8-38).

---

* If a crack penetrates through the compressive skin (e.g., by scratching) into the tension zone shown in Fig. 8-37, the crack may become rapidly self-propagating. The aftermath of this effect can be observed in a broken window of a car.

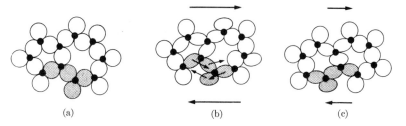

(a)   (b)   (c)

Fig. 8–39. Viscous flow in glass. Only a few of the most highly strained bonds are broken at any one time.

The mechanism of adsorption can operate because of the polarization of the structure within the layer. The result is that wet clay becomes an extremely plastic mass which may be reshaped with very minor loads. These characteristics of clays are undesirable if the engineer is interested only in strength, but the resulting plasticity can be used advantageously if the shaping of materials into usable construction materials is the primary concern. During any extrusion process the planar crystals become oriented to permit the sliding of one layer over another.

After the adsorbed water dries, there is an increase in resistance to slip; the "lubricating" surface film has been removed and the van der Waals attractions between layers become more effective. Consequently, clay in a dried brick, in a stabilized roadbed, or in a sand foundry mold possesses sufficient strength for its purpose.

Viscous deformation of glass. The plastic slip which is common to metals and clays requires movement of one crystal plane over another. Since large numbers of atoms within adjacent planes must be moved simultaneously from positions of low energy when slip occurs, it is necessary to apply an initial stress.

However, there are no planes or other long-range regularities in liquids or amorphous solids; therefore many interatomic distances are not at the minimum energy spacings with respect to all their neighbors. The first small increment of applied shear stress may be sufficient to break the most highly stressed bonds and to cause a rearrangement that results in a small amount of permanent strain. This movement, called *viscous flow*, does not require a measurable initial stress.

Viscous flow may be illustrated by the behavior of glass at high temperatures. In glass, the application of the initial shear stresses to start viscous flow breaks only those bonds which are already strained (Fig. 8–39b). The resulting rearrangement permits a gradual movement which subjects other bonds to higher stresses, and these intensified shearing stresses cause more extensive rearrangement and more movement. Viscous flow rates are directly related to applied shear stresses.

There is also a greater chance that the stressed bonds depicted in Fig. 8–39 will be broken by superimposed shear stresses when the atoms are undergoing the vigorous thermal vibration caused by high temperatures; consequently lower external forces are then required to produce flow. For example, the viscosities of liquids (e.g., asphalt and tar) decrease as they are heated, and the fluidity of glass and other amorphous solids decreases with lower temperatures. The rate of flow in glass at ambient temperatures is extremely slow.

References for Further Reading

8-1. BURKE, J. E. (editor), *Progress in Ceramic Science*, Vol. I. New York: Pergamon Press, 1961. A series of review articles on (1) glass strength, (2) vaporization of oxides, (3) chemistry of cement hydration, (4) deformation and fracture of ionic crystals, (5) chemical approach to problems of the glass state. For the advanced undergraduate.

8-2. BURKE, J. E. (editor), *Progress in Ceramic Science*, Vol. II. New York: Pergamon Press, 1962. A series of review articles. (1) Dislocation etch pits in nonmetallic crystals. (2) Catalyzed crystallization of glass. (3) Radiation damage. (4) Thermal conductivity of ceramic dielectrics. For the advanced undergraduate.

8-3. EITEL, W., *The Physical Chemistry of the Silicates*. Chicago: The University of Chicago Press, 1954. A detailed reference book on the chemistry of ceramic materials. For the instructor and ceramic specialist.

8-4. GRIM, R. E., *Clay Mineralogy*. New York: McGraw-Hill, 1953. An advanced book on the structure and properties of clay minerals.

8-5. HAUTH, W. F., "Crystal Chemistry in Ceramics," *Bulletin American Ceramic Society*, **30**, 1951. Part 3 is on silicate structure, Part 5 on the sheet structure minerals, Part 6 on clays and micas, Part 7 on polymorphism, Part 8 on the structural chemistry of glass. A bibliography is included.

8-6. ILER, R. V., *The Colloid Chemistry of Silica and the Silicates*. Ithaca, N. Y.: Cornell University Press, 1955. An advanced book dealing with the submicroscopic characteristics of the siliceous materials.

8-7. KINGERY, W. D., *Introduction to Ceramics*. New York: John Wiley & Sons, 1960. The standard ceramic textbook for the advanced student and instructor.

8-8. KLINGSBERG, C., *Physics and Chemistry of Ceramics*. New York: Gordon and Breach, 1963. For the instructor; this is a publication of a symposium on the newer applications of physical and chemical theory to ceramic research.

8-9. National Bureau of Standards, *Mechanical Behavior of Crystalline Solids*. National Bureau of Standards Monograph 59, 1963. A series of six lectures on the relationship of properties of ceramics to their crystalline structure. Specialized but introductory.

8-10. NORTON, F. H., *Ceramics for the Artist Potter*. Reading, Mass.: Addison-Wesley, 1956. Nontechnical but complete. Emphasis is on art products.

8-11. NORTON, F. H., *Elements of Ceramics*. Reading, Mass.: Addison-Wesley, 1952. An introductory presentation of ceramic materials for the student who has had chemistry. As much emphasis on the production of ceramic materials as on their properties.

8-12. PHILLIPS, C. J., *Glass, Its Industrial Applications*. New York: Reinhold, 1960. Written for the engineer. No prior knowledge of glass is required.

8-13. RYSHKEWITCH, E., *Oxide Ceramics*. New York: Academic Press, 1960. Presents the physical chemistry and technology of ionic ceramics. Specialized but easily followed by the engineer.

8-14. STANWORTH, J. E., *Physical Properties of Glass*. Oxford: Clarendon Press, 1950. For the advanced student and the instructor. The properties are correlated with the structure.

8-15. VAN VLACK, L. H., *Physical Ceramics for Engineers*, Reading, Mass.: Addison-Wesley, 1964. Sequel to this text, but may be studied simultaneously.

Problems

8-1. Periclase (MgO) has an fcc structure of O^{2-} ions with Mg^{2+} ions in all the 6-fold sites. (a) The radii are 1.32 A and 0.78 A respectively; what is the atomic packing factor? (b) What would this factor be if $r/R = 0.414$?
Answer: (a) 0.63   (b) 0.79

8-2. CsCl has a simple cubic structure of Cl^- ions with Cs^+ ions in all the 8-fold sites. (a) The radii are 1.81 A and 1.65 A, respectively; what is the atomic packing factor? (b) What would this factor be if $r/R = 0.732$?

8-3. Fluorite (CaF_2) has an fcc structure of Ca^{2+} ions with F^- ions in all the 4-fold sites. (a) The radii are 1.06 A and 1.33 A, respectively; what is the atomic packing factor? (b) What ion-size ratio(s) r/R would be required for maximum packing factors in this structure?
Answer: (a) 0.58   (b) When $r/R = 0.732$, APF $= 0.63$; when $r/R = 0.225$, APF $= 0.75$.

8-4. Estimate the density of cubic ZnS (sphalerite) which has an fcc structure of sulfur atoms and zinc atoms in half the 4-fold sites. (See Example 8-2 for CN = 4.)

8-5. Estimate the density of γ-Al_2O_3 which has an fcc structure of O^{2-} ions with Al^{3+} ions in two-thirds of the 6-fold sites.
Answer: 4.1 gm/cm^3

8-6. Estimate the density of corundum (Al_2O_3) which has an hcp structure of O^{2-} ions with Al^{3+} ions in two-thirds of the 6-fold sites.

8-7. A cubic form of ZrO_2 is possible when one Ca^{2+} ion is added in a solid solution for every six Zr^{4+} ions present. Thus the cations form an fcc structure, and O^{2-} ions are located in the 4-fold sites. (a) How many O^{2-} ions are there for every 100 cations? (b) What fraction of the 4-fold sites is occupied?
Answer: (a) 185.7 O^{2-} ions   (b) 92.9%

8-8. (a) What type of vacancies, anion or cation, would be required to dissolve MgF_2 in LiF? (b) What type would be required to dissolve LiF in MgF_2?

8-9. A solid solution contains 30 mole percent MgO and 70 mole percent LiF. (a) What are the weight percents of Li^+, Mg^{2+}, F^-, O^{2-}? (b) What is the density?
Answer: (a) Li^+, 16 w/o; Mg^{2+}, 24 w/o; F^-, 44 w/o; O^{2-}, 16 w/o   (b) 2.63 gm/cm^3

8-10. Estimate the density of the ZrO_2-CaO solid solution in Problem 8-7.

8-11. If the size of cubic $BaTiO_3$ (Fig. 8-8) were determined by the Ba^{2+} and O^{2-} ions, what radius would the center site (the site where the Ti^{4+} is located) have?
Answer: 0.625 A

• 8-12. Brucite [$Mg(OH)_2$] is formed by hydrating MgO. What is the percent gain in weight?

• 8-13. Gibbsite [$Al(OH)_3$] is calcined so that all of the hydrogen is removed as H_2O. What is the percent weight loss?
Answer: 34.6%

• 8-14. Kaolinite (Fig. 8-18) is calcined and H_2O is released. What is the maximum weight loss?

• Problems preceded by a bullet are based, in part, on optional sections.

TABLE 8-3

MAGNETIC MOMENTS OF IONS

Ion	3-d electrons	Magnetic moment, Bohr magnetons*
V^{3+}	2	2
V^{5+}	0	0
Cr^{3+}	3	3
Fe^{3+}	5	5
Fe^{2+}	6	4
Mn^{2+}	5	5
Mn^{4+}	3	3
Ni^{2+}	8	2
Co^{2+}	7	3
Cu^{+}	10	0
Cu^{2+}	9	1
Mg^{2+}	0	0
Zn^{2+}	10	0
O^{2-}	0	0

* Bohr magnetons $= \frown\!\blacktriangleright - \frown\!\centerdot\,$ (see Fig. 5–23).

• 8–15. Coesite, the high-pressure polymorph of SiO_2, has a density of 2.9 gm/cm^3. What is the ionic packing factor?

Answer: 0.57

8–16. Table 8-3 shows the magnetic moments of various cations. What is the magnetic moment of a unit cell of $[CoFe_2O_4]_8$? (Cf. Fig. 8–30.)

8–17. What is the magnetic moment of a unit cell of magnetite $[Fe_3O_4$ or $Fe^{2+}Fe_2^{3+}O_4]_8$? The eight ions in the 4-fold sites are Fe^{3+} and are aligned in one direction. The balance of the ions are in 6-fold sites and are aligned in the antiparallel direction.

Answer: 32 Bohr magnetons

8–18. What is the magnetic moment of a unit cell of $[MgFe_2O_4]_8$? The Fe^{3+} ions have the same sites as those in $[NiFe_2O_4]_8$.

8–19. Magnesite ($MgCO_3$) is a raw material for making the MgO which is used as a high-temperature brick (>3000°F). How much MgO will one ton of magnesite make?

Answer: 960 lb

• 8–20. $AlPO_4$ can form the same crystal structures as SiO_2. Explain.

8–21. The composition of mullite is approximately $Al_6Si_2O_{13}$. This is frequently considered to be $3Al_2O_3 \cdot 2SiO_2$. What is the percentage of (a) Al_2O_3? (b) SiO_2? (c) Al? (d) Si? (e) O?

Answer: (a) 71.8% (b) 28.2% (c) 38% (d) 13% (e) 49%

9

multiphase materials.
equilibrium relationships

9–1 Introduction. The three preceding chapters have been concerned successively with metallic, organic, and ceramic phases, and with the dependence of their properties on phase structure. In each chapter only single-phase materials were considered. However, although many useful engineering materials consist predominantly of one phase, a greater number are mixtures of phases; for example, steel, solder, portland cement, grinding wheels, paints, and glass-reinforced plastics. The mixture of two or more phases in one material permits interaction among the phases, and the resulting properties are usually different from the properties of individual phases. It is frequently possible, also, to modify these properties by changing either the shape or the distribution of the phases (see Chapter 11).

QUALITATIVE PHASE RELATIONSHIPS

9–2 Solutions versus mixtures. Different components can be combined into a single material by means of *solutions* or of *mixtures*. Solid solutions have already been discussed in Sections 4–2ff, 6–5, and 8–5, and we are all familiar with liquid solutions. The compositions of solutions can vary widely, because (1) one atom may be substituted for another at lattice points of the phase structure, or (2) atoms may be placed in the interstices of the structure. The solute does not change the structural pattern of the solvent. A mixture, on the other hand, contains more than one phase (structural pattern). Sand and water, rubber with a carbon filler, and tungsten carbide with a nickel binder are examples of mixtures. In each of these aggregates there are two different phases, each with its own atomic arrangement.

It is, of course, possible to have a mixture of two different solutions. For example, in a lead-tin solder, one phase is a solid solution in which tin has replaced some of the lead in the fcc structure, and the other phase has the structure of tin (body-centered tetragonal). At elevated temperatures, lead atoms may replace a limited number of atoms in the tin structure. Thus an ordinary 60-40 solder (60% Sn-40% Pb) contains two structures, each a solid solution.

9–3 Solubility. Figure 9–1 shows the *solubility* of ordinary sugar in water; the curve is a *solubility curve*. All compositions shown to the left of the curve will form only one phase, because all the sugar is dissolved in the liquid phase. With the higher percentages of sugar shown to the right of the curve, however, it is impossible to dissolve the sugar completely, with the result that we have a mixture of

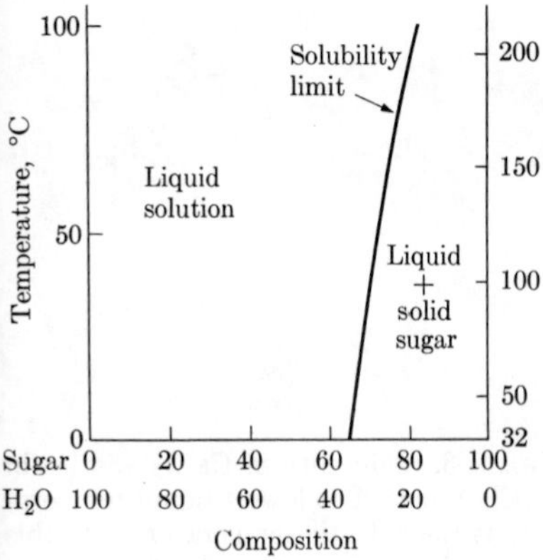

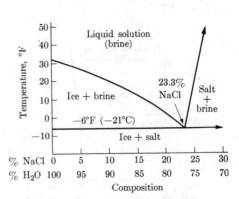

FIG. 9–1. Solubility of sugar in water. The limit of sugar solubility in water is shown by the solubility curve. Note that the sum of the sugar and water content at any point on the abscissa is 100%.

FIG. 9–2. Solubility of NaCl salt in brine (right upward-sloping line) and solubility of ice in brine (left curve).

two phases, solid sugar and liquid "syrup." This example shows the change of solubility with temperature, and also demonstrates a simple method for plotting temperature (or any other variable) as a function of composition. From left to right, the abscissa of Fig. 9–1 indicates the percentage of sugar. The percentage of water may be read directly from right to left, since the total of the components must, of course, equal 100%.

Figure 9–2 shows a two-component system which has more engineering importance than our first example. Here, the extremes of the abscissa indicate 100% H_2O and 30% NaCl. Note from the figure that (1) the solubility of NaCl in a brine solution decreases with decreasing temperature, (2) the solubility of H_2O in a brine solution also decreases with decreasing temperature, and (3) intermediate compositions have melting temperatures lower than that of either pure ice (32°F) or pure salt (1473°F). (1) and (3) are well-known facts, and (2), the less familiar limited solubility of ice in the aqueous liquid, can be verified by a simple experiment. A salt and water solution, e.g., sea water with 1.5% NaCl, can be cooled to less than 32°F and, according to Fig. 9–2, it will still be entirely liquid until 30.5°F is reached. This is in agreement with observations of any arctic saline sea.* When such a salty liquid is cooled below 30.5°F, ice crystals will form, and because the solution cannot contain more than 98.5% H_2O at that temperature, these crystals must separate from the liquid. At 0°F, the maximum amount of H_2O possible in a brine solution is 79%, as can be verified by making a slush at 0°F and separating the ice from this liquid; the ice will be pure H_2O and the remaining liquid will be saltier (i.e., lower in H_2O) than the original brine solution.

---

* There can be a slight variation if the salt content is not exactly 1.5%.

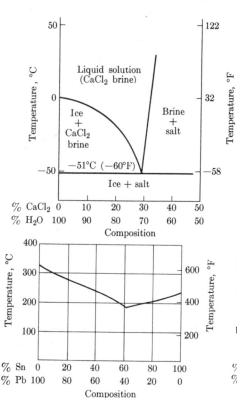

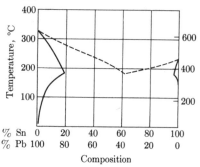

Fig. 9–3. Solubility of CaCl₂ and ice in CaCl₂ brine. The lowest liquid temperature is the eutectic temperature. At this temperature, the two solubility curves meet.

Fig. 9–4. Solubility of Pb and Sn in molten solders. The eutectic composition, 60 Sn-40 Pb, is frequently used for solders because of its low melting properties.

Fig. 9–5. Solid solubility. Solubility of Sn in the fcc structure of solid lead (left curve). Solubility of Pb in the bct structure of solid tin (right curve).

Fig. 9–6. Pb-Sn diagram. Such a diagram indicates the composition and quantities of phases for any lead-tin mixture at any temperature. (ASM *Handbook of Metals* Cleveland: American Society for Metals, 1948.)

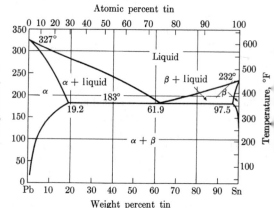

Another example of engineering importance is a mixture of H_2O and $CaCl_2$ (Fig. 9–3). Calcium chloride rather than NaCl is used to remove ice from highways in very cold climates. The reason is apparent from a comparison of Figs. 9–3 and 9–2. An aqueous solution of calcium chloride remains liquid at temperatures as low as $-60°F$, while a similar solution of NaCl will freeze at $-6°F$. The lowest temperature at which a solution will remain completely liquid is called the *eutectic temperature*, and the solution which possesses this lowest freezing point is called the *eutectic composition*. The eutectic composition for the H_2O-NaCl system of Fig. 9–2 is 76.7% H_2O and 23.3% NaCl. From Fig. 9–3, the eutectic composition for H_2O-$CaCl_2$ is 71% H_2O and 29% $CaCl_2$. The intersection of the solubility curves in such diagrams marks the eutectic composition for the two components in a liquid solution.

These melting-freezing relationships are quite common in all types of two-component combinations. Figure 9–4 shows the solubility curves for lead and tin. The low-melting "60-40" alloy is used in many solders because this eutectic composition permits the formation of metal-bonded joints with a minimum of heating. If the solder contained more lead (say 70% lead and 30% tin), during cooling the liquid metal would become saturated with lead at a temperature above the eutectic temperature and some lead would precipitate from the liquid metal solution. As with the brine and ice in Fig. 9–2, there would be a temperature range where liquid and solid would coexist. Experiments have demonstrated that at 260°C (500°F), 19% (12 w/o) of the lead atoms in the solid phase of this alloy may be replaced by tin atoms.*

Figure 9–5 shows the solubility curves for tin in the *solid* lead structure and for lead in the *solid* tin structure. In these particular alloys, the temperature at 360°F is the eutectic temperature and represents (1) the lowest temperature at which any liquid in the series can exist, (2) a temperature above and below which the solid solubility decreases, and (3) a temperature above which any excess over the solid solubility limit is liquid, and below which any excess over the solid solubility limit is solid.

9–4 Phase diagrams. Figure 9–6 is a completed *phase* (equilibrium) *diagram* for the lead-tin system. This diagram can be used as a "map" from which the phases present at any particular temperature of composition can be read if the alloy is at equilibrium.

For example, at 50% tin and 100°C the "map" indicates two solid phases: α is a solid solution of lead with some dissolved tin; β is almost pure tin with very little

---

* Inasmuch as the lead atoms are heavier than the tin atoms, 19% of the tin atoms represent only 12% of the weight. The convention established in Section 4–3 will be followed. *Unless stated otherwise, the compositions of liquids and solids are expressed in weight percent. Unless stated otherwise, the compositions of gases are expressed in volume or molecular percent.* The bottom abscissa of phase diagrams will express weight percent unless stated otherwise; the atomic percent is sometimes also included as a top abscissa for convenience.

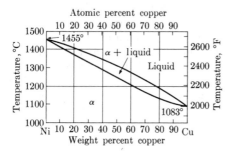

FIG. 9–7. Ni-Cu diagram. All solid compositions give only one phase. This phase is fcc. (ASM *Handbook of Metals.* Cleveland: American Society for Metals, 1948.)

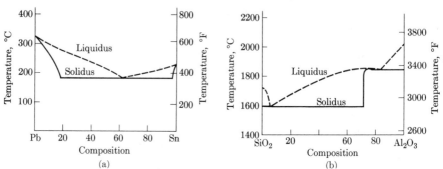

FIG. 9–8. Liquidus and solidus. (a) For the Pb-Sn system. (See Fig. 9–6.) (b) For the SiO_2-Al_2O_3 system. (See Fig. 9–9.)

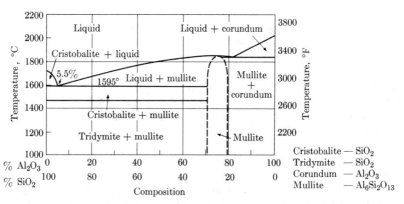

FIG. 9–9. SiO_2-Al_2O_3 diagram. The phase diagrams for nonmetals are used in the same manner as those for metals. The only difference is the longer time required to establish equilibrium. (Adapted from S. Aramaki and R. Roy, *Journal of the American Ceramic Society,* **42**, 644, 1959.) Some recent studies propose that the eutectic temperature is 1547°C. (Majumdar, A. J., and J. H. Welch, *Trans. British Ceramic Society,* **62**, 603, 1963.)

dissolved lead. At 200°C, an alloy of 10% tin and 90% lead lies in an area which is entirely in the α phase. It is a solid solution of lead with some tin dissolved in it. At the same temperature, but for 30% tin and 70% lead, the "map" indicates a mixture of liquid and α solid solution; if this latter composition were heated to a temperature of 300°C, it would become all liquid.

The phase fields in equilibrium diagrams, of course, depend on the particular alloy systems being depicted. When copper and nickel are mixed, the phase diagram is as shown in Fig. 9–7. This "map" is comparatively simple, since only two phases are present. In the lower part of the diagram all compositions form only one solid solution and therefore only one crystal structure. Both the nickel and the copper have face-centered cubic structures. Since the atoms of each are nearly the same size, it is possible for nickel and copper atoms to replace each other in the crystal structure in any proportion. When an alloy containing 60% copper and 40% nickel is heated, the solid phase exists until a temperature of about 2200°F is reached. Above this temperature and up to 2330°F the solid and liquid solutions coexist. Above 2330°F only a liquid phase remains.

9–5 Freezing ranges. As shown in the foregoing phase diagrams, the range of temperatures over which freezing occurs varies with the composition of the alloy. This situation influences the plumber, for example, to select a high lead alloy as a "wiping" solder when he needs a solder which will not freeze completely at one temperature. If he chooses an 80Pb-20Sn solder, the freezing range is from 530 to 360°F as compared with 370 to 360°F for a 60Sn-40Pb solder.

The terms *liquidus*, the locus of temperatures above which all compositions are liquid, and *solidus*, the locus of temperatures below which all compositions are solid, are applied in this connection. Every phase diagram for two or more components must show a liquidus and solidus boundary and an intervening freezing range (Fig. 9–8). Whether the components are metals or nonmetals (Fig. 9–9), there are certain locations on the phase diagram where the liquidus and solidus meet. For a pure component, this point lies at the edge of the diagram. When it is heated, a pure material will remain solid until its melting point is reached, and will then change entirely to liquid before it can be raised to a higher temperature.

The solidus and liquidus must also meet at the eutectic. In Fig. 9–6 the liquid solder composed of 61.9% tin and 38.1% lead is entirely solid below the eutectic temperature and entirely liquid above it.

9–6 Equilibrium. Phase diagrams are usually equilibrium diagrams. That is, they indicate the phases which will be present when the components are in equilibrium with each other and no further net reaction occurs. Under such conditions each phase is entirely saturated with all other phases which are present, but not supersaturated. In practice, it may take some time for equilibrium to develop. This situation will be considered in the next chapter. An equilibrium diagram is extremely useful because it does indicate (1) what phases will be present under conditions of equilibrium, and (2) the direction toward which reaction is tending to occur if equilibrium does not exist. For example, heating a lead-tin alloy containing 90% lead and 10% tin to 200°C produces only one phase, the fcc solid solution of lead containing some tin. If this solution is quenched rapidly, so that the metal comes to room temperature before the β phase has had an opportunity to precipitate from the α solid solution, only one phase will be present. However, given time, the β phase will precipitate from the α solid solution phase, and two phases will then be present concurrently, as indicated by the phase diagrams.

Example 9–1

Sterling silver, an alloy containing approximately 92.5% silver and 7.5% copper (Fig. 9–10), is heated slowly from room temperature to 2000°F. What phase(s) will be present as heating progresses?

Answer:

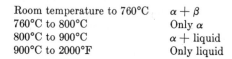

Room temperature to 760°C	$\alpha + \beta$
760°C to 800°C	Only α
800°C to 900°C	$\alpha +$ liquid
900°C to 2000°F	Only liquid

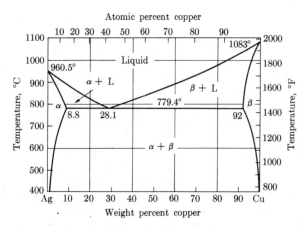

FIG. 9–10.   Ag-Cu diagram.   (ASM *Metals Handbook.*   Cleveland: American Society for Metals, 1948.)

Example 9–2

A combination of 90% SiO_2 and 10% Al_2O_3 is melted at 1800°C, and then cooled extremely slowly to 1400°C. What phase(s) will be present in the cooling process?

Answer:

1800°C to 1660°C	Only liquid
1660°C to 1595°C	Liquid + mullite ($Al_6Si_2O_{13}$)
1595°C to 1470°C	Mullite + cristobalite (SiO_2)
<1470°C	Mullite + tridymite (SiO_2)

The cooling would have to be extremely slow, because the process of changing the strong Si—O bonds from one structure to another is very slow.

QUANTITATIVE PHASE RELATIONSHIPS

9–7 Phase compositions. In addition to serving simply as a "map," a phase diagram permits the determination of the *chemical compositions* of the phases present under conditions of equilibrium. In a one-phase area, the determination of the phase composition is automatic; it has the same composition as the over-all combination.

In a two-phase area, equilibrium will mutually saturate the two phases, and the composition of the two phases will therefore be depicted by the solubility curves of the phase diagram. For example, Fig. 9–11 shows the phase diagram for phenol (C_6H_5OH) and water. At 25°C there are two liquids present in a 50-50 water-phenol combination. Since the water is saturated with phenol, its composition will be 92% water and 8% phenol, and since the phenol is saturated with water, its composition will be 71% phenol and 29% water. Any combination between a and b at 25°C (77°F) will be composed of a mixture of the two liquids, each with the composition just described. A similar group of data may be determined for the two phases at 50°C (122°F). Once the temperature is raised above the solubility curve, only one phase remains, with its composition fixed by the over-all composition.

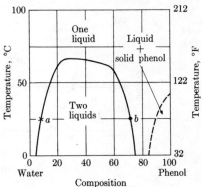

FIG. 9–11. Water (H_2O) and phenol (C_6H_5OH) diagram. Two liquids may coexist for the temperatures and compositions indicated.

Example 9–3

Sixty-seven pounds of water are combined with 21 lb of phenol. What are the phase compositions at 86°F, 140°F, and 158°F?

Answer:

$$\frac{67}{21 + 67} = 76.1\% \text{ water}, \qquad \frac{21}{21 + 67} = 23.9\% \text{ phenol.}$$

Temperature	Composition of water-rich phase	Composition of phenol-rich phase
86°F (30°C)	91% H_2O; 9% C_6H_5OH	30% H_2O; 70% C_6H_5OH
140°F (60°C)	80% H_2O; 20% C_6H_5OH	40% H_2O; 60% C_6H_5OH
158°F (70°C)	76.1% H_2O; 23.9% C_6H_5OH	

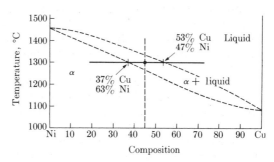

FIG. 9–12.   1300°C Ni-Cu isotherm (cf. Fig. 9–7).

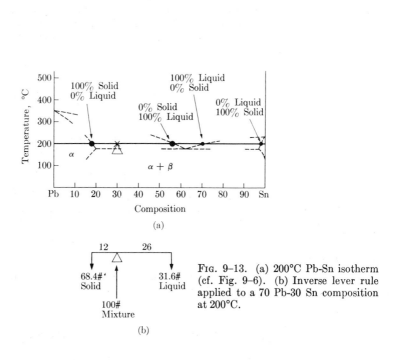

(a)

(b)

FIG. 9–13.   (a) 200°C Pb-Sn isotherm (cf. Fig. 9–6).   (b) Inverse lever rule applied to a 70 Pb-30 Sn composition at 200°C.

Example 9–4

An alloy containing 92 lb of magnesium and 8 lb of aluminum is typical of the magnesium alloys used for aircraft parts. What are the phase compositions at 1200°F, 1000°F, 800°F, 600°F, and 400°F? (See Fig. 9–38 for the phase diagram.)

Answer:

Temperature, °F	Phases	Phase composition
1200	Liquid	L—92% Mg, 8% Al
1000	Liquid and ε	L—81% Mg, 19% Al; ε—94% Mg, 6% Al
800	ε	ε—92% Mg, 8% Al
600	δ and ε	δ—57% Mg, 43% Al; ε—94% Mg, 6% Al
400	δ and ε	δ—57% Mg, 43% Al; ε—96% Mg, 4% Al

9–8 Relative amounts of phases. In Section 9–4 we discussed the method of determining what phases are present in a material at equilibrium, and in Section 9–7 we discussed the determination of the *chemical composition* of these phases. In this section we shall show how to determine the relative *amounts* of the phases present at a specific temperature.

The chemical composition of a phase is usually expressed as the percent of component A or component B. For instance, in Example 9–4 the *chemical composition* of δ is 43% Al and 57% Mg at 400°F.

Figures 9–12 and 9–13 will help in comprehending the procedure for determining the relative *amounts* of each phase present at a specific temperature. In Fig. 9–12 at 1300°C a solid solution exists only for mixtures containing less than 37% copper. For mixtures containing more than 53% copper only a liquid solution exists. In the two-phase region between these two compositions, the relative amounts of the two phases will vary. It may be expected that halfway between these two compositions (i.e., at 45% copper) 50% liquid and 50% solid will exist. This is the case. It will also be the case at any other *temperature level* for an alloy composition exactly halfway between the 100% solid and 100% liquid points.

The above reasoning provides a method for calculating the relative amounts of the two phases which exist in any two-phase area of a phase diagram. In the lead-tin diagram of Fig. 9–6, at the 200°C isotherm (isolated in Fig. 9–13) there is only one phase between the lead-rich end and the 18% tin composition. At the 18% level there is no liquid present, only solid. Increasing the tin content beyond 18% at 200°C will produce increasing amounts of liquid, until only liquid exists at 56% tin. Between 18% and 56% tin, the amount of liquid solution increases from zero to 100% and the amount of solid solution decreases from 100% to zero. Subtracting 18 from 56 indicates that the addition of 38 percentage units of tin makes a complete change in the amount of each of the two phases. At 30% tin, which is 12 units of tin beyond the point where there is no liquid, there will be 12/38, or 31.6% liquid. Similarly, with 30% tin and 70% lead at 200°C, (56 − 30)/38, or 68.4% solid is to be expected.

The lever rule. The so-called *lever rule* is a useful tool for calculating relative amounts of phases. For example, in the Pb-Sn diagram of Fig. 9–6 or 9–13, the relative amounts of solid and liquid in an alloy of 30% tin and 70% lead at 200°C can be calculated by considering the 30% tin point as the fulcrum of a lever. The amount of solid present, which would in this case contain 18% tin, is necessarily greater than the amount of liquid, which contains 56% tin and 44% lead. In our analogy, the amount of solid is proportional to the distance from the fulcrum to the end of the lever marking the liquid composition. Conversely, the amount of liquid is proportional to the distance from the fulcrum to the other end, which marks the solid composition. This *inverse* relationship, which places the fulcrum and total composition at the "center of gravity" between the phases, serves as a simple rule for calculating the relative amounts of the equilibrated phases.

Example 9–5

Determine the relative amounts of the phases in a 92% Mg-8% Al alloy at 1200°F, 1000°F, 800°F, 600°F, and 400°F. (Compare with Example 9–4.)

Answer:

Temperature, °F	Phases	Amounts of each phase	
1200	Liquid	100% liquid	
1000	Liquid + ε	$\frac{94-92}{94-81} = 15.4\%$ liquid;	$\frac{92-81}{94-81} = 84.6\%$ ε
800	ε	100% ε	
600	δ + ε	$\frac{94-92}{94-57} = 5.4\%$ δ;	$\frac{92-57}{94-57} = 94.6\%$ ε
400	δ + ε	$\frac{96-92}{96-57} = 10.3\%$ δ;	$\frac{92-57}{96-57} = 89.7\%$ ε

Material balances. The validity of the above calculations becomes more apparent after some *material balances* are taken. In a material balance, the quantities of the components in each of the phases should add up to the total quantity of the components in the multiple-phase system. This check also affords an excellent opportunity for verifying the accuracy of calculations.

Example 9–6

Perform a material balance on the distribution of lead and tin in a eutectic lead-tin solder at 212°F. The basis is:

100 gm solder = 61.9 gm tin and 38.1 gm lead (from Fig. 9–6).

Answer:

Phase	Chemical composition	Amounts of each phase	Pb	Sn	Check
α	96% Pb 4% Sn	$\frac{100-61.9}{100-4} = 39.7 \frac{\text{gm } \alpha}{100 \text{ gm solder}}$	38.1 gm	1.6 gm	39.7 gm
β	0% Pb 100% Sn	$\frac{61.9-4}{100-4} = 60.3 \frac{\text{gm } \beta}{100 \text{ gm solder}}$	0 gm	60.3 gm	60.3 gm
Check		100 gm alloy	38.1 gm Pb	61.9 gm Sn	100 gm alloy

A similar material balance can be taken for any other composition or temperature within a two-phase region. Obviously, in a single-phase region there are no such calculations to be made, since the total amount of this phase is 100%, and the composition of this phase is the same as the over-all composition of the alloy.

9–9 Equilibration.   Changes from one phase to another or in the composition of any one phase involve rearrangements of the atoms in a material. The time required for such changes depends on the temperature and the complexity of the change. Polymorphic changes (Section 3–18) of a pure metal require a minimum of rearrangement and can occur quite rapidly. In iron, the atoms simply shift from a face-centered structure to a body-centered structure (or vice versa). The distance of movement is not great, and the energy required to separate the original bonds is nearly equal to that released in the formation of the new bonds. On the other hand, the rearrangement of polyatomic structures requires more movement of the atoms and the disruption of much stronger bonds, which slows down the transformation rate considerably.

Atomic movements are also necessary in the melting or freezing of any combination of two components. Figure 9–14, which is a detailed area of Fig. 9–7, shows successively the compositions of the liquid and solid phases which are in equilibrium at the start, within, and at the end of the freezing range of a 50-50 Cu-Ni alloy. At 2400°F, where freezing starts, the equilibrium solid contains only 35% copper and 65% nickel. Therefore, as freezing proceeds, extra nickel atoms must move (diffuse) toward the new solid crystals and excess copper atoms must diffuse away from the solidifying surface. At 2355°F (1290°C) and under equilibrium, the atoms have moved so that the liquid contains 55% copper and the solid contains 62% nickel. At the solidus, the final small amount of liquid contains 66% copper and only 34% nickel. Since the solid changes from 35% to 50% copper and 65% to 50% nickel as the temperature decreases from the liquidus to the solidus, nickel must move within the solid to allow copper to enter if equilibrium is to be maintained. The over-all sequence is shown schematically in Fig. 9–15.

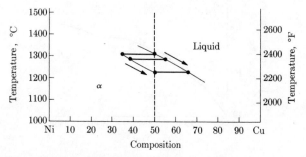

Fig. 9–14. Composition changes during solidification (Ni-Cu). Each phase increases in copper content as cooling progresses.

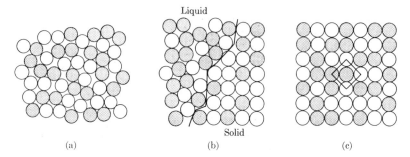

(a)   (b)   (c)

FIG. 9–15. Composition changes during solidification.   (a) Liquid, 49% B (shaded); (b) liquid, 64% B, and solid, 33% B; (c) solid, 49% B.

FIG. 9–16. Solidification segregation (70–30 brass), ×100. Segregation may arise from rapid solidification during which there has been insufficient time for diffusion to provide equilibrium. The lighter colored patterns *within* the grains are copper-rich dendrites which are surrounded by zinc-rich (darker) areas. (D. K. Crampton, Chase Brass and Copper Co.)

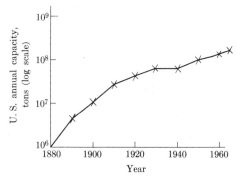

FIG. 9–17. Steel production in the United States. On the average, each engineer specifies the use of more than one ton of steel per day.

A segregation of the atoms may remain in the solid if the cooling is slow enough to permit diffusion in the liquid (where it can take place quite rapidly) but too fast for complete diffusion to occur in the solid* (Fig. 9–16).

• **Example 9–7**

Describe the diffusion necessary for the equilibrium solidification of a melt containing 75% SiO_2 and 25% Al_2O_3 (Fig. 9–9).

Answer: The liquid phase above 1750°C has an amorphous structure composed of SiO_4 tetrahedra and AlO_6 octahedra (Figs. 8–9, 8–16c, and 8–17).

Below the liquidus, the aluminum, silicon, and oxygen atoms segregate from the liquid in the ratios of 6, 2, and 13, respectively, to form the crystal structure of mullite, $Al_6Si_2O_{13}$. The remaining liquid is reduced in alumina and enriched in silica until the eutectic composition is reached, at 1595°C. At this temperature, if equilibrium is to be maintained, the remaining aluminum atoms and some of the silicon and oxygen atoms form mullite. The excess silicon and oxygen form cristobalite.

Because strong Si—O and Al—O bonds must be broken, this diffusion process is extremely slow.

IRON-CARBON ALLOYS

9–10 Introduction. Steels, which are primarily alloys of iron and carbon, offer illustrations of the majority of reactions and microstructures available to the engineer for adjusting material properties. Also, the iron-carbon alloys have become the most predominant among structural engineering materials. Current production of iron and steel exceeds 120,000,000 tons per year (Fig. 9–17), a rate equivalent to more than 400 tons of steel per year for each engineer in this country. It is almost certain that an engineer will at some time find it part of his task to make, to specify, or to utilize steel in one form or another.

The versatility of the steels as engineering materials is evidenced by the many kinds of steel that are manufactured. At one extreme are the very soft steels used for deep-drawing applications such as automobile fenders and refrigerator panels. At the other are the extremely hard and tough steels used for gears and bulldozer blades. Some steels must have abnormally high resistance to corrosion. Steels for such electrical purposes as transformer sheets must have special magnetic characteristics so that they may be magnetized and demagnetized many times each second with low power losses. Other steels must be completely nonmagnetic, for such applications as wrist watches and minesweepers. Phase diagrams can be used to help explain each characteristic described above.

9–11 The Fe-C phase diagram. Pure iron changes its crystal structure from body-centered to face-centered cubic as it is heated beyond 1670°F (910°C). This change and a subsequent one at 2550°F (1400°C) are indicated in Fig. 9–18, and are compared with phase changes in water.

---

* Diffusion will always be much more rapid in a liquid than in a solid because the atoms are more tightly bonded in the latter.

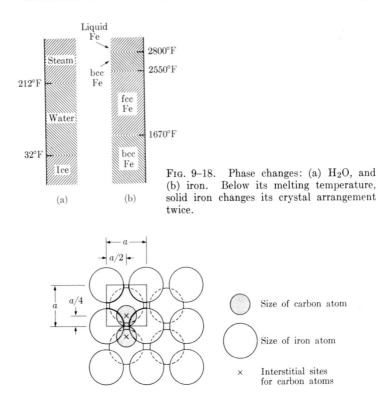

FIG. 9-18. Phase changes: (a) H_2O, and (b) iron. Below its melting temperature, solid iron changes its crystal arrangement twice.

FIG. 9-19. Carbon solution in bcc ferrite. The largest opening in the bcc iron crystal is appreciably smaller than the carbon atom. Therefore the solubility of carbon in ferrite is very low.

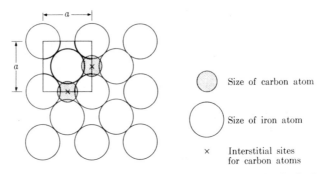

FIG. 9-20. Carbon solution in fcc austenite. The largest opening in the fcc iron crystal is almost the size of the carbon atom. Therefore as much as 2 weight percent (9 atom percent) carbon may be dissolved [(100) plane].

Ferrite, or α-iron. The structural modification of pure iron at room temperature is called either *α-iron* or *ferrite*. Ferrite is quite soft and ductile; in the purity which is encountered commercially, its tensile strength is less than 45,000 psi. It is a ferromagnetic material at temperatures under 1414°F.

Since ferrite has a body-centered cubic structure, the interatomic spaces are small and pronouncedly oblate, and cannot readily accommodate even a small spherical carbon atom (Fig. 9–19). Therefore, solubility of carbon in ferrite is very low. The carbon atom is too small for substitutional solid solution, and too large for extensive interstitial solid solution (Section 4–3).

Austenite, or γ-iron. The face-centered modification of iron is called *austenite*, or *γ-iron*. It is the stable form of pure iron at temperatures between 1670°F and 2550°F. Making a direct comparison between the mechanical properties of austenite and ferrite is difficult because they must be compared at different temperatures. However, at its stable temperatures, austenite is soft and ductile and consequently is well suited to fabrication processes. Most steel forging and rolling operations are performed at 2000°F or above, when the iron is face-centered cubic. Austenite is not ferromagnetic at any temperature.

The face-centered cubic structure of iron (Fig. 9–20) has larger interatomic spacings than does ferrite. Figures 9–20 and 9–19 provide a direct comparison between the possibility for interstitial solid solution in austenite and in ferrite. Even so, in the fcc structure the holes are barely large enough to crowd the carbon atoms into the interstices, and this crowding introduces strains into the structure. As a result, not all the holes can be filled at any one time. The maximum solubility is only 2% (8.7 a/o) carbon (Fig. 9–21). By definition, steels contain less than 2% carbon; thus steels may have their carbon completely dissolved in austenite at high temperatures.

δ-iron. Above 2550°F austenite is no longer the most stable form of iron, since then the crystal structure changes back to a body-centered-cubic phase called *δ-iron.* δ-iron is the same as α-iron except for its temperature range, and so it is commonly called δ-ferrite. The solubility of carbon in δ-ferrite is small, but it is appreciably larger than in α-ferrite, because of the higher temperature.

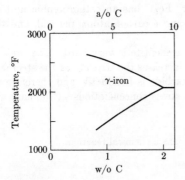

Fig. 9–21. Solubility of carbon in austenite (γ-iron).

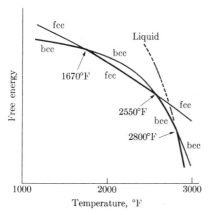

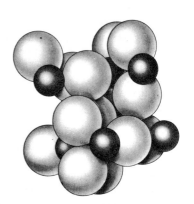

FIG. 9–22. Free energy of ferrite and austenite (schematic). Ferrite is bcc iron and austenite is fcc iron. The phase with the lowest free energy is stable. (See Fig. 10–8.)

FIG. 9–23. Fe₃C structure. The unit cell is orthorhombic, with 12 iron atoms and 4 carbon atoms. (R. W. G. Wycoff, *Crystal Structure.* New York: Interscience Publishers, 1948.)

Because of the relative free energies* of ferrite and of austenite, ferrite has two temperature ranges of stability, which makes it unique among common engineering materials. The most stable form of any material is the form with the minimum free energy (see Section 10–6 for a more complete explanation). Figure 9–22 shows the free energy for both ferrite and austenite. Below 1670°F and above 2550°F, the body-centered-cubic structure has a lower free energy than the face-centered-cubic structure.

Cementite, or iron carbide. In iron-carbide alloys, carbon in excess of the solubility limit must form a second phase, which is often iron carbide† (cementite). Iron carbide has the chemical composition of Fe_3C. This does not mean that iron carbide forms molecules of Fe_3C, but simply that the crystal lattice contains iron and carbon atoms in a three-to-one ratio. Fe_3C has an orthorhombic unit cell (Figs. 9–23 and 3–20) with 12 iron atoms and 4 carbon atoms per cell, and thus has a carbon content of 6.67%.

As compared with austenite and ferrite, cementite is very hard. The presence of iron carbide with ferrite in steel greatly increases the strength of the steel (Section 11–4). However, because pure iron carbide is nonductile and therefore relatively weak by itself, it cannot adjust to stress concentrations. (Compare with ceramic materials in Section 8–11.)

---

* Free energy is the energy which can enter into a chemical reaction.

† See Section 11–11 for an exception.

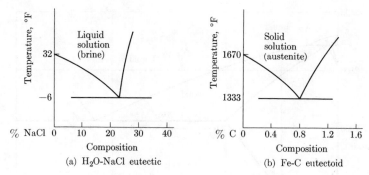

FIG. 9–24. Liquid versus solid solutions.

The eutectoid reaction. In Fig. 9–24 a comparison is made between the addition of common salt to water and the addition of carbon to austenite. In each case, the addition of the solute lowers the stable temperature range of the solution phase. These two examples differ in only one respect: in the ice-salt system, a *liquid solution* exists above the eutectic temperature; in the iron-carbon system, a *solid solution* exists, so that a true eutectic reaction does not occur upon cooling. However, because of the analogy of this reaction to the eutectic reaction, it is called *eutectoid* (literally, eutectic-like).

$$\text{Eutectic:} \qquad L \xrightarrow[\text{heating}]{\text{cooling}} S_1 + S_2. \qquad (9\text{--}1)$$

$$\text{Eutectoid:} \qquad S_A \xrightarrow[\text{heating}]{\text{cooling}} S_B + S_C. \qquad (9\text{--}2)$$

The eutectoid temperature for iron-carbon alloys is 1333°F (723°C). The corresponding eutectoid composition is 0.80% carbon. Figure 9–25 shows the completed iron-carbon phase diagram in the composition ranges normally encountered, and in Fig. 9–26 the eutectoid region is enlarged.

Example 9–8

Plot the percentage of ferrite, austenite, and carbide in an alloy of 0.60% carbon, 99.40% iron as a function of temperature.

Answer: At 1334°F:

$$\% \text{ ferrite} = \frac{0.80 - 0.60}{0.80 - 0.025} = 26\%.$$

At 1332°F:

$$\% \text{ ferrite} = \frac{6.67 - 0.60}{6.67 - 0.025} = 91\%.$$

At other temperatures and for other phases, results are shown in Fig. 9–27.

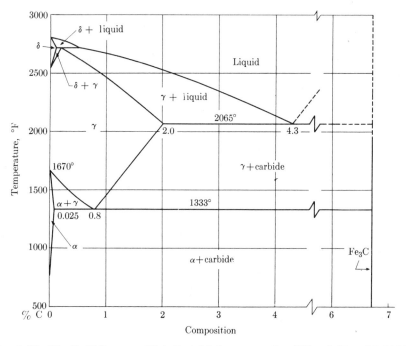

FIG. 9–25. The Fe-C diagram. Note that this is a composite of Figs. 9–21 and 9–24(b).

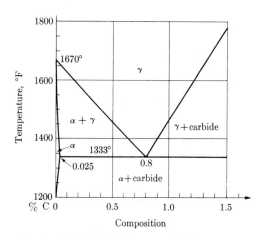

FIG. 9–26. Eutectoid region of the Fe-C diagram. The heat treatment of iron and steel depends on these phase relations.

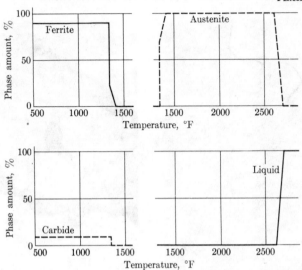

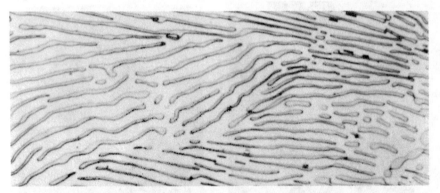

FIG. 9–27. Equilibrium amounts of phases (0.6% carbon-99.4% iron alloy). See Example 9–8.

FIG. 9–28. Pearlite, ×2500. This microstructure is a lamellar mixture of ferrite (lighter matrix) and carbide (darker). Pearlite forms from austenite of eutectoid composition. Therefore the amount and composition of pearlite is the same as the amount and composition of eutectoid. (J. R. Vilella, U. S. Steel Corp.)

9–12 Pearlite. The Fe-C eutectoid reaction involves the simultaneous formation of ferrite and carbide from austenite of eutectoid composition. There is nearly 12% carbide and slightly more than 88% ferrite in the resulting mixture. Since the carbide and ferrite form simultaneously, they are intimately mixed. Characteristically, the mixture is lamellar, i.e., it is composed of alternate layers of ferrite and carbide (Fig. 9–28). The resulting microstructure, called *pearlite*, is very important in iron and steel technology, because it may be formed in almost all steels by means of suitable heat treatments.

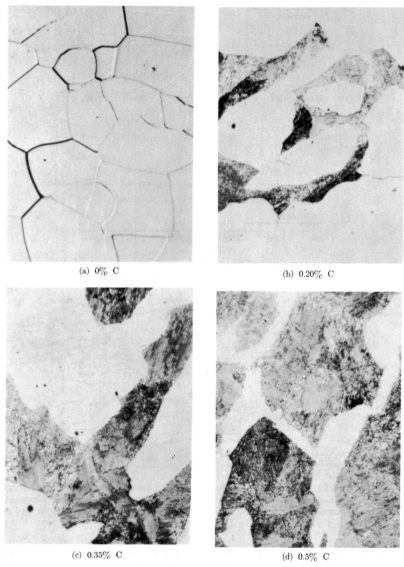

(a) 0% C

(b) 0.20% C

(c) 0.35% C

(d) 0.5% C

FIGURE 9–29

Pearlite is a specific mixture of two phases formed by transforming austenite of eutectoid composition to ferrite and carbide. This distinction is important, since mixtures of ferrite and carbide may be formed by other reactions as well. However, the microstructure resulting from other reactions will not be lamellar (com-

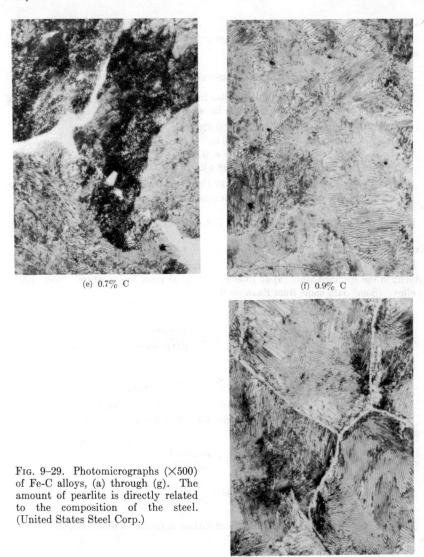

(e) 0.7% C   (f) 0.9% C

FIG. 9–29. Photomicrographs (×500) of Fe-C alloys, (a) through (g). The amount of pearlite is directly related to the composition of the steel. (United States Steel Corp.)

(g) 1.2% C

pare Figs. 11–13 and 9–28) and consequently the properties of such mixtures will be different. (See Section 11–4.)

Since pearlite comes from austenite of eutectoid composition, the amount of pearlite present is equal to the amount of eutectoid austenite transformed (Fig. 9–29).

Example 9–9

Determine the amount of pearlite in a 99.6% Fe-0.4% C alloy which is cooled slowly from 1600°F. Basis: 100 lb of alloy.

Answer: From 1600 to 1480°F: 100 lb austenite with 0.4% C.

From 1480 to 1333°F(+): ferrite separates from austenite and the carbon content of the austenite increases.

At 1333°F(+): composition of ferrite = 0.025% C,
    amount of ferrite = 51.6 lb,
    composition of austenite = 0.80% C,
    amount of austenite = 48.4 lb.

At 1333°F(−): amount of pearlite = 48.4 lb.   (It came from, and replaced, the austenite of eutectoid composition.)

Each of the above calculations assumes sufficient time for equilibrium to be attained.

Example 9–10

From the results of the example above, determine the amount of ferrite and carbide present in the specified alloy (a) at 1330°F, and (b) at room temperature. Basis: 100 lb of alloy. (Some data come from Example 9–9.)

Answer: (a) at 1330°F:

Amount of carbide: $48.4 \dfrac{0.8 - 0.025}{6.67 - 0.025} = 5.7 \dfrac{\text{lb carbide}}{100 \text{ lb steel}}$

Amount of ferrite:

$$48.4 - 5.7 = 42.7 \text{ lb ferrite formed with the pearlite}$$
$$\underline{51.6 \text{ lb ferrite formed before the pearlite}}$$
$$94.3 \text{ lb ferrite total/100 lb steel}$$

Alternate calculations:

Amount of carbide: $\dfrac{0.4 - 0.025}{6.67 - 0.025} = 5.7 \dfrac{\text{lb carbide}}{100 \text{ lb steel}}$

Amount of ferrite: $\dfrac{6.67 - 0.4}{6.67 - 0.025} = 94.3 \dfrac{\text{lb ferrite}}{100 \text{ lb steel}}$

(b) At room temperature (the solubility of carbon in ferrite at room temperature may be considered zero for these calculations):

$$\frac{0.4 - 0}{6.67 - 0} = 6.0 \frac{\text{lb carbide}}{100 \text{ lb steel}}$$

$$\frac{6.67 - 0.4}{6.67 - 0} = 94.0 \frac{\text{lb ferrite}}{100 \text{ lb steel}}$$

Additional carbide is precipitated from the ferrite below the eutectoid point because the solubility of carbon in ferrite decreases to nearly zero. This additional carbide is not part of the pearlite. (Each of these calculations assumes that equilibrium prevails.)

TABLE 9-1

NOMENCLATURE FOR AISI AND SAE STEELS

AISI or SAE number	Composition
10xx	Plain carbon steels
11xx	Plain carbon (resulfurized for machinability)
13xx	Manganese (1.5-2.0%)
23xx	Nickel (3.25-3.75%)
25xx	Nickel (4.75-5.25%)
31xx	Nickel (1.10-1.40%), chromium (0.55-0.90%)
33xx	Nickel (3.25-3.75%), chromium (1.40-1.75%)
40xx	Molybdenum (0.20-0.30%)
41xx	Chromium (0.40-1.20%), molybdenum (0.08-0.25%)
43xx	Nickel (1.65-2.00%), chromium (0.40-0.90%) molybdenum (0.20-0.30%)
46xx	Nickel (1.40-2.00%), molybdenum (0.15-0.30%)
48xx	Nickel (3.25-3.75%), molybdenum (0.20-0.30%)
51xx	Chromium (0.70-1.20%)
61xx	Chromium (0.70-1.10%), vanadium (0.10%)
81xx	Nickel (0.20-0.40%), chromium (0.30-0.55%), molybdenum (0.08-0.15%)
86xx	Nickel (0.30-0.70%), chromium (0.40-0.85%), molybdenum (0.08-0.25%)
87xx	Nickel (0.40-0.70%), chromium (0.40-0.60%), molybdenum (0.20-0.30%)
92xx	Silicon (1.80-2.20%)

xx—carbon content, 0.xx%.   B—Prefixed to show bessemer steel.
Mn—All steels contain 0.50% ±   C—Prefixed to show open-hearth steel.
    manganese.   E—Prefixed to show electric furnace steel.

9-13 Nomenclature for steels. The importance of carbon in steel has made it desirable to indicate the carbon content in the identification scheme of steel types. A four-digit numbering scheme is used, in which the last two digits designate the number of hundredths of percent of carbon content (Table 9-1). For example, a 1040 steel has 0.40% carbon (plus or minus a small workable range). The first two digits indicate the type of alloying element that has been added to the iron and carbon. The classification (10xx) is reserved for plain carbon steels with only a minimum amount of other alloying elements.

These designations for the steels are accepted as standard by both the American Iron and Steel Institute and the Society of Automotive Engineers (AISI and SAE). Many commercial steels are not included in this classification scheme because of larger additions or more subtle variations in alloy contents. Usually, however, such steels have more specialized applications and may not be stocked as regular warehouse items.

MULTICOMPONENT PHASE SYSTEMS

• **9–14 Ternary plots.** Many engineering materials have more than two components. For example, most steels have a third element such as manganese, nickel, molybdenum, or chromium in addition to iron and carbon. A ceramic magnet may contain Fe_2O_3, MnO, and NiO. A rubber tire usually contains rubber, sulfur, and a filler such as carbon.

The pattern encountered in a three-component system is what would be expected on the basis of experience with two-component systems. Solid solutions occur with two solutes rather than one; solubility limits exist; and eutectics are found where solubility limits intersect. Thus there can be *ternary eutectics* (and ternary eutectoids).

It is difficult to present a three-component system with as much detail as a two-component system because one added variable enters; e.g., two of three compositions must be stated in a three-component system, whereas only one of two components is required to be stated in a two-component system. (The final component is fixed after the others have been given.) Thus, if we are going to present ternary (i.e., three-component) phase relationships in two-dimensional graphs, it is necessary to fix one of the three variables. This may be accomplished by (1) fixing a phase (liquidus plots), (2) fixing temperature (isothermal plots), or (3) fixing the percentage of one of the components (pseudo-binaries). We shall limit our discussion to a brief consideration of the last two.

Isothermal plots. The composition of the material at any point within a three-component system may be designated by making use of a principle of plane geometry which states that *the sum of the perpendicular distances from any point within an equilateral triangle to the three sides is constant and equal to the altitude of the triangle.* Thus, if 100% represents the height of the triangle in Fig. 9–30 and each corner is one of three components, the distance a represents the percent of component A, b represents the percent of component B, and c represents the percent of component C. In accord with the lever rule discussed in Section 9–8, the total composition is located at the "center of gravity" of the three components.

Such a triangular diagram is useful for indicating properties and data of several types. Figure 9–31, for example, shows the index of refraction for various three-component glasses. Figure 9–32 gives the heat of combustion of mixtures of fuels. Figure 9–33 shows the room-temperature phase of stainless steels composed of Fe-Cr-Ni (only the iron-rich corner is shown).

Pseudobinaries. Figure 9–34 shows five Fe-C diagrams, each with a different amount of chromium present in addition to the iron and carbon. Only the first of the five is a true binary because of the chromium addition to the others; however, we apply the name *pseudobinary* to the others and handle them as binary diagrams.

From Fig. 9–34 it may be observed that as the chromium content of the steel is increased (Fig. 9–35) the carbon content of the eutectoid composition progressively decreases, and that the eutectoid temperature also changes. Figure 9–36 presents a compilation of the effects of other alloys on the eutectoid temperatures and compositions.

• **Example 9–11**

Assume that Fig. 9–29(d) is the microstructure for a steel containing 0.4% Mo and 99.6% Fe and C. Estimate how much carbon is present.

Answer: About $\frac{3}{4}$ of this steel is pearlite and $\frac{1}{4}$ is separate ferrite. Figure 9–36 indicates that the eutectoid will have 0.6% carbon when 0.4% molybdenum is present. Basis: 100 lb of steel:

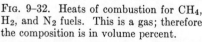

75 lb pearlite containing 0.60% C = 0.45 lb carbon

25 lb ferrite containing nil C = nil lb carbon

0.45 lb carbon/100 lb steel

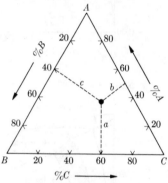

FIG. 9–30.   Three-component diagram. Any composition containing *A*, *B*, and *C* may be represented by a point on the diagram.

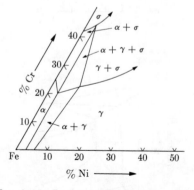

FIG. 9–31.   Index of refraction of BaO-B_2O_3-SiO_2 glasses. (Adapted from E. M. Levin and G. Ugrinic, *J. Research Natl. Bur. Standards*, **51**, 55, 1953.)

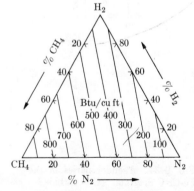

FIG. 9–32.   Heats of combustion for CH_4, H_2, and N_2 fuels. This is a gas; therefore the composition is in volume percent.

FIG. 9–33.   Isothermal diagram (phases in Fe-Cr-Ni alloys at room temperature). One of the common stainless steels contains 18% Cr and 8% Ni. Therefore it is austenitic. (Adapted from ASM data.)

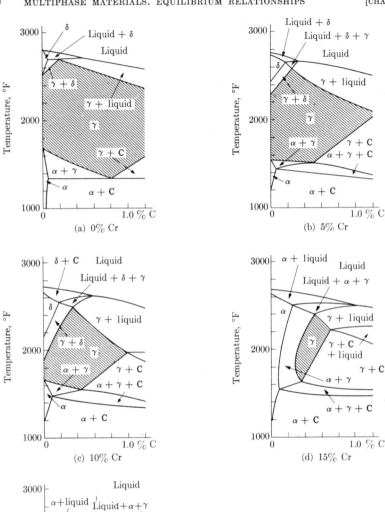

Fig. 9–34.   Pseudobinaries in the Fe-Cr-C diagram.   (C = carbide.)

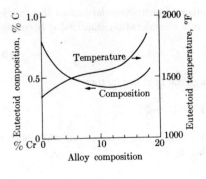

FIG. 9–35. Eutectoids in Fe-Cr-C alloys. Chromium additions change the temperature and carbon content of the eutectoid. (Cf. Fig. 9–34.)

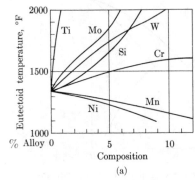

(a)

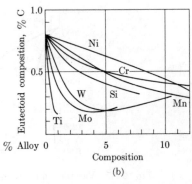

(b)

FIG. 9–36. Eutectoids in Fe-X-C alloys. Effect of alloy additions on (a) the temperature of the eutectoid reaction, and (b) the carbon content of the eutectoid. (Adapted from ASM data.)

• **9–15 Phase rule.** We have made no effort to discuss environmental variables other than temperature in the preceding discussions. The most common additional variable is pressure; in addition, electric fields and magnetic fields also exist as variables. Multiparameter conditions such as these serve to focus our attention on a basic rule known as the *phase rule:*

$$P = C + E - V. \tag{9–3a}$$

The above rule states that the maximum number of phases P which may co-exist under equilibrium conditions is equal to the sum of the number of components C and the number of environmental factors, E, minus the variance V of the system. *Phases* were described in Section 3–24 as a structurally homogeneous part of a material system. A *component* may be elements such as Pb and Sn in Fig. 9–6, or they may be compounds such as SiO_2 and Al_2O_3 in Fig. 9–9. The prime requirement is that they should not dissociate over the range of environmental conditions which are being considered.

It is legitimate to consider any number of *environmental factors* that might be required. Thus, if temperature is the only consideration, Eq. (9–3a) becomes

$$P + V = C + 1. \tag{9–3b}$$

Or if both the temperature and the magnetic field are factors,

$$P + V = C + 2 \tag{9–3c}$$

is appropriate. This latter form of Eq. (9–3) is also encountered when both temperature and pressure are environmental factors.

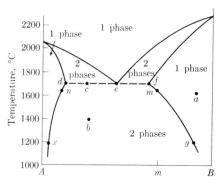

FIG. 9–37. Variance in phase equilibria. Equation (9–3b) indicates that $V = 3 - P$ in this binary system. (See text.)

The *degree of freedom*, or *variance*, refers to the number of unassigned variables. This may best be described by the use of an actual example. Consider Fig. 9–37 where Eq. (9–3b) is applicable. Locations a, b, and c have one, two, and three equilibrated phases, respectively. In a one-phase area, $V = C + 1 - P = 2$, and we have the opportunity to choose *either or both*, temperature and composition. In a two-phase area, our freedom of choice is limited; if we choose a temperature, say 1200°C, there is no choice in phase compositions. They must be x and y. Conversely, if we require a specific composition in a two-phase equilibrium, say m, there is no choice of temperature. In this example, it is fixed at 1650°C. Finally, in order to have three phases in a binary system, there is *no choice* of temperature or composition and our variance is zero, because the temperature must be the eutectic temperature and the compositions must be d, e, and f (in this example).

The phase rule may be used to formulate certain rules of geometry which apply to phase diagrams. These are listed in Table 9–2, and are useful in the preparation of phase diagrams. (See Figs. 9–38 through 9–50.)

The phase rule becomes particularly useful when we are dealing with multicomponent systems to determine whether the microstructures (Chapter 11) are in equilibrium or not.

TABLE 9–2

BOUNDARIES IN PHASE DIAGRAMS

I. BINARY DIAGRAMS

(a) Single-phase regions (or compositions) are separated by two-phase regions, and two-phase regions are separated by single-phase regions (or compositions). This produces a 1-2-1-2-1-2-. . . sequence across the isotherm of a diagram.

(b) One-phase regions come in contact only at invariant temperatures.

(c) Invariant temperatures involve the termination of three two-phase regions.

(d) Solubility lines extrapolate into two-phase regions.

(e) A single-phase region meets an invariant temperature where two solubility lines cross.

(f) The two-phase region which lies between two three-phase invariant temperatures has the two phases which are common to the two invariant reactions.

(g) Phases with congruent transformation may be treated as single-component systems at their transformation point.

II. TERNARY DIAGRAMS

(a) Except for invariant conditions, four regions must meet at a point *within* an isothermal diagram (or *within* a diagram with one component fixed).

(b) The four regions around the point include 1, 2, 3, and 2 phases in sequence.

Additional phase diagrams. (See p. 270 for the location of various diagrams.)

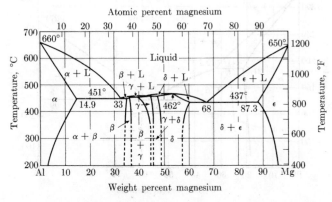

FIG. 9–38. **Al–Mg.** *Metals Handbook,* page 1163, Cleveland: American Society for Metals, 1948.

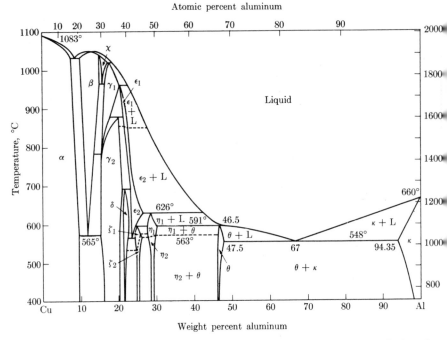

FIG. 9–39. **Al–Cu.** *Metals Handbook*, page 1159, Cleveland: American Society for Metals, 1948.

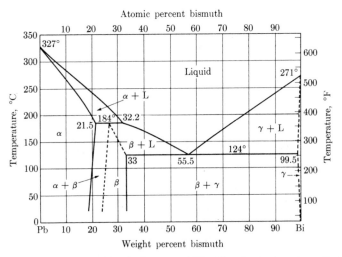

FIG. 9–40. **Bi–Pb.** *Metals Handbook*, page 1179, Cleveland: American Society for Metals, 1948.

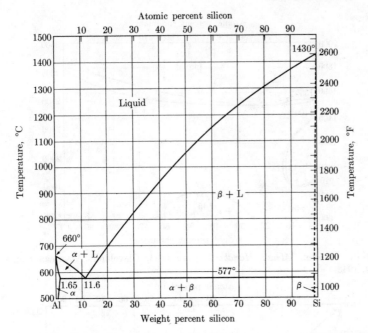

Fig. 9–41. **Al–Si.** *Metals Handbook,* page 1166, Cleveland: American Society for Metals, 1948.

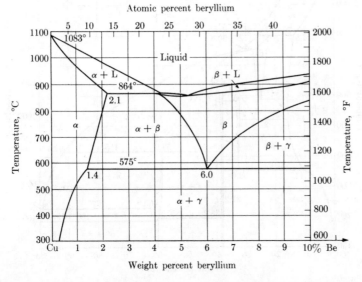

Fig. 9–42. **Be–Cu.** *Metals Handbook,* page 1176, Cleveland: American Society for Metals, 1948.

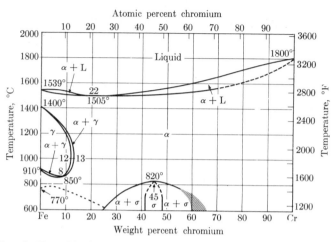

FIG. 9–43. **Cr–Fe.** *Metals Handbook*, page 1194, Cleveland: American Society for Metals, 1948.

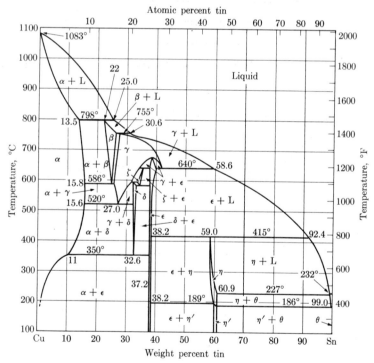

FIG. 9–44. **Cu–Sn.** *Metals Handbook*, page 1204, Cleveland: American Society for Metals, 1948.

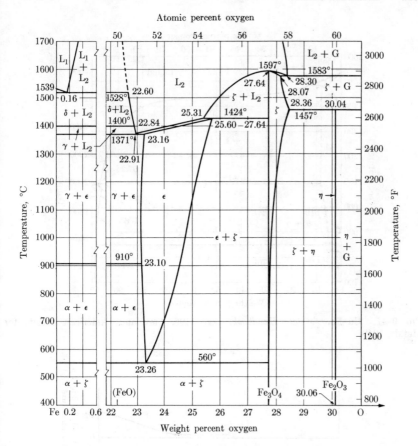

FIG. 9–45. **Fe–O.** *Metals Handbook,* page 1212, Cleveland: American Society for Metals, 1948.

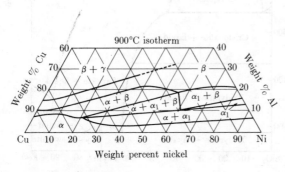

FIG. 9–46. **Al–Cu–Ni.** *Metals Handbook,* page 1243, Cleveland: American Society for Metals, 1948.

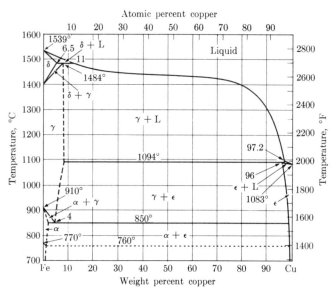

FIG. 9–47. **Cu–Fe.** *Metals Handbook*, page 1196, Cleveland: American Society for Metals, 1948.

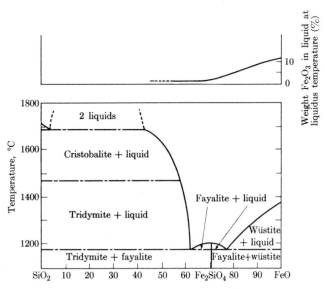

FIG. 9–48. **FeO–SiO₂.** N. L. Bowen and J. F. Schairer, *American Journal of Science*, 5th Series, **24**, 200, 1932.

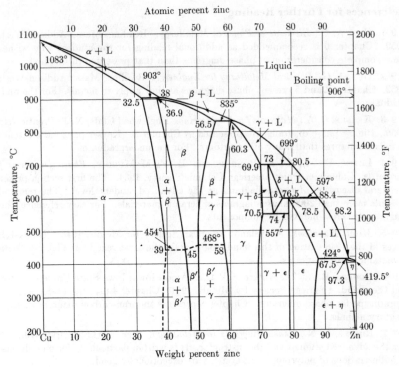

Fig. 9–49. **Cu–Zn.** *Metals Handbook*, page 1206, Cleveland: American Society for Metals, 1948.

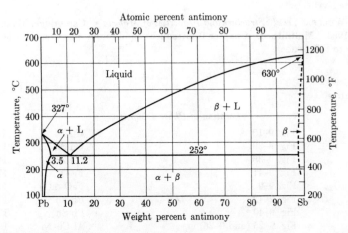

Fig. 9–50. **Pb–Sb.** *Metals Handbook*, page 1237, Cleveland: American Society for Metals, 1948.

References for Further Reading

9-1. GUY, A. G., *Elements of Physical Metallurgy*. Reading, Mass.: Addison-Wesley, 1959. Chapter 6 is recommended as additional reading for the student who wishes a more complete consideration of phase diagrams than that presented in this text.

9-2. GUY, A. G., *Physical Metallurgy for Engineers*. Reading, Mass.: Addison-Wesley, 1962. Chapters 4 and 5 present phase diagrams as they apply to metals. For the undergraduate.

9-3. KEYSER, C. A., *Materials for Engineering*. Englewood Cliffs, N. J.: Prentice-Hall, 1956. Binary phase diagrams are presented in Chapter 8. Keyser pays more attention to microstructures than many other authors. For the undergraduate.

9-4. LEVIN, E. M., C. R. ROBBINS and H. F. McMURDIE, *Phase Diagrams for Ceramists*. Columbus, Ohio: American Ceramic Society, 1964. The first section presents a general discussion of phase diagrams at the advanced student level. The remainder presents more than 2000 phase diagrams of ceramic materials. For easy reference, these diagrams are cross-indexed by components.

9-5. *Metals Handbook*. Cleveland: American Society for Metals, 1948. The last 125 pages of the 1948 edition of this handbook contain the most readily available collection of metallic phase diagrams.

9-6. ROGERS, B. A., *The Nature of Metals*. Ames, Iowa: Iowa State University Press, and Cleveland: American Society for Metals, 1951. Chapter 4 uses the Pb-Sn system as a prototype for phase diagrams. Chapter 8 presents the iron-carbon diagram in an elementary manner.

9-7. RHINES, F. N., *Phase Diagrams in Metallurgy*. New York: McGraw-Hill, 1956. For the advanced student and the instructor. It is written particularly for metallurgists. The illustrations of polycomponent systems are exceptionally good.

9-8. VAN VLACK, L. H., *Physical Ceramics for Engineers*. Reading, Mass.: Addison-Wesley, 1964. Chapter 6 pays specific attention to ternary phase diagrams. Undergraduate level.

9-9. WULFF, J., *et al.*, *Structure and Properties of Materials*. Cambridge, Mass.: M.I.T. Press, 1963. Multilithed. Chapter 9 introduces equilibrium diagrams at a level comparable to this text.

Problems

Location of Phase Diagrams

Ag-Cu	Fig. 9–10	Cu-Ni	Fig. 9–7
Al-Cu	Fig. 9–39	Cu-Sn	Fig. 9–44
Al-Mg	Fig. 9–38	Cu-Zn	Fig. 9–49
Al-Si	Fig. 9–41	Fe-O	Fig. 9–45
Al_2O_3-SiO_2	Fig. 9–9	FeO-SiO_2	Fig. 9–48
Be-Cu	Fig. 9–42	Pb-Sb	Fig. 9–50
Bi-Pb	Fig. 9–40	Pb-Sn	Fig. 9–6
C-Fe	Fig. 9–25 (and 9–26)	Al-Cu-Ni	Fig. 9–46
Cr-Fe	Fig. 9–43	C-Cr-Fe	Fig. 9–34
Cu-Fe	Fig. 9–47	Cr-Fe-Ni	Fig. 9–33

9–1. The solubility of tin in solid lead at 200°C is 18% Sn. The solubility of lead in the molten metal at the same temperature is 44% Pb. What is the composition of an alloy containing 40% liquid and 60% solid α at 200°C?

Answer: 66.8% Pb, 33.2% Sn

9–2. A lead battery grid contains 92% Pb-8% Sb. (a) What is the composition of the final liquid to solidify? (b) How much β will be present at 200°C?

9–3. (a) At what temperature would a monel metal alloy (70% nickel, 30% copper) contain $\frac{2}{3}$ liquid and $\frac{1}{3}$ solid, and (b) what would be the composition of the liquid and of the solid?

Answer: (a) 1370°C (b) liquid 34% Cu-66% Ni, solid 22% Cu-78% Ni

9–4. An alloy of 50 gm Cu and 30 gm Zn is melted and cooled slowly. (a) At what temperature will there be 40 gm α and 40 gm β? (b) 50 gm α and 30 gm β? (c) 30 gm α and 50 gm β?

9–5. (a) Making use of Fig. 9–10, show what equilibrium phase(s) exist in a sterling silver alloy containing 92.5% silver and 7.5% copper as it is progressively cooled from 2100°F. (b) If such an alloy were cooled fast enough to reach room temperature without precipitation of the copper-rich phase, would it be stronger or weaker than 100% pure silver? Explain.

Answer: (a) 2100°F to 1650°F, liquid; 1650°F to 1475°F, liquid + α; 1475°F to 1400°F, α only; below 1400°F, $\alpha + \beta$; (b) stronger, solid solution.

9–6. A 90-10 Cu-Sn bronze is slowly cooled to room temperature from a liquid. At each 100°C interval, (a) what is the composition of the α phase, and (b) approximately how much α is present?

9–7. Make a material balance for a 92-8 Ag-Cu alloy at 500°C (equilibrium conditions). *Answer:* 93.8 lb α, 98% Ag-2% Cu; 6.2 lb β, 1% Ag-99% Cu

9–8. (a) What are the compositions of the phases in a 10% magnesium-90% aluminum alloy at 600°C, 400°C, 200°C? (b) What are the amounts of these phases at each of the temperatures in part (a)? (c) Make a material balance for the distribution of the magnesium and aluminum in the above alloy at 600°C.

9–9. An alloy of 95.5% Al and 4.5% Cu is heated to 1000°F. (a) It is cooled very fast. What phases are present? Why? (b) It is cooled slowly enough for equilibrium to develop. What phases are present? (c) Where would the first precipitate occur in (b)? Why?   *Answer:* (a) only κ (b) $\kappa + \theta$ (c) grain boundaries

9–10. A beryllium bronze contains 98% Cu-2% Be. Make a material balance for 600°C.

9–11. Make a material balance for a 90–10 Mg-Al alloy at 400°F. (Assume equilibrium.) *Answer:* 84.6 lb ϵ, 96% Mg-4% Al; 15.4 lb δ, 57% Mg-43% Al

9–12. How much mullite would be present in a 60% SiO_2-40% Al_2O_3 brick at the following temperatures under equilibrium conditions: (a) 2550°F, (b) 2900°F, (c) 2912°F?

9–13. A 60% Al_2O_3-40% SiO_2 brick contains 75% mullite. Does it have more or less mullite than the equilibrium amount at 1400°C?   *Answer:* Less (85% mullite)

9–14. A die-casting alloy of 95 Al-5 Si is cooled so that the metal contains primary α and a eutectic mixture of $(\alpha + \beta)$. What fraction of the casting is primary α?

9–15. (a) Determine the compositions of Al-Si alloys that would contain $\frac{1}{3}$ liquid and $\frac{2}{3}$ solid when brought to equilibrium at 600°C. (b) Give the compositions of the liquids. *Answer:* (a) 96 Al-4 Si, 70 Si-30 Al (b) 91 Al-9 Si, 87 Al-13 Si

9–16. Based on Figs. 9–6 and 9–27, make a graph for an alloy containing 80% Pb and 20% Sn showing (a) the fraction of liquid versus temperatures, (b) the fraction of α versus temperature, and (c) the fraction of β versus temperature.

9–17. The following observations were made in a study of the phase equilibria existing at various temperatures in the system Xm-Yz. On the basis of these observations, draw the equilibrium phase diagram for the Xm-Yz system.

Total Composition	Tem-perature	Structure and Composition of Phases Observed in Equilibrium
10 w/o Xm	275°C	Fcc, 8 w/o Xm; Liq, 13 w/o Xm
	250	Fcc, 10 w/o Xm
	100	Fcc, 10 w/o Xm
20 w/o Xm	225°C	Fcc, 17 w/o Xm; Liq, 26 w/o Xm
	150	Fcc, 20 w/o Xm
	50	Fcc, 19 w/o Xm; Hex, 25 w/o Xm
30 w/o Xm	200°C	Liq, 30 w/o Xm
	185	Fcc, 22 w/o Xm; Hex, 27 w/o Xm; Liq, 32 w/o Xm
	175	Hex, 28 w/o Xm; Liq, 38 w/o Xm
	100	Hex, 30 w/o Xm
40 w/o Xm	150°C	Hex, 30 w/o Xm; Liq, 47 w/o Xm
	125	Hex, 33 w/o Xm; Liq, 56 w/o Xm; Rhomb, 99.5 w/o Xm
	50	Hex, 32.5 w/o Xm; Rhomb, 99.9 w/o Xm
70 w/o Xm	200°C	Liq, 70 w/o Xm
	150	Liq, 64 w/o Xm; Rhomb, 99.6 w/o Xm
	125	Hex, 33 w/o Xm; Liq, 56 w/o Xm; Rhomb, 99.5 w/o Xm
	100	Hex, 32.8 w/o Xm; Rhomb, 99.7 w/o Xm

Pure Xm melts at 271°C; pure Yz melts at 327°C.

Answer: See Bi-Pb diagram.

9–18. Draw on cross-section paper the equilibrium diagram for alloys of metals *A* and *B* from the following data. Label all areas of your diagram.

Melting point of *A*	700°C
Melting point of *B*	1000°C
Eutectic temperature	500°C
Composition of liquid in equilibrium at the eutectic temperature:	30 w/o *A*
	70 w/o *B*
Solubilities at 500°C:	*B* in *A* = 15 w/o
	A in *B* = 20 w/o
Solubilities at 70°C:	*B* in *A* = 15 w/o
	A in *B* = 8 w/o

9-19. Making use of the iron-carbon diagram, calculate the amount of α and the amount of carbide present at 1300°F in a metal containing 2% carbon and 98% iron.

Answer: 30⁻% carbide, 70⁺% ferrite

9-20. Describe the phase changes which occur on heating a 0.20% carbon steel from room temperature to 2200°F.

9-21. Calculate the percent ferrite, carbide, and pearlite, at room temperature, in iron-carbon alloys containing (a) 0.5% carbon, (b) 0.8% carbon, (c) 1.5% carbon.

Answer: (a) 7.5% carbide, 92.5% α, 62% pearlite; (b) 12% carbide, 88% α, 100% pearlite; (c) 22.5% carbide, 77.5% α, 88% pearlite.

9-22. (a) Determine the phases present, the composition of each of these phases, and the relative amounts of each phase for 1.2% carbon steel at 1600°F, 1400°F, 1300°F. (Assume equilibrium.)   (b) How much pearlite is present at each of the above temperatures?

• 9-23. A steel contains 98.5% Fe, 0.5% C, and 1.0% silicon. (a) What is the eutectoid temperature?   (b) How much pearlite may be formed?   (c) What will be present other than pearlite?

Answer: (a) 750°C (1380°F) (b) 76% pearlite (0.65% carbide in eutectoid) (c) separate ferrite

• 9-24. Modify Fig. 9-26 for a steel containing (a) 1% Mn, (b) 1% Cr, (c) 1% W, (d) 1% Ni. (The new solubility curves remain essentially parallel to the previous ones.)

• 9-25. Calculate the quantities of the phases at 100°F intervals from 1200°F to 1600°F for the following steels: (a) 0.8% carbon, 99.2% iron; (b) 1.2% carbon, 98.8% iron; (c) 0.6% carbon, 0.6% molybdenum, and 98.8% iron.

Answer: (a) 1200°F, 88α-12**C**; 1300°F, 88α-12**C**; 1400 to 1600°F, 100γ; (b) 1200°F, 82α-18**C**; 1300°F, 82α-18**C**; 1400°F, 95γ-5**C**; 1500°F, 98γ-2**C**; 1600°F, 100γ; (c) 1200, 1300, 1400°F, 91α-9**C**; 1500 and 1600°F, 100γ (**C** = carbide).

9-26. A steel has the following composition. Give it an AISI number: C 0.38, Mn 0.75, Cr 0.87, Mo 0.18, Ni 0.03.

9-27. A steel has the following composition. Give it an AISI number: C 0.21, Mn 0.69, Cr 0.62, Mo 0.13, Ni 0.61.

Answer: AISI 8620

9-28. On the basis of this chapter, would you choose a high- or low-carbon steel for an automobile fender?   Give reasons.

9-29. A liquid containing 90% Ni and 10% Cu is cooled relatively quickly (so that there is time for diffusion in the liquid, but not in the solid) from the bottom of the container upward. Describe the compositional differences in the final solid casting.

• 9-30. (a) On a ternary diagram, locate the composition of polyvinyl chloride with C, H, and Cl as components. Locate the composition (b) of vinylidene chloride, and (c) of ethylene. (Use weight percent.)

• 9-31. On a ternary diagram, locate the composition (a) of acetone, (b) of melamine, and (c) of phenol. (Use weight percent.)

Answer: (a) 62.1% C, 10.3% H, 27.6% O (b) 28.6% C, 4.8% H, 66.6% N (c) 76.7% C, 6.4% H, 17.0% O

• Problems preceded by a bullet are based, in part, on optional sections.

9–32. β-brass is a bcc solid solution; β is a random solid solution; β' is an ordered solid solution. What precautions are necessary in rolling or extruding this metal?

9–33. Show the sequential changes in phases when the composition of an alloy is changed from 100% Cu to 100% Al (a) at 700°C, (b) at 450°C, (c) at 900°C.

Answer: (c) At 900°C: α, $\alpha + \beta$, β, $\beta + \gamma_1$, γ_1, $\gamma_1 + \epsilon_1$, ϵ_1, $\epsilon_1 + L$, L

9–34. Show the sequential changes in phases when the composition of an alloy is changed from 100% Mg to 100% Al (a) at 300°C, (b) at 500°C, (c) at 445°C.

9–35. (a) Formulate a general rule about the sequential *number* of phases in Problems 9–33 and 9–34. (b) Check your rule in other phase diagrams.

9–36. If carbon atoms were forced into the larger "holes" in the fcc iron structure (Fig. 9–20), what common type of structure would result? (Cf. Fig. 8–5.)

• 9–37. What phases are present at 900°C in an alloy of (a) 60 Cu-40 Ni? (b) 60 Cu-25 Ni-15 Al? (c) 60 Cu-10 Ni-30 Al?

Answer: (a) α (b) $\alpha + \beta$ (c) $\beta + \gamma$

• 9–38. What phases are in equilibrium at room temperature in stainless steels of (a) 18 Cr-8 Ni-74 Fe? (b) 18 Cr-5 Ni-77 Fe? (c) 18 Cr-1 Ni-81 Fe?

• 9–39. What phases are present (a) at room temperature, (b) at 2000°F in stainless steels of 12 Cr-88 Fe? 17 Cr-83 Fe?

Answer: (a) $\alpha + (\sigma?)$, $\alpha + \sigma$ (b) $\alpha + \gamma$, α

• 9–40. What phases are present at 2000°F for stainless steels of (a) 15 Cr-0.5 C-bal. Fe? (b) 18 Cr-0.5 C-bal. Fe? (c) 18 Cr-0.1 C-bal. Fe?

• 9–41. Cite the invariant temperatures of (a) the Cu-Sn system; (b) the Cu-Fe system; (c) the Cu-Zn system.

Answer: (c) When C = 2: 903°C, 835°C, 699°C, 597°C, 557°C, 424°C; when C = 1: 1083°C, 419.5°C.

10

reactions within solid materials

10–1 Introduction. Chemical reactions which produce new phases in solids frequently have important engineering consequences. Often, as we shall see in Chapter 11, they have desirable reactions, but sometimes they must be avoided. We shall first categorize some of the more commonly encountered solid-phase reactions, and, because reactions are not instantaneous, we shall then give attention to the time required for solid-phase reactions to occur. Finally, we must examine metastable and transition phases. The contribution of these reactions toward properties will be considered in Chapters 11 and 12.

SOLID-PHASE REACTIONS

10–2 Polymorphic phase transformations. Pure materials may undergo phase transformations from one polymorphic form to another.

Polymorphic transformation: Solid $A \rightleftarrows$ Solid B.   (10–1)

Our prototype of this reaction, discussed in Section 9–11, was the $\alpha \rightleftarrows \gamma$ transformation of iron at 910°C (1670°F). Other familiar polymorphic changes (out of many) include the α-to-β transformation in titanium and the quartz-to-tridymite-to-cristobalite changes in SiO_2. These transformations result from temperature changes. The polymorphic transformation between graphite and diamond is a consequence of pressure variations.

Density and volume changes accompany phase transformations because the polymorphic structures do not have identical atomic packing factors. These packing factors are 0.68 and 0.74, respectively, for the bcc and fcc phases of iron; hence there is a noticeable dimensional change at 1670°F (Fig. 10–1a). However, the heating or cooling must be quite slow for the change to occur precisely at the transformation temperature without a lag.

The transformation temperature was defined in Fig. 9–22 as the temperature at which the two phases have identical amounts of energy available for chemical reaction. Thus below 1670°F austenite is more reactive than ferrite because it has more free energy; consequently, austenite is unstable and ferrite is stable. Immediately above 1670°F, the opposite is true; then austenite is the stable phase of pure iron because the bcc iron reacts to form fcc iron.

Polymorphic reactions require only minor atom movements because the composition of the reactant and the product are identical [Eq. (10–1)]. However, it is still necessary to break the existing bonds and reform the atoms into the new structure.

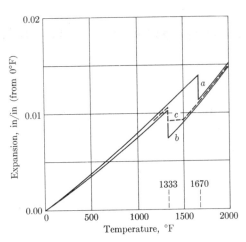

FIG. 10–1. Dimensional changes with phase transformations in iron and iron-carbon alloys. (a) Pure iron. (b) 99.2 Fe-0.8 C. (c) 99.6 Fe-0.4 C. Very slow changes in temperature permit an equilibrium, with transformation at the temperatures indicated by the phase diagrams (Fig. 9–26).

10–3 Eutectoid reactions. The equilibrium temperature between two polymorphic phases is altered when one of the phases dissolves a second component to a greater extent than the other. Again let us use the ferrite-austenite transformation as an example, and refer to Fig. 9–25. For reasons cited in Section 9–11, carbon has greater solubility in austenite than in ferrite. As a result, the stability range of austenite is extended to higher and lower temperatures when carbon is present with iron. Figures 9–25 and 9–26 indicate that the lower end of the temperature range drops from 1670°F for pure iron to 1333°F for an alloy with 0.8 w/o carbon. Presumably this temperature would be still lower for higher percentages of carbon, except for the fact that cementite (Fe_3C) is formed. In Chapter 9 we referred to this lowest temperature as the eutectoid temperature, and discussed the fact that it involved (in a binary alloy) a eutectoid reaction of three phases:

$$\text{Eutectoid:} \qquad \text{Solid } A \underset{\text{heating}}{\overset{\text{cooling}}{\rightleftarrows}} \text{Solid } B + \text{Solid } C. \qquad (10\text{–}2)$$

Materials of eutectoid composition may have their transformation completed at a single temperature (Fig. 10–1b) if sufficient time is given during heating or cooling. Other compositions (Fig. 10–1c) require a range of temperatures even under equilibrium conditions.

The transformation of austenite to pearlite containing ferrite and carbide is typical of many reactions within solids in that it starts at the grain boundaries and proceeds into the former grains (Fig. 10–2a). This sequence of reaction is to be expected, since it will be recalled from Section 4–9 and Fig. 4–15 that the atoms at the grain boundaries have higher energies than the atoms within the grains. Therefore, the atoms along the boundary require less additional energy to break away from their existing neighbors and to form a new structure.

However, grain boundaries are not the only locations of more energetic atoms. Those atoms around point or line defects (Sections 4–7 and 4–8) have extra energy

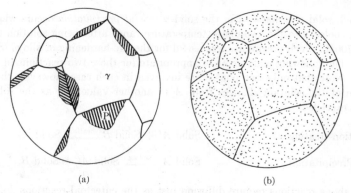

(a)   (b)

FIG. 10–2. Phase transformations. (a) Nucleation at grain boundaries ($\gamma \to \alpha +$ carbide in steel). (b) Nucleation at imperfections within crystals ($\kappa \to \kappa + \theta$ in an Al-Cu alloy).

and can serve as locations for the nucleation of reactions (Fig. 10–2b). These locations increase in importance as the temperature is lowered.

A eutectoid reaction requires diffusion because the product phases are not identical to the reactant phases. This is illustrated in Fig. 10–3 for pearlite formation, where carbon must diffuse from areas forming ferrite into areas forming carbide. Of course, this process requires some time for completion.

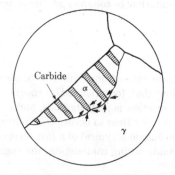

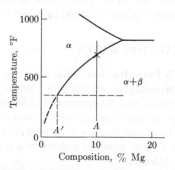

FIG. 10–3. Pearlite formation. Carbon must diffuse from the eutectoid austenite (0.8± %) to form carbide (6+ %). The ferrite which is formed has negligible carbon.

FIG. 10–4. Solution-treating and precipitation. One phase is dissolved in the other at elevated temperatures. Cooling produces a solid precipitation reaction (90 Al-10 Mg alloy).

10–4 Solution and precipitation within solids. These two reactions are opposite to each other and may be illustrated in Fig. 10–4. At temperatures below 700°F, an alloy with 90% Al and 10% Mg contains two phases, α and β. Above 700°F, all the magnesium may be contained in fcc α; consequently, as the metal is heated, solid β is *dissolved* in the solid α. *Solid precipitation* occurs when this alloy is cooled into the two-phase temperature range after being solution-treated above 700°F. Such precipitation is useful for the age-hardening of alloys (Section 11–7). The following equations are appropriate for these two reactions in binary alloys. Note that only two phases are involved in each case; however, the composition of the solution changes from A to another value, A', as the solubility limit is exceeded.

Solution-treating: Solid A' + Solid B $\xrightarrow{\text{heating}}$ Solid A.   (10–3)

Precipitation: Solid A $\xrightarrow{\text{cooling}}$ Solid A' + Solid B.   (10–4)

The above reactions require diffusion just as the eutectoid reactions do. Consider, for example, the composition of 95.5 w/o Al and 4.5 w/o Cu, which is a widely used aluminum alloy. As shown in Fig. 9–39, there are two phases, θ and κ, in equilibrium below 500°C. $CuAl_2$ comprises the θ phase, so that it contains an appreciably larger fraction of copper atoms than the κ phase. During solution-treatment these copper atoms must move through the κ structure to take on random substitutional positions; during precipitation, the copper atoms must be collected onto the growing $CuAl_2$ (that is, θ) particles.

Precipitation, like phase transformations, is nucleated at boundaries and other imperfections within a material. Here, as before, the grain boundary precipitation is predominant at those temperatures just below the solubility limit where the atoms can diffuse easily, and intragrain precipitation is common at lower temperatures where diffusion rates are restricted.

REACTION RATES

10–5 Introduction. Rates for various reactions range from those which are almost instantaneous to those which are so slow that for practical purposes the reactions may be considered nonexistent. No reaction is *instantaneous*, and even those we call "instantaneous" actually require a finite time to occur. The burning of the gas-air mixture in an internal combustion engine is typical of a fast reaction, but if there were not a delay of a few milliseconds during combustion, the engine would knock.

The crystallization of glass is an example of a very *slow* reaction. Glass is a supercooled liquid and, like other materials, it should crystallize below its melting point. However, the rate of crystallization at room temperature is so slow that we still have samples of noncrystalline glass made in early historic times (Fig. 10–5). Thus, glass is considered to be a *metastable phase*.

10–6 Effect of temperature on reaction rates. The time requirement for reaction arises because (1) existing bonds must be broken, (2) atoms must be moved to or from the reaction site, and (3) a new boundary is required whenever a new phase is to be nucleated. Each of the above steps requires a supply of

Fig. 10–5. Early historical glass (1400 B.C.). This glass has not crystallized during this long period even though it is a supercooled liquid. (Corning Glass Works.)

energy; therefore, it should be anticipated that each will be sensitive to the temperature of the material.

When only the first two of the above energy requirements must be considered, the reaction rate (= reciprocal time $1/t$) has the following exponential relationship with temperature:

$$\text{Rate} = \frac{1}{t} = Ae^{-Q/RT}. \tag{10–5}$$

The terms include: a reaction constant A; the absolute temperature T in °K; the "gas constant" R which is equal to 1.987 cal/mole·°K; and an activation energy Q in cal/mole. These terms may be compared directly with those in Section 4–12, because atom movements are involved. Since $\ln x = 2.3 \log_{10} x$, Eq. (10–5) may be rewritten as

$$\log_{10} \frac{1}{t} = \log_{10} A - \frac{Q}{2.3RT}, \tag{10–6a}$$

or

$$\log \frac{1}{t} = \log A - \frac{Q}{4.575T}. \tag{10–6b}$$

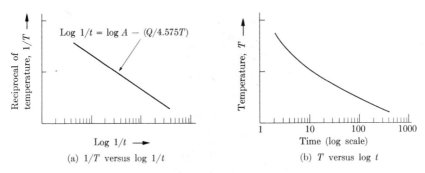

FIG. 10-6. Reaction time versus temperature. Two common methods of presentation are shown.

The relationship expressed in Eqs. (10–6) is shown graphically in Fig. 10–6. A straight-line relationship exists when $1/T$ is plotted against log $(1/t)$ on a semilogarithmic graph.

Example 10–1

At 212°F, the first precipitation of $CuAl_2$ from a supersaturated solid solution of copper in aluminum was detected after three minutes, and at 70°F, after three hours. It is desired to slow down this reaction so that no precipitation is observed in three days. To what temperatures should the metal be cooled?

Answer:

Temperature	Time
$212°F = 373°K$	180 sec (3 min)
$70°F = 294°K$	10,800 sec (3 hr)
$T = x$	259,200 sec (3 days)

$$\log \frac{1}{180} = \log A - \frac{Q}{4.575(373)} = -2.255,$$

$$\log \frac{1}{10,800} = \log A - \frac{Q}{4.575(294)} = -4.033.$$

Solving simultaneously, we obtain

$$\log A = 4.36,$$

$$Q = 11,400 \text{ cal/mole},$$

$$\log \frac{1}{259,200} = 4.36 - \frac{11,400}{4.575T} = -5.42,$$

$$x = 255°K = 0°F.$$

This may also be solved graphically if $1/T$ is plotted against $1/t$ on semilog paper.

The general relationship cited in Eqs. (10–6) is not applicable in those transformation reactions which are required to *nucleate a new phase* near the trans-

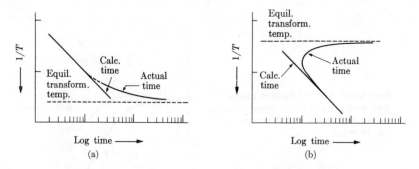

FIG. 10–7. Reaction lag for nucleation of a new phase. (a) Heating reactions. (b) Cooling reactions. There is a deviation from the calculated time for transformations near the transformation temperature. (Note: Both coordinate directions have been inverted from Fig. 10–6a.)

formation temperature, when the reaction time may be significantly longer (Fig. 10–7) and a deviation from an extrapolated line is to be expected. Extra energy is associated with any phase surface because the atoms along the interface are less tightly bound than in the interior of the phase. When a new phase must be nucleated, extra energy is therefore required to form the interface between the new particle and the parent phase. Since this extra energy is not available at the equilibrium temperature, reaction will be infinitely slow at that temperature.

• *Supercooling.* The reaction lag for nucleation of a new phase (Fig. 10–7b) has a basis which may be explained more precisely than is done by the qualitative statements of the last paragraph. The energy change which is of importance in a chemical reaction is the decrease in *free energy* of the reaction. This is called the *driving force* ΔF, and is shown in Fig. 10–8 for water and ice.

$$\Delta F = F_{\text{product}} - F_{\text{reactants}}. \tag{10-7}$$

The driving force favors ice formation below 32°F because ΔF is negative and energy is released by the reaction, $H_2O_{\text{water}} \rightarrow H_2O_{\text{ice}}$.

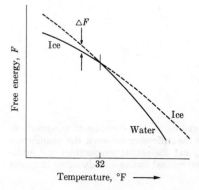

FIG. 10–8. Free energy of water and ice. Above 32°F, ice has a higher free energy than water. It gives up this energy by changing to the lower-free-energy form of water. (See Fig. 9–22.) The driving force is equal to ΔF.

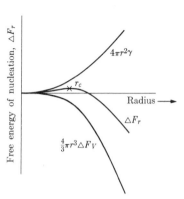

FIG. 10–9. Critical nucleus radius, $\times$. Any nucleation of a new phase requires an initial increase in net energy. (Cf. Eq. 10–8.)

The energy released during the nucleation of a new phase of radius r is $\frac{4}{3}\pi r^3 \Delta F_V$, where ΔF_V is the change in free energy per unit volume. However, energy is required to produce the new surface between the nucleated phase and the parent phase. This is equal to $4\pi r^2\gamma$, where γ is the interface energy per unit area. Thus, the total change in energy ΔF_r for a precipitate of radius r is

$$\Delta F_r = 4\pi r^2\gamma + \tfrac{4}{3}\pi r^3\Delta F_V. \qquad (10\text{–}8)$$

Although ΔF_V is negative for any spontaneous reaction, γ is always positive; therefore, we can plot Eq. (10–8) as shown in Fig. 10–9. Below a critical nucleus radius r_c, net energy is required for the nucleation of a new phase and nucleation cannot be spontaneous. Cooling beyond the equilibrium temperature, i.e., *supercooling*, increases the value of ΔF and therefore markedly reduces both the critical radius and the maximum amount of nucleation energy (Fig. 10–10). Thus there is a much greater probability that the necessary number of atoms can receive the appropriate amount of energy from some local energy source, such as a grain boundary or crystal imperfections. As a result, a reaction which takes infinitely

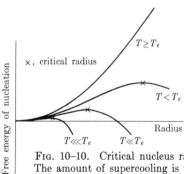

FIG. 10–10. Critical nucleus radius $\times$, as a function of temperature. The amount of supercooling is the difference between the equilibrium transformation temperature T_e and the actual temperature T. Additional supercooling decreases the critical radius and therefore increases the probability of nucleation.

long at the equilibrium temperature occurs in much less time with supercooling (Fig. 10–7b). Of course, extremely low temperatures restrict atom movements so that the time for reaction is extended even in the presence of nuclei.

• **Example 10–2**

Consider the polymorphic transformation, $A \rightleftarrows B$. The interface energy between A and B is 500 ergs/cm^2, and the values of ΔF_V for $A \rightarrow B$ are -100 cal/cm^3 at 1000°C and -500 cal/cm^3 at 900°C. (1 cal/cm^3 = 4.185 × 10^7 ergs/cm^3.) (a) Determine the critical nucleus radius for the nucleation of B within A at each temperature. (b) Calculate the energy that must be supplied for reaction to proceed in each case.

Answer:

(a)
$$r_c = \text{radius when } \frac{d\,\Delta F_r}{dr} = 0,$$

$$\Delta F_r = 4\pi r^2 \gamma + \tfrac{4}{3}\pi r^3 \,\Delta F_V,$$

$$\frac{d\,\Delta F_r}{dr} = 0 = 8\pi r\gamma + 4\pi r^2 \,\Delta F_V,$$

$$r_c = \frac{-2\gamma}{\Delta F_V}.$$

At 1000°C,
$$r_c = \frac{-2(500)}{-4.185 \times 10^9} = 24 \text{ A.}$$

At 900°C,
$$r_c = \frac{-2(500)}{-20.925 \times 10^9} = 4.8 \text{ A.}$$

(b)
$$\Delta F_r = 4\pi r^2 \left(\gamma + r\,\frac{\Delta F_V}{3} \right).$$

At 1000°C,　　$\Delta F_r = 4\pi(2.4 \times 10^{-7})^2 \left[500 + \dfrac{(2.4 \times 10^{-7})(-4.185 \times 10^9)}{3} \right]$

$$= 1.2 \times 10^{-10} \text{ erg.}$$

At 900°C,　　$\Delta F_r = 4\pi(0.48 \times 10^{-7})^2 \left[500 + \dfrac{(0.48 \times 10^{-7})(-20.925 \times 10^9)}{3} \right]$

$$= 0.048 \times 10^{-10} \text{ erg.}$$

• *Nucleating surfaces.* Less interface energy is required if an existing surface is available. If, for example, a plane surface of the product phase is already present, transformations can proceed without any increased surface area. Very often impurity particles may be present (by chance or by intent) and their surfaces may serve as a nucleating surface. If the impurity and the product phase have similar structures and thus comparable interfaces of low energy, the impurity may serve as a base for the transformation. Less surface energy is required under such conditions and the transformation can proceed more rapidly.

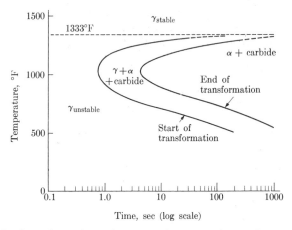

FIG. 10–11. Isothermal-transformation curves for $\gamma \rightarrow \alpha$ + carbide (a eutectoid steel). (Adapted from U. S. Steel Corp. data.)

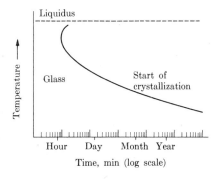

FIG. 10–12. Isothermal-transformation curve for glass crystallization (schematic).

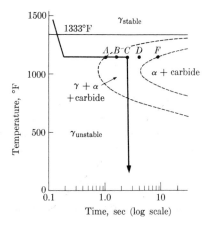

FIG. 10–13. Interrupted quench (eutectoid steel). This technique is used in establishing isothermal-transformation curves. The initial quench is made into a hot bath and it is held there for a prescribed time before the second quench to room temperature.

Fig. 10–14.   Start of transformation at
1150°F ($\gamma \rightarrow \alpha +$ carbide). M is steel which
has not transformed to $\alpha +$ carbide.   P is
pearlite, i.e., lamellar ($\alpha +$ carbide).   (Point
A in Fig. 10–13.)

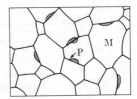

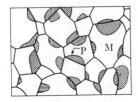

Fig. 10–15. Transformation 25% complete at
1150°F. (Point B in Fig. 10–13.)

Fig. 10–16. Transformation 75% complete at
1150°F. (Point D in Fig. 10–13.)

10–7 Isothermal transformation. The combined effect of temperature and
available free energy on a transformation is frequently indicated by *isothermal-
transformation curves* (Figs. 10–11 and 10–12). These may also be called *C-curves*
(because of their shape) or *T-T-T curves* (i.e., Temperature-Time-Transformation).
The data for Fig. 10–11 were obtained as follows. Small samples of steel were
heated into the austenite temperature range sufficiently long to assure complete
transformation to austenite. These samples were then quenched to a lower temperature (e.g., 1150°F) and held there for varying lengths of time before being
quenched further to room temperatures (Fig. 10–13). The change $\gamma \rightarrow \alpha +$
carbide (pearlite) was not observed in samples held at 1150°F for less than one
second, and complete transformation to $\alpha +$ carbide was not observed until after
more than 10 seconds had elapsed (Figs. 10–14 through 10–16). Similar data
were obtained for other temperatures until the completed diagram shown in
Fig. 10–11 was established.

The isothermal-transformation diagram shows that reactions occur slowly both
at relatively low temperatures and at temperatures close to the transformation
temperature. At intermediate temperatures, more rapid transformation occurs
because (1) there is sufficient driving force to help nucleate the new phases, and
(2) thermal diffusion is still quite rapid. With extremely fast cooling (severe
quenching), it is often possible to miss the "knee" of the transformation curve for
the beginning of the transformation, and to cool the steel to room temperature
without transformation to ferrite and carbide. In fact, this is the purpose of
quenching steel in regular heat-treating operations (Section 11–9).

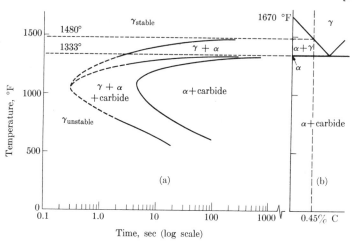

Fig. 10–17. Isothermal-transformation diagram for SAE 1045 steel. The reaction is faster than for eutectoid steel (Fig. 10–11). (Adapted from U. S. Steel Corp. data.)

The example just considered is the transformation of a eutectoid steel when there has been no advance separation of ferrite (or cementite) from the austenite prior to the formation of the pearlite. Figure 10–17(a) shows a similar transformation diagram for an SAE 1045 steel. Two features are different from those in Fig. 10–11. (1) Some ferrite may separate from the austenite above the eutectoid temperature. This could be predicted from the phase diagram which is shown at the right side of the figure. (2) The isothermal transformation of 0.45 carbon steel occurs somewhat faster than the transformation of eutectoid steel. Comparison of the "knees" of the two curves shows this difference: the higher carbon steel starts to transform in about one second; in the 0.45% carbon steel, the reaction starts sooner. In fact, in the latter case the reaction occurs sufficiently fast so that we are not able to measure the rate at the "knee" of the curve with the interrupted-quench technique described above. A lower carbon content permits faster reaction, since part of the transformation delay is associated with the movement of the carbon atoms.

The times required for the transformation of steel may be contrasted with the times required for the crystallization of glass (Fig. 10–12). The C-curves are very similar except for the scale of the abscissa. The slower rates for glass are a direct result of the stronger bonds and a more complicated arrangement between the atoms, a combination which provides less chance for atoms to rearrange themselves from the glassy structure into the crystalline structure (Fig. 8–22). Consequently, it is possible to retain the vitreous structure down to room temperatures without accelerated cooling rates.

By definition, the isothermal-transformation curves which have been presented *are not equilibrium diagrams*. They indicate the changes which will occur with time as a variable. An equilibrium diagram shows no change with time.

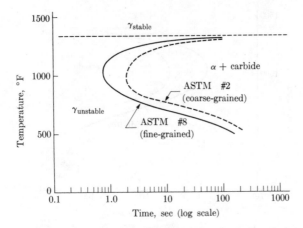

FIG. 10–18. Grain-boundary nucleation. The effect of grain size on the *start* of austenite transformation is shown for eutectoid steels. The fine-grained steel has more grain boundary area from which transformation can start.

10–8 Control of reaction rates.   Many times it is not necessary to exercise any deliberate control of a reaction rate.   For example, linseed oil may be used as a vehicle in a paint and left to cross-link by oxidation as fast as oxygen naturally becomes absorbed by the paint film.   In practice, the technologist is often in a position to influence rates of reaction, and there are several ways in which he may accelerate or retard a reaction, as he chooses.   The most common method of control is by temperature regulation, as described in the preceding sections.   Reaction rates may also be adjusted (1) through a control of the number of nucleation sites, or (2) by a modification of the diffusion rates.

Control through grain size.   Since a reaction may be initiated at a grain or phase boundary, one procedure of rate control is an adjustment of these surfaces.   This is done in the manufacture of quick-setting portland cement by grinding it more finely than regular cement so that there is more surface area and more rapid hydration.   Likewise, a steel with fine austenitic grain size has a faster transformation reaction ($\gamma \rightarrow \alpha +$ carbide) than a steel with a coarse austenitic grain size.   In the former there is more grain-boundary area from which a reaction may be initiated, so that more nucleation can occur in a given interval, thus shortening the time required for the total process (Fig. 10–18).

Control through diffusion retardation.   The term *retarder* is self descriptive.   The most significant effect of the addition of alloying elements to steels is to retard the $\gamma \rightarrow \alpha +$ carbide reaction by reducing the rate of diffusion of the carbon atoms to the reaction site.   This effect is indicated in Fig. 10–19 for two steels which are similar, except for the presence of a small amount of molybdenum in one of them.   With one or two minor exceptions, the addition of any alloying element within steel has a retarding effect on this transformation.   This has a major engineering consequence because, as we shall see in subsequent sections, the purpose of quench-

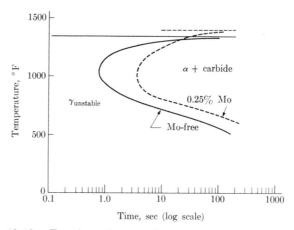

FIG. 10–19.   Transformation retardation.   Molybdenum, like other alloying elements, retards the *start* of transformation of austenite.

ing is to cool the steel fast enough *to avoid* the $\gamma \rightarrow \alpha$ + carbide reaction. Thus, alloying elements are used in steel to displace the transformation curves to the right (that is, to take longer times) and provide more time for removing the heat within larger sections of steel.

METASTABLE PHASES

10–9 Introduction.   Many of the materials of engineering contain phases which are *metastable*, that is, they maintain their existence although they have more energy than the equilibrium phase does.   Glass, which was cited as such a phase in Section 10–5, remains as a metastable phase because energy is required in order to *initiate* crystallization.

An analogy may be made with the box of Fig. 10–20, where the right-hand position would be considered more stable than the left-hand position because the center of gravity (and therefore the potential energy) is lower.   Additional energy

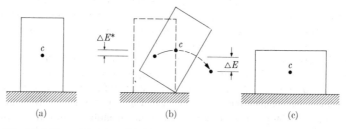

FIG. 10–20.   Stability.   Position (a) is only metastable because it has more potential energy ΔE than position (c).   An activation energy ΔE^* is required before the box may go to the more stable position.   (C = center of gravity.)

ΔE^* is necessary before the box can be moved from the metastable to the stable position. It is this extra energy requirement which maintains the metastability of the box in the left-hand position.

The additional, or activation, energy which is required to crystallize glass is used to break the interatomic bonds prior to the rearrangement of the atoms. This energy (and more) would be returned if new bonds were formed in a crystal; however, this energy is not available for the initial reaction. Therefore, the glass remains until some outside source of energy, such as heat or high-intensity radiation, is made available.

Materials may also be metastable to their surroundings. For example, iron would be expected to react with air to give Fe_2O_3, releasing energy and thereby becoming more stable; however, it remains as metal for extended periods of time. Similar metastability occurs for other metals, for rubber, and for all plastics, because they would also release energy by oxidation. Here, as with glass, the metastability of the material is protected by the energy required to break the bonds already existing prior to oxidation.

Transition phases present another example of metastability and are rather common in materials. These phases have lower energy than the initial phase but more energy than the stable form. Thus they can spontaneously form under appropriate conditions, but in turn are subject to eventual transformation to still more stable phases.

10–10 Martensite—a transition phase. The isothermal transformation relationships shown in Fig. 10–11 for a eutectoid steel and in Fig. 10–17 for an SAE 1045 steel indicate that the lower the temperature, the longer is the time required for transformation. Furthermore, as temperatures decrease, the free-energy difference between the fcc austenite and the combination of bcc ferrite plus carbide becomes larger. Consequently, the austenite is more unstable. At sufficiently low temperatures, but usually still above room temperatures, the

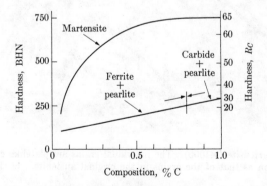

FIG. 10–21. Hardness of annealed iron-carbon alloys (α + carbide) and martensite versus carbon content. This difference in hardness is the reason for the quenching of steel.

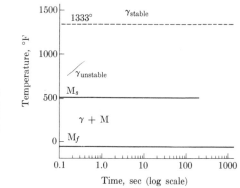

Fig. 10–22. Martensite formation in a 1080 steel. Temperatures are shown at the start (upper line) and finish (lower line) of the austenite → martensite transformation.

face-centered structure does change to a body-centered structure, but all of the carbon present remains in solution. Consequently, the resulting body-centered structure is tetragonal (bct) rather than cubic; it is called *martensite*.

Since martensite has a noncubic structure, and since carbon is still present in the lattice, slip does not occur readily, and therefore martensite is hard, strong, and brittle. Figure 10–21 shows a comparison of the hardness of martensite with that of pearlite-containing alloys as a function of carbon content. This enhanced hardness is of major engineering importance, since it provides a steel which is extremely resistant to abrasion and deformation.

Figure 10–22 shows the temperature M_s at which austenite starts to change to martensite in a 1080 steel. With still lower temperatures more and more austenite changes to martensite, until at room temperature relatively little austenite remains (Fig. 10–23). There is practically no time lag* for this reaction because no

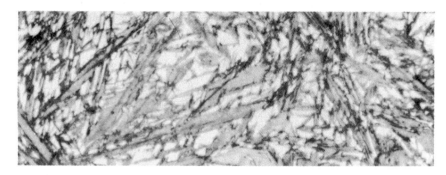

Fig. 10–23. Martensite (×1000). The individual grains are platelike crystals with the same composition as that of the grains in the original austenite. (J. R. Vilella, U. S. Steel Corp.)

---

* Measurements indicate that only a small fraction of a second is required at any given temperature.

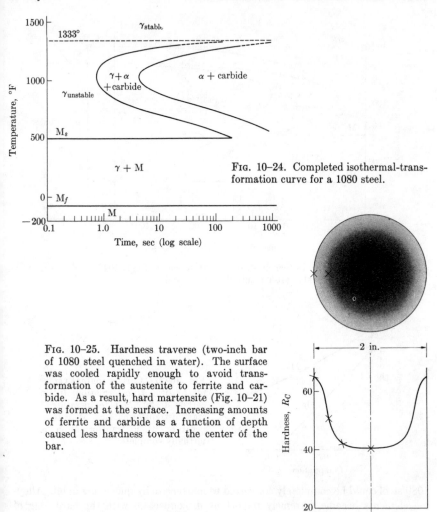

Fig. 10–24. Completed isothermal-transformation curve for a 1080 steel.

Fig. 10–25. Hardness traverse (two-inch bar of 1080 steel quenched in water). The surface was cooled rapidly enough to avoid transformation of the austenite to ferrite and carbide. As a result, hard martensite (Fig. 10–21) was formed at the surface. Increasing amounts of ferrite and carbide as a function of depth caused less hardness toward the center of the bar.

carbon diffusion occurs. Because all of the carbon remains in solution, martensite has a single-phase microstructure.

Figure 10–24 combines the information of Figs. 10–22 and 10–11. It is immediately evident that if martensite is to be obtained, the austenite must be cooled sufficiently fast so that it does not have time to change to ferrite and carbide at the higher temperatures. At 1000°F the time limit for 1080 steel is less than one second. The usual way to obtain martensite in a 1080 steel is to quench it severely in water. Even so, it is impossible to form martensite in the center of a large piece of this steel, because the heat at the center cannot be removed quickly enough. This is demonstrated in Fig. 10–25. On the other hand, a thin section of

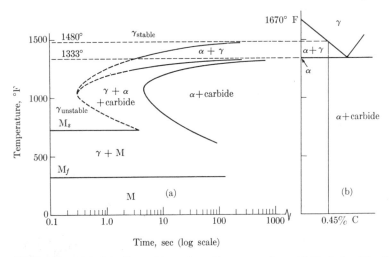

FIG. 10–26. Completed isothermal-transformation curve for a 1045 steel. The Fe-C diagram (right) is applicable after reaction is completed.

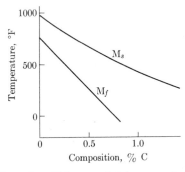

FIG. 10–27. Carbon content versus martensitic transformation (plain carbon steels). M_s is temperature at start of transformation. M_f is temperature when transformation is virtually complete.

1080 steel could be completely converted to martensite by quenching in oil. Alloying elements become extremely important in connection with the hardening of steel. Since almost all alloy additions to steels retard the transformation rate, more time is available to cool the steel and still avoid the formation of ferrite and carbide.* Longer cooling times permit less severe quenching, with a consequent reduction in the accompanying thermal stresses from which cracks may result. Furthermore, with alloy steels it is possible to obtain martensite at a greater depth below the surface without severe quenching.

Martensite formation temperatures vary with the carbon and alloy contents of steel. This is evident from a comparison of Figs. 10–24 and 10–26. Figure 10–27

---

* Alloying elements *do not* reduce the cooling rate; rather they reduce the transformation rate.

summarizes the effect of carbon additions on the temperature of start of transformation (M_s) and the temperature at which the austenite $\rightarrow$ martensite transformation is virtually finished (M_f). Usually there is a very minor amount of retained austenite even at very low temperatures.

10–11 Tempered martensite. The existence of martensite as a metastable
phase which contains carbon in solid solution in a body-centered tetragonal structure does not alter the iron-carbon phase diagram (Fig. 9–25). With sufficient
time at temperatures below the eutectoid, the super-saturated solution of carbon
in iron transforms to ferrite and carbide (Eq. 10–9). This process is known commercially as *tempering*.

$$\text{M} \xrightarrow{\hspace{2cm}} \alpha + \text{carbide}. \tag{10–9}$$
$$\underset{\text{(martensite)}}{} \qquad \underset{\substack{\text{(tempered} \\ \text{martensite)}}}{}$$

The resulting ferrite and carbide microstructure is not lamellar like that of pearlite (Fig. 9–28), but contains many dispersed carbide particles because there are
numerous nucleation sites within the martensitic steel. This *tempered martensite**
is softer and much tougher than the metastable martensite.

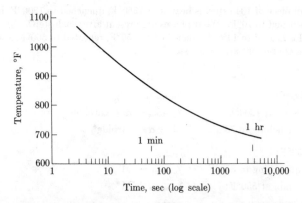

FIG. 10–28. Temperature versus tempering time. Time is required to
soften martensite ($R_C = 65$) to tempered martensite ($R_C = 50$) in a
1080 steel. Typically, less time is required at higher temperatures.

The extent of these property changes depends on the size of the resulting carbide particles in the ferrite matrix, and therefore the mechanical properties can
be controlled and adjusted by means of the tempering process (Section 11–9).

As with most reactions, the time required for softening decreases as the tempering temperature is increased. Figure 10–28 indicates the time required for the

---

* Note that tempered martensite does not have the crystal structure of martensite.
Rather, it is a two-phase microstructure, $\alpha +$ carbide.

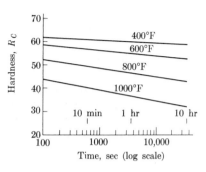

FIG. 10–29. Hardness versus tempering time (1080 steel quenched to maximum hardness). The softening arises from the transformation of martensite to α + carbide (tempered martensite). See Fig. 11–2.

hard martensite ($R_C = 65$) in a 1080 steel to be tempered to $R_C = 50$. Conversely, Fig. 10–29 shows the progress of this softening with time for the same steel.

Since the M $\rightarrow$ α + carbide transformation requires nucleation, diffusion, and grain growth, it has rate-versus-temperature relationships similar to those described in Fig. 10–6 and Eqs. (10–5) and (10–6).

Example 10–3

(a) A small piece of 1045 steel is heated to 1550°F, quenched to 1200°F, held for 5 sec, and then quenched to 70°F. What phases are present after each step? (b) A small piece of 1080 steel is heated to 1450°F, quenched to 350°F, reheated to 550°F, and held 1 min. What phases are present after each step?

Answer:

(a) At 1550°F: γ_{stable}

    After 5 sec at 1200°F: $\gamma_{unstable} + \alpha$ + carbide

    After quenching to 70°F: M + α + carbide*

(b) At 1450°F: γ_{stable}

    After quenching to 350°F: $\gamma_{unstable} + M$

    After 1 min at 550°F: $\gamma_{unstable} + M^*$

[*Note:* With additional time at 550°F, both γ and M will transform to α + carbide.]

References for Further Reading

10–1. BIRCHENALL, C. E., *Physical Metallurgy*. New York: McGraw-Hill, 1959. Chapters 11–13 discuss reactions in solids more thoroughly than does this text. Advanced undergraduate level.

10–2. CHALMERS, B., *Physical Metallurgy*. New York: John Wiley & Sons, 1959. Chapter 8 provides a thorough discussion of solid-state transformations. Advanced undergraduate level.

---

* The reactions of Eq. (10–9) and Fig. 10–22 are *not* reversible below the eutectoid temperature.

10-3. KINGERY, W. D., *Introduction to Ceramics.* New York: John Wiley & Sons, 1960. Chapter 10 presents nucleation, crystal growth, and solid-state reactions as they apply to ceramics. Advanced undergraduate level.

10-4. MASON, C. W., *Introductory Physical Metallurgy.* Cleveland: American Society for Metals, 1947. Chapter 7 uses iron and steel to illustrate phase changes and resulting microstructures.

10-5. NORTON, F. H., *Elements of Ceramics.* Reading, Mass.: Addison-Wesley, 1952. Chapter 13 has sections on solid reaction rates and solid-state reactions in the firing of ceramic ware. Chapter 14 presents properties of typical ceramic materials. Chapter 15 discusses thermochemical changes.

10-6. ROGERS, B. A., *The Nature of Metals.* Ames, Iowa: Iowa State University Press, and Cleveland: American Society for Metals, 1951. Chapter 9 discusses the hardening of steel, particularly with respect to cooling rates. Introductory level.

10-7. SCHMIDT, A. X. and C. A. MARLIES, *Principles of High Polymer Theory and Practice.* New York: McGraw-Hill, 1948. Sections 226-230 discuss factors controlling equilibrium and rate. Activation energy is considered as an energy barrier. Section 804 discusses catalysts, inhibitors, and promotors.

10-8. SMOLUCHOWSKI, R., *et al., Phase Transformation in Solids.* New York: John Wiley & Sons, 1951. For the instructor and interested undergraduate student. Most types of solid phase reactions are presented here.

10-9. WULFF, J., *et al., Structure and Properties of Materials.* Cambridge, Mass.: M.I.T. Press, 1962. Lithoprinted. Chapter 10 of Vol. I presents nonequilibrium phase transformations. Chapter 4 of Vol. II presents rates of reactions as they apply to solids. Introductory, but a more rigorous presentation than in this text.

Problems

10-1. (a) Cite the eutectoid reaction in the Fe-O system (Fig. 9-45). (b) What is the $Fe^{3+}:Fe^{2+}$ ratio in the oxide of eutectoid composition? (c) How much metallic iron is in the two-phase product below the eutectoid temperature?
    Answer: (a) $\epsilon \xrightarrow{\text{cooling}} \alpha + \zeta$ (b) 0.13   (c) 16.0%

10-2. Refer to the Cu-Sn diagram in Chapter 9. Locate and state the reactions (on cooling) for four eutectoid transformations.

10-3. How much $CuAl_2$, or θ, will precipitate from a solution-treated alloy of 95% Al-5% Cu if it is cooled slowly to 400°C?
    Answer: 6%

10-4. The first noticeable crystallization of glass is found in 12 hr at 2000°F and in $2\frac{1}{2}$ days at 1500°F. (a) How long would it take for similar crystallization at 1000°F? (b) At 500°F?

10-5. Austenite is undercooled to 450°F and held at that temperature for 100 sec before transformation can be detected. At 800°F, the time required for the start of transformation is 1 sec. Calculate the time required for transformation at 675°F. [*Note:* 800°F is below the "knee" of the isothermal-transformation curve for the transformation of austenite to ferrite and carbide.]
    Answer: 4 sec

10–6. The following data are applicable for the average times and temperature for a certain solid-transformation reaction $(A \rightarrow B)$. What temperature would accomplish the same reaction in 1 sec?

Transformation temperature	Time	Rate
380°C	10 sec	0.1 sec^{-1}
315°C	100 sec	0.01 sec^{-1}

10–7. (a) If Fig. 10–20 shows a 4-lb brick, 8 in. $\times$ 4 in., what is the activation energy necessary for its movement to a lower energy condition? (b) How much energy is released by the "reaction"?
Answer: (a) 0.15 ft-lb   (b) −0.67 ft-lb

10–8. A small piece of 1045 steel is heated to 1550°F, quenched to 1300°F, held at that temperature for 5 sec, and then quenched at 70°F. What phases are present? [*Hint:* Check the method for making isothermal-transformation diagrams.]

10–9. A small piece of 1080 steel is heated to 1450°F, quenched to −70°F, reheated to 600°F, and held 10 sec. What phases are present at the end of this time?
Answer: Martensite (with some possible change to α + carbide)

10–10. A small wire of 1045 steel is subjected to the following treatments as successive steps:

(1) Heated to 1600°F, held there for 1 hr.
(2) Quenched to 500°F, held there 2 sec.
(3) Quenched to 70°F, held there 100 sec.
(4) Reheated to 1000°F, held there 1 hr.
(5) Quenched to 70°F and held.

Describe the phases or structures present *after each step* of this heat-treatment sequence.

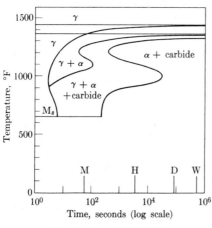

Fig. 10–30. A.I.S.I. 4140.

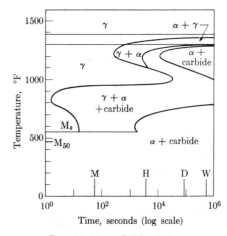

Fig. 10–31. A.I.S.I. 4340.

10–11. (a) Repeat Problem 10–10 with steps (1), (2), (5). (b) Repeat Problem 10–10 with steps (1), (3), (4), (5). (c) Repeat Problem 10–10 with steps (1), (2), (4), (5).

10–12. Sketch an isothermal-transformation diagram for a steel of 1.0 w/o C and 99.0 w/o Fe.

10–13. Sketch an isothermal-transformation diagram for a 1020 steel.

Answer: M_s = 850°F, M_f = 550°F; $\alpha + \gamma$ are stable between 1333 and 1575°F after long times; at 1000°F the curve is further to the left than in 1045 steel.

10–14. A small piece of 4140 steel (Fig. 10–30) is quenched from all austenite to 1200°F, held one hour, and quenched to 1000°F. What phases are present?

10–15. A small piece of 4140 steel (Fig. 10–30) is heated to 1500°F until equilibration, quenched to 700°F, held 10 min, then reheated to 1000°F. What phases are present?

Answer: $\alpha +$ carbide. [*Note:* The reaction does not form γ below the eutectoid temperature.]

10–16. A small piece of 4340 steel (Fig. 10–31) is heated to 1320°F until equilibrium, quenched to 470°F. What phases are present? How much of each? (The eutectoid for 4300 steels contains 0.65% carbon.)

10–17. A 4140 steel (Fig. 10–30) is heated to 1320°F until equilibrated, quenched to 1050°F and held 1 min. What phases are present? How much of each? (See the note of Problem 10–15.)

Answer: 94% α, 6% carbide. [*Note:* The ferrite did not change to austenite.]

10–18. Why are Figs. 10–24 and 10–26(a) not equilibrium diagrams?

10–19. In your own words, explain why the formation of martensite is *not* time-dependent.

10-20. Compare and contrast (a) pearlite, (b) martensite, and (c) tempered martensite.

11

modification of properties
through changes in microstructure

11–1 Introduction. The fact that phases and microstructures in a material can be modified permits the engineer to choose a combination with the properties most suitable for a given application. Recall from Chapter 6 that the microstructures of single-phase metals can be adjusted (1) by plastic deformation, and (2) by recrystallization, which in turn modify the properties. Additional choices of properties are available for single-phase materials through (3) the appropriate selection of solid solution or copolymer compositions, and (4) crystal or molecular orientation.

Multiple-phase materials can have their properties modified and controlled through these same procedures that are available for single-phase materials. Furthermore, there are additional means of control of microstructures in materials with more than one phase present: (1) The *relative amounts of the phases* may be varied. (2) The *size of the phase grains* within the microstructure may be varied. (3) The *shape and distribution of the phases* can be modified. Each of these three microstructural variations provides means of modifying the properties of materials. The resulting microstructures, their relationship to properties, and procedures of control will be the subject of this chapter. Considerable attention will be given to steels, since they are widely used, have been thoroughly analyzed, and provide a suitable prototype for other microstructures.

11–2 Multiphase microstructures. Specific attention has already been given to pearlite as a multiphase microstructure (Fig. 9–28). In this example the microstructure contained a *mixture* of ferrite and carbide, which was lamellar in shape and distribution because growth proceeded inward from the boundaries of the former austenite grains (Fig. 10–2a). However, all microstructures which contain ferrite and carbide are not the same. This is observed in Fig. 11–1(a), where the ferrite is present in two generations. The initial ferrite formed before the austenite of eutectoid composition changed to pearlite. Hence it is sometimes called *proeutectoid ferrite*, in contrast to the ferrite within the pearlite, which is called *eutectoid ferrite*. (See Example 9–10.)

A second microstructural modification involves the thicknesses of the ferrite and carbide lamellae in pearlite. The diffusion shown in Fig. 10–3 can proceed over greater distances as the transformation temperature is increased or the cooling rate decreased. Therefore, these factors will produce thicker lamellae in the pearlite than when transformation must occur at lower temperatures. The effect of this variable on properties will be discussed later in this chapter.

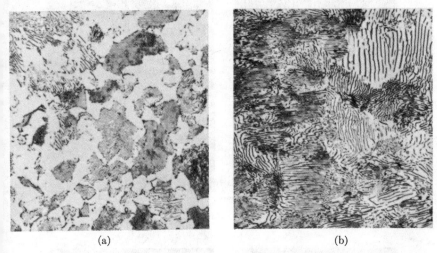

(a)   (b)

Fig. 11–1. Microstructure of pearlitic steels, ×500. (a) 0.40% carbon. (b) 0.80% carbon. The larger white ferrite areas of the 0.40% carbon steel formed before the eutectoid reaction produced the lamellar ferrite in the pearlite (gray). The 0.80% carbon steel contains only eutectoid ferrite. (Compare with Figs. 9–26 and 9–28.) (J. R. Vilella, United States Steel Corp.)

Microstructures of ferrite and carbide are not always lamellar. Tempered martensite (Fig. 11–2) has a dispersion of carbide particles within a matrix of ferrite. Such a dispersion originates because the microstructure of the parent martensite (Fig. 10–23) provided many nucleating sites on which transformation could start. It is important to note that increased temperatures permit a growth of the carbide particles, with an accompanying decrease in hardness. This growth, which does not alter the relative amounts of the ferrite and carbide phases, occurs through a precipitation of the carbon that is in the ferrite onto the larger carbide particles, and an accompanying solution of the smaller carbide particles into the ferrite.

Other materials besides steel have related microstructures; for example, certain aluminum alloys contain a dispersion of small $CuAl_2$ particles with a soft aluminum matrix. In gray cast iron, graphite is present as flakes within a ferrite-plus-carbide matrix. Likewise, the microstructures of nonmetallic materials range from plastics, with glass-fiber reinforcement, and rubber, containing colloidal carbon, to clays which have been plasticized by interparticle water.

Pores are a very important microstructural feature in many materials and may be considered as a phase of zero composition. In electrical and magnetic ceramics, they are undesirable and are to be avoided. However, they are necessary in other materials, such as thermal insulations and powdered metal bearings. Even when they are desired, their amount, size, shape, and distribution must be controlled if the material is to have optimum properties.

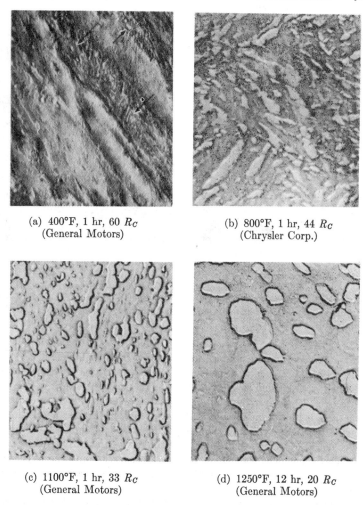

(a) 400°F, 1 hr, 60 R_C
(General Motors)

(b) 800°F, 1 hr, 44 R_C
(Chrysler Corp.)

(c) 1100°F, 1 hr, 33 R_C
(General Motors)

(d) 1250°F, 12 hr, 20 R_C
(General Motors)

Fig. 11–2. Electron micrographs of tempered martensite (×11,000). Each of these is eutectoid steel which was previously quenched to maximum hardness (R_c 65). (*Electron Microstructure of Steel.* Philadelphia, American Society for Testing and Materials, 1950.)

PROPERTIES VERSUS MICROSTRUCTURES

11–3 Additive properties of microstructures. Two phases never have completely identical properties because, as we have seen, each is structurally different. This generalization also applies to the properties of multiphase materials. Certain of these properties are additive and may be determined by suitably weighted averages of the properties of each of the individual phases. Other properties are

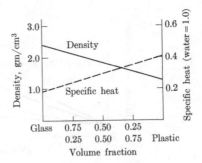

FIG. 11–3. Additive properties of two-phase mixtures of plastic–glass fiber composites. Equation (11–1) applies.

interactive, because the behavior of each phase depends on the nature of the adjacent phase.

The density of a multiphase microstructure may be calculated directly from the density ρ of each phase and the corresponding volume fraction f:

$$\rho_{\text{material}} = f_1\rho_1 + f_2\rho_2 + f_3\rho_3 + \cdots. \tag{11–1}$$

With only two phases present, the density varies linearly with the fraction which is present (Fig. 11–3). When there is pore space, the $f\rho$ product is zero because the phase has no density.

The specific heat of a multiphase microstructure has a similar additive relationship which is also proportional to the volume fraction. The averages of both these properties, density and specific heat, depend on volume because the contribution of one phase does not affect the contribution of the adjacent phase. Likewise, neither property is influenced by the size of the grains in the phase mixture.

The thermal and electrical conductivities of multiphase microstructures are also additive. However, a more complex weighting procedure is necessary because the shape and distribution of each phase is important. The three simplified examples which may be cited are shown in Fig. 11–4; although these examples apply equally to either thermal or electrical conductivity, thermal conductivity notations will be incorporated into the following equations. *Parallel conduction* ap-

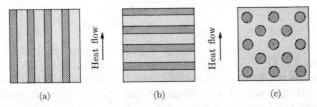

FIG. 11–4. Conductivity versus phase distribution (idealized). (a) Parallel conductivity [Eq. (11–2)]. (b) Series conductivity [Eq. (11–4)]. (c) Conductivity through a material with a dispersed phase [Eq. (11–5)].

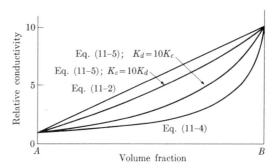

FIG. 11–5.   Conductivity versus volume fraction.   (Adapted from Kingery, W. D., *Introduction to Ceramics.* New York: John Wiley & Sons, 1960, page 502.)

plies in the first case; therefore,

$$k_m = f_1 k_1 + f_2 k_2 + \cdots, \qquad (11\text{–}2)$$

and the average conductivity for the material k_m is a summation of the volume (or cross-sectional area) contribution of all phases. *Series conduction* applies in Fig. 11–4(b); therefore

$$\frac{1}{k_m} = \frac{f_A}{k_A} + \frac{f_B}{k_B} + \cdots, \qquad (11\text{–}3)$$

or, for a two-phase microstructure,

$$k_m = \frac{k_A k_B}{f_A k_B + f_B k_A}. \qquad (11\text{–}4)$$

In this case the conductivity of the material is less than that obtained by a linear interpolation from the phase volumes (Fig. 11–5).

If one phase is dispersed in another, as is common, a still more complicated interpolation results:

$$k_m = k_c \frac{1 + 2f_d \dfrac{1 - k_c/k_d}{2k_c/k_d + 1}}{1 - f_d \dfrac{1 - k_c/k_d}{2k_c/k_d + 1}}. \qquad (11\text{–}5)$$

In this equation the subscript c refers to the continuous phase and d to the dispersed phase. The above equation is plotted for two examples: when the $k_c/k_d = 10$, and when the $k_d/k_c = 10$. The results fall between the two curves defined by Eqs. (11–2) and (11–4). Kingery[*] has studied thermal conductivity in $MgO\text{-}Mg_2SiO_4$ mixtures and finds substantial agreement with Eq. (11–5). How-

---

[*] See the reference for Fig. 11–5.

ever, cognizance had to be taken of the fact that the continuous and dispersed phases were interchanged as the volume fraction of either phase increased from zero to 100 percent. Therefore, his experimental curve switches from one dispersion curve of Fig. 11–5 to the other.

Example 11–1

Fifty w/o SiO_2 flour (i.e., SiO_2 powder) is added to a phenol-formaldehyde resin as a filler. (a) What is the density of the mixture? (b) What is the thermal conductivity?

Answer: From Appendix E:

$$\rho_{SiO_2} = 2.65 \text{ gm/cm}^3, \qquad \rho_{pf} = 1.3 \text{ gm/cm}^3,$$

$$k_{SiO_2} = 0.03 \text{ cal·cm/}^\circ\text{C·cm}^2\text{·sec,}$$

$$k_{pf} = 0.0004 \text{ cal·cm/}^\circ\text{C·cm}^2\text{·sec.}$$

(Basis: 100 gm.)

(a)
$$\begin{array}{llll}
50 \text{ gm} & SiO_2 = 18.8 \text{ cm}^3 & SiO_2; & f_{SiO_2} = 0.33 \\
50 \text{ gm} & pf \; = 38.4 \text{ cm}^3 & pf; & f_{pf} \; = 0.67 \\
\cline{2-2}\cline{4-4}
& 57.2 & & \phantom{f_{pf} \;=} 1.0
\end{array}$$

By Eq. (11–1),

$$\rho_m = (0.33)(2.65) + (0.67)(1.3) = 1.75 \text{ gm/cm}^3.$$

(b) By Eq. (11–5),

$$k_m = 0.0004 \; \frac{1 + 2(0.33) \dfrac{1 - 0.0004/0.03}{2(0.0004/0.03) + 1}}{1 - (0.33) \dfrac{1 - 0.0004/0.03}{2(0.0004/0.03) + 1}}$$

$$= 0.0009 \; \frac{\text{cal·cm}}{^\circ\text{C·cm}^2\text{·sec}} \cdot$$

(b) Alternate: Since

$$k_{pf} \ll k_{SiO_2}, \qquad k_m \cong k_c \left(\frac{1 + 2f_d}{1 - f_d} \right),$$

$$k_m \cong 0.0004 \left[\frac{1 + 2(0.33)}{1 - 0.33} \right] = 0.001 \; \frac{\text{cal·cm}}{^\circ\text{C·cm}^2\text{·sec}} \cdot$$

11–4 Interactive properties. Properties such as hardness and strength cannot be interpolated between the properties of the contributing phases because the behavior of each phase depends on the nature of the adjacent phase. For example, a finely dispersed, less ductile particle of a rigid phase inhibits slip and prevents shear of a ductile matrix.

This interdependence of the mechanical properties of phases makes it possible to strengthen materials by the addition of "fillers." For example, the addition of carbon to rubber, of sand to clay, of sand to tar or asphalt, or of wood flour to plastics increases their resistance to deformation or flow. The effect on strength

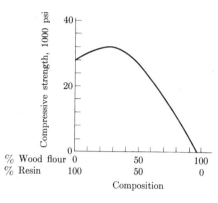

FIG. 11–6. Strength of mixtures (wood flour filler in phenol-formaldehyde resin). The mixture of wood flour and resin is stronger than either alone. The wood flour prevents slip in the resin; the resin bonds the particles of wood flour.

in the latter example is shown graphically in Fig. 11–6. Although a phenol-formaldehyde resin has considerable strength alone, it is subject to eventual shear failure under stress, and the incorporation of a second phase produces added resistance to deformation. At the other end of the composition range, the strength of wood flour alone is nil; there are no forces which hold the individual particles of cellulose into a coherent mass. The addition of the resin to the fine particles serves to cement the wood flour together. Maximum strength is developed with intermediate compositions, with the two phases strengthening each other.

Highway construction is another example of the use of phase mixtures. For obvious reasons, roadbeds composed solely of clay would be unsatisfactory, as would those made completely of gravel or sand. However, an appropriate combination of clay and gravel produces a practical, stabilized roadbed (Fig. 11–7). The clay is strengthened by the hard gravel, and the gravel is bound by the clay into a coherent mass that resists concentrated loads.

Mixtures of ferrite and carbide in steel are less obvious but equally common. Carbide is harder than the accompanying ferrite, and so it increases the resistance of steel to deformation. Figure 11–8 shows graphically the *hardnesses* of carbon steels which have been annealed (i.e., cooled slowly from austenitic temperatures to ensure coarse pearlite). The microstructures are shown in Fig. 11–1. The 0.40% carbon steel contains approximately 50% pearlite (6% carbide); the 0.80%

FIG. 11–7. Stabilized roadbed. The mixture of gravel and clay is more durable than either gravel or clay alone.

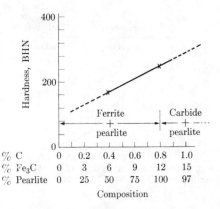

FIG. 11–8. Hardness versus carbon content of annealed steels. The steels contain mixtures of coarse pearlite and ferrite. The hardness depends on the amount of carbide. (Adapted from E. C. Bain, *Alloying Elements in Steel*. Cleveland: American Society for Metals, 1939.)

carbon steel is all·pearlite (12% carbide). Slip occurs more readily in the former than in the latter.

In addition to being harder, steels with higher carbon contents are stronger. Both the *yield strength* and the *tensile strength* are shown in Fig. 11–9. Note, however, that the curves in this figure cannot be extrapolated to very high values at 100% iron carbide. Because iron carbide is very weak by itself, since it is lacking in ductility and cannot adjust to stress concentrations, an extension of Fig. 11–9 to 100% iron carbide will show the curves dropping to approximately 5000 psi.

Figure 11–10 shows the effect of iron carbide on *ductility*. As expected, ductility decreases with increased carbon content. Therefore for automobile fenders the manufacturer chooses a very low-carbon steel that can be rolled into a thin sheet and deep-drawn to take the sharp curvatures required for styling. By contrast, the dies and shears used in forming and cutting these fenders are made of high-carbon steels which may be made hard and strong.

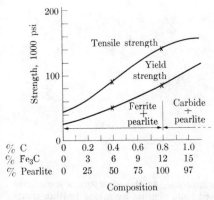

FIG. 11–9. Strength versus carbon content of annealed steels. (Cf. Fig. 11–1.)

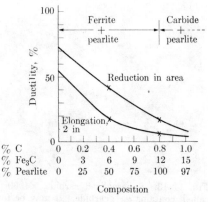

FIG. 11–10. Ductility versus carbon content of annealed steels. (Cf. Fig. 11–1.)

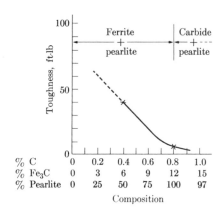

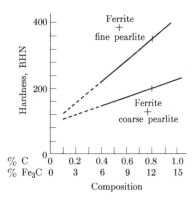

FIG. 11-11. Toughness versus carbon content of annealed steels. (Cf. Fig. 11-1.)

FIG. 11-12. Effect of particle size on hardness of steel. The harder, finer pearlite was formed by faster cooling.

The *toughness* of a steel is also important if the engineer is designing or using equipment which is subject to impact, since a brittle (opposite of tough) steel will break under comparatively light blows. Fractures are more readily propagated in high-carbon steels because there are more carbide paths through which cracks may progress (Fig. 11-11).

Effects of phase size on mechanical properties. The coarseness of the microstructure of a material directly affects its mechanical properties. The addition of very fine sand to asphalt will produce a more viscous mixture than will the addition of an equal weight (or volume) percent of gravel. Similarly, steel with a very finely mixed microstructure of ferrite and carbide will be much harder and stronger than will steel of the same carbon content but with a much coarser microstructure.

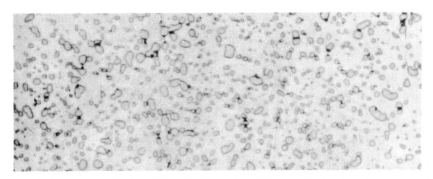

FIG. 11-13. Spheroidized carbide, ×1000. *Spheroidite*, as this structure is sometimes called, contains α + carbide. It may be formed from pearlite by a long heating treatment. There is less interfacial surface in this structure than in pearlite. Spheroidite may also be formed by tempering martensite [Fig. 11-2(d)]. (J. R. Vilella, U. S. Steel Corp.)

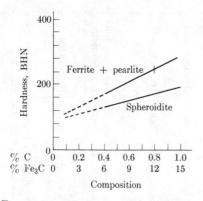

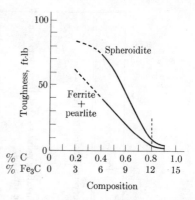

FIG. 11-14. Effect of particle shape on hardness. The spheroidite (Fig. 11-13) provides less resistance to slip than does the lamellar pearlite (Fig. 9-28).

FIG. 11-15. Effect of particle shape on toughness. In spheroidite, cracks cannot travel very far in the brittle carbide without encountering tougher ferrite. (Cf. Figs. 11-13 and 9-28.)

A comparison is made in Fig. 11-12. The lower set of data describes a steel which was cooled slowly to produce a coarse pearlite structure; the upper set is for a steel that was cooled more rapidly, to form a much finer pearlite.

The same variation in properties is observable in martensitic steels tempered at different temperatures. Initial tempering produces a very fine mixture of carbide particles in a ferrite matrix (Fig. 11-2a). Figures 11-2(b), (c), and (d) show samples tempered at higher temperatures, which permits the carbide particles to grow. The hardness values in the legend indicate the degree of softening. When the harder particles are agglomerated, there are larger areas of the soft ferrite matrix in which slip can occur without restriction.

Effects of phase shape and distribution on mechanical properties. The shape and distribution of microstructure phases also affect the properties of a material. For example, in pearlite the carbide is lamellar. However, if the pearlitic steel were held just under the eutectoid temperature for a long period of time, the carbide would *spheroidize** and develop the structure shown in Fig. 11-13. The effect of spheroidization on hardness is shown in Fig. 11-14; the hardness decreases because the spheroidized structure reinforces the metal less. The shape of the phases also rather markedly affects the toughness of the mixture (Fig. 11-15). A spheroidized structure is tougher because cracks in the carbide cannot propagate very far before entering tough ferrite.

---

* The boundary area between two phases (or grains) is a site of higher energy than the lattice itself because the boundary atoms are not as closely aligned as the atoms within a crystal (Fig. 4-15 and Section 4-9). Since the boundary atoms have higher energy, the boundaries will be spontaneously eliminated if the atomic mobility is sufficient. Boundary area may be reduced by grain growth (Fig. 11-2) or by spheroidization (Fig. 11-13). High temperatures will facilitate either of these reactions.

TABLE 11-1

COMMON HEAT-TREATING PROCESSES

Process	Example	Purpose	Procedure
Annealing	Cold-worked metals (Section 6–8)	To remove strain hardening and increase ductility	Heat above recrystallization temperature.
Annealing	Glass	To relieve residual strains	Heat above annealing point so that the atoms can adjust to the stresses.
Annealing	Steel (Section 11–6)	To soften	Heat 50°F above final ferrite stability and slow (furnace) cool.
Normalizing	Steel (Section 11–6)	Homogenization and strain relief	Heat to 100°F into the fully austenitic range, and air cool.
Process annealing	Low-carbon steel (Section 11–6)	To remove strain hardening and increase ductility	Heat briefly close to, but below, the eutectoid temperature.
Spheroidizing	High-carbon steel (Section 11–6)	To soften and toughen	Heat for a sufficiently long time close to, but below, the eutectoid temperature to spheroidize the carbides.
Quenching	Steel (Section 11–9)	To harden	Quench from austenite to martensite. (This is followed by tempering.)
Tempering	Quenched steel (Section 10–11)	To toughen	Quench. Heat briefly, or at low temperatures, to start the $M \rightarrow \alpha + $ carbide reaction.

Process	Material	Purpose	Description
Tempering	Glass (Section 8–11)	To strengthen	Heat above strain point. Quench in oil to place surface under compression.
Austempering	Steel (Section 11–8)	To harden without developing brittle martensite	Quench from austenite to a temperature below the "knee" of the transformation curve, but above the martensite transformation temperature. Hold until bainite formation is complete.
Marquenching (interrupted quench or martempering)	Steel (Section 11–9)	To harden without quench cracking	Quench from austenite to a temperature below the "knee" of the transformation curve, but above the martensite transformation temperature. Hold until temperature has equalized. Cool slowly to martensite. (This is followed by tempering.)
Solution treating	Stainless steel (Section 10–4)	To produce a single-phase alloy	Heat above the solubility curve into a single-phase area and quench to room temperature.
Age-hardening (precipitation hardening)	Aluminum alloys (Section 11–7)	To harden	Solution treat. Cool fast to provide supersaturation. Reheat to an intermediate temperature until the initial precipitation *starts*. Cool to surrounding temperatures.
Malleabilizing	Malleable cast iron (Section 11–11)	To increase ductility in a casting	Form white cast iron with quick solidification. Reheat to dissociate carbides.
Firing (vitreous sintering)	Brick (Section 13–6)	Agglomeration	Heat above the initial eutectic to form a glassy bond.
Solid sintering	Powdered metals (Section 13–6)	Agglomeration	Heat close to, but below, the melting temperature so that solid diffusion can consolidate the material into an integrated mass.

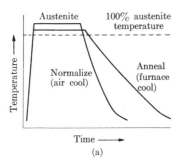 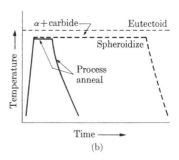

FIG. 11–16. Softening and toughening processes. (a) Annealing and normalizing, and (b) process annealing and spheroidizing. (Example: eutectoid steel.)

CONTROL OF MICROSTRUCTURES

11–5 Introduction. The most common method of altering microstructures is by various *heat treatments*, each designed to produce a particular phase relationship. The more common treatments for metallic materials are summarized in Table 11–1 (pages 308–309). Although heat treatments are less highly developed for non-metallic materials, they are receiving increasing industrial attention.

11–6 Annealing processes. The term *annealing* is used to denote either a softening or a toughening process. In Section 6–8, the word *annealing* was used to indicate the softening which accompanies recrystallization of strain-hardened metals. The glass technologist uses *annealing* to denote a heat treatment for removing residual stresses to reduce the probability of crack development in brittle glass. The word *annealing* has a specific connotation when it describes a heat treatment for steel, which involves heating the steel into the austenitic range and subsequently cooling it slowly (Fig. 11–16a). This process produces a very soft microstructure because the slow cooling process permits the formation of a *coarse pearlite* (Fig. 11–12).

Process annealing. It is often desirable to relieve stresses in steels which have been cold-drawn (e.g., wire products), without forming austenite. This process, called *process annealing*, involves heating the steel to temperatures just under the eutectoid (Fig. 11–16b). If the sole purpose is to relieve stresses, only a short heating period is necessary.

Spheroidizing. This annealing heat treatment is used to achieve maximum ductility in steels or in any two-phase metal. It may be accomplished in one of two ways, each of which is in reality an extended process-annealing operation carried out over a sufficient length of time to permit agglomerization of the carbides into large spherical particles (Fig. 11–13). If the carbide within the pearlite is to be spheroidized, a considerable length of heating time is required. Ordinarily, some 12 to 15 hours are necessary, at temperatures close to the eutectoid. On the other hand, tempered martensite requires only an hour or two for spheroidization and growth, depending on the temperature.

Normalizing. The simplest annealing heat-treatment process consists of heating the steel to form austenite and then removing it from the furnace and letting it cool in the air. This process, called *normalizing*, is similar to full annealing, except that normalized metal cools much faster (Fig. 11–16a) and is finer in microstructure than annealed metals. The cooling rate depends on the size of the steel part being treated. A large piece, of course, cools more slowly because a larger quantity of heat must be removed per unit of surface area. This process is used to homogenize steel in the austenite temperature range.

11–7 Age-hardening processes. A very noticeable increase in hardness may develop during the *initial stages of precipitation* from a supersaturated solid solution [Section 10–4 and Eq. (10–4)]. In fact, the start of the precipitation in Example 10–1 was detected by this increased hardness. This hardening is commonly called *age-hardening* because it develops with time. (It is also called *precipitation hardening*.) The prime requirement for an alloy which is to be age-hardened is that solubility decreases with decreasing temperature so that a supersaturated solid solution may be obtained. Numerous metal alloys have this characteristic.

The process of age-hardening involves a *solution treatment* [Eq. (10–3)] followed by a quench to supersaturate the solid solution. Usually the quenching is carried to a temperature where the precipitation rate is exceedingly slow. After the quench, the alloy is reheated to an intermediate temperature at which precipitation is initiated in a reasonable length of time. These are steps XA and AB in Fig. 11–17.

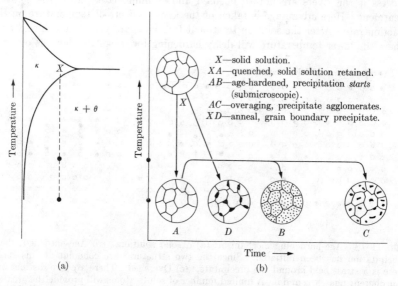

X—solid solution.
XA—quenched, solid solution retained.
AB—age-hardened, precipitation *starts* (submicroscopic).
AC—overaging, precipitate agglomerates.
XD—anneal, grain boundary precipitate.

Fig. 11–17.   Age-hardening process (95.5% Al-4.5% Cu alloy). See Table 11–2. The precipitate is still submicroscopic at the time of maximum hardness.

TABLE 11-2

PROPERTIES OF AN AGE-HARDENABLE ALLOY
(95.5% Al-4.5% Cu)

Treatment (See Fig. 11–17)		Tensile strength, psi	Yield strength, psi	Ductility, % in 2 in.
A	Solution-treated and quenched	35,000	15,000	40
B	Age-hardened	60,000	45,000	20
C	Overaged	~25,000	~10,000	~20
D	Annealed	25,000	10,000	15

An interesting example of the utility of the age-hardening process is the way it is used in airplane construction. Aluminum rivets are easier to drive and fit more tightly if they are soft and ductile, but in this condition they lack the desired strength. Therefore the manufacturer selects an aluminum alloy which can be quenched as a supersaturated solution, but which will age-harden at room temperature. The rivets are used while they are still soft and ductile, and they harden after they have been riveted in place. Since hardening sets in fairly rapidly at room temperature, there arises the practical problem of delaying the hardening process if the rivets are not to be used almost immediately after the solution treatment. Here advantage is taken of the known effects of temperature on the reaction rate. After the solution treatment the rivets are stored in a refrigerator, where the lower temperature will delay hardening for reasonable lengths of time.

● Solute atom   o Solvent atom

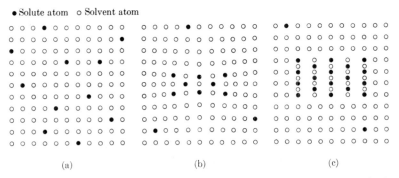

(a)   (b)   (c)

FIG. 11–18. Age-hardening mechanism: (a) α solid solution. (b) Age-hardened; the β precipitation has been initiated. Since the two structures are coherent at this stage, there is a stress field around the precipitate. (c) Overaged. There are two distinct and noncoherent phases, α and β. A limited number of solute atoms will provide the greatest interference to dislocation movements in (b). (Guy, A. G., *Elements of Physical Metallurgy.* Reading, Mass.: Addison-Wesley, 1959, page 448.)

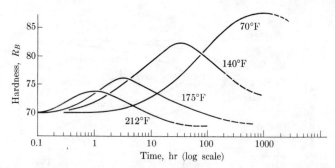

Fig. 11–19. Overaging. The precipitates are carbides and nitrides (note R_B scale). (Adapted from Davenport and Bain, "The Aging of Steel." *Trans. A. S. M.*, **23**, 1061, 1935.)

Detailed studies have produced the following interpretation of the age-hardening phenomenon. The supersaturated atoms (Cu atoms in Example 10–1 and Fig. 11–17) tend to accumulate along specific crystal planes in the manner indicated in Fig. 11–18(b). The concentration of the copper (solute) atoms in these positions lowers the concentrations in other locations, producing less supersaturation and therefore a more stable crystal structure. At this stage, the copper atoms have not formed a phase which is wholly distinct; a *coherency* of atom spacing exists across the boundary of the two structures. Dislocation movements occur with difficulty across these distorted regions, and consequently the metal becomes harder and more resistant to deformation under high stresses.

Overaging. A continuation of the local segregation process over long periods of time leads to true precipitation and *overaging*, or softening. For example, the development of a truly stable structure in an alloy of 96% aluminum and 4% copper involves an almost complete separation of the copper from the fcc aluminum at room temperature. Nearly all the copper forms $CuAl_2$ (θ in Fig. 11–17a). Because the growth of the second phase provides larger areas which have practically no means of slip resistance, a marked softening occurs.

Figure 11–19 shows data for the aging and overaging of a low-carbon, nitrogen-bearing steel. All the nitrogen present can be dissolved in the steel at 1200°F; however, the solubility of nitrogen in ferrite drops to nearly zero at lower temperatures, so that precipitation is started. The initial hardening is followed by softening as the resulting precipitate is agglomerated. Two effects of the aging temperature may be observed: (1) precipitation, and therefore hardening, starts more rapidly at higher temperatures; (2) overaging, and therefore softening, occurs more rapidly at higher temperatures. These two phenomena overlap to affect the maximum hardness that is attained. Lower temperatures permit greater increases in hardness, but longer times are required.

Combined hardening. Occasionally it is desirable to combine two methods of hardening. The cold-working of an alloy which has previously been age-hardened increases the hardness still further. However, there are some practical difficulties

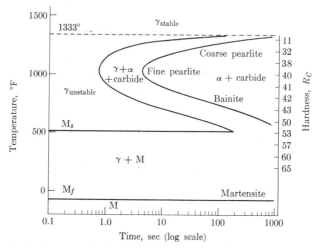

FIG. 11–20.   Isothermal transformation temperature versus hardness (eutectoid steel).   High transformation temperatures permit coarser microstructures and therefore softer steels.

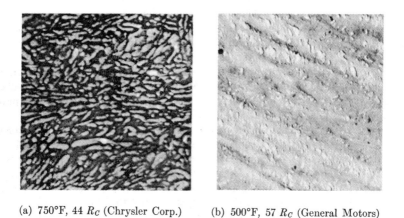

(a) 750°F, 44 R_C (Chrysler Corp.)   (b) 500°F, 57 R_C (General Motors)

FIG. 11–21.   Electron micrographs of bainite (×11,000).   Each of these is a eutectoid steel which has undergone isothermal transformation.   Compare with Fig. 11–2.   (*Electron Microstructure of Steel*.   Philadelphia: American Society for Testing and Materials, 1950.)

TABLE 11–3

TENSILE STRENGTHS OF A STRAIN- AND AGE-HARDENED
ALLOY (98% Cu-2% Be)

Annealed (1600°F)	35,000 psi
Solution-treated (1600°F) and cooled fast	72,000
Age-hardened only	175,000
Cold-worked only (37%)	107,000
Age-hardened, then cold-worked	200,000 (cracked)
Cold-worked, then age-hardened	195,000

encountered in this process. Age-hardening increases resistance to slip and therefore increases the energy required for cold-working, and it also decreases ductility
so that rupture occurs more readily during cold-working. A possible alternative
is to cold-work prior to the precipitation-hardening treatment. The metal is then
cold-worked more readily and the age-hardening reaction occurs at a lower temperature because the slip planes serve as nuclei for the precipitation. However,
the temperature of the aging process which follows cold-working may relieve some
of the strain hardening and cause a slight loss in hardness. Although it does not
produce hardnesses as great as those obtained from the reverse order, the final
hardness is greater than that developed by using either method alone (Table 11–3).

11–8 Isothermal transformation processes.   If the samples used as examples
in Section 10–7 were tested, there would be a definite correlation between hardness, on the one hand, and the temperature of transformation on the other. This
correlation is presented graphically as the right ordinate in Fig. 11–20. Such
isothermal transformations at high temperatures produce coarse pearlitic structures;
therefore the properties are nearly identical with those produced by annealing.
Isothermal transformation at lower temperatures produces finer pearlite because
there is less thermal movement to assist diffusion of the carbon from the areas
forming ferrite to the areas forming carbide.

   Bainite.   If transformation occurs isothermally at a temperature below the
"knee" of the isothermal transformation curve, the resulting microstructure is
not pearlite. Instead of developing a lamellar structure, the carbide is finely dispersed in a ferrite matrix, forming a microstructure called *bainite* (Fig. 11–21).
Bainite and tempered martensite (Fig. 11–2) have rather similar structures, and
their properties are similar. The microstructure and properties of both vary with
the temperature of transformation. High temperatures produce larger carbides
and therefore softer, more ductile steels.

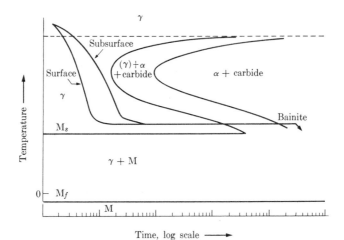

FIG. 11–22. Austempering. This heat treatment isothermally transforms austenite to bainite (α + carbide). The properties of bainite are nearly identical with those of tempered martensite.

The production of bainite has been developed into a commercial process called *austempering*. Figure 11–22 shows this process schematically. Cooling, which must be sufficiently rapid to avoid transformation to pearlite, is usually accomplished in a molten lead or a fused-salt bath, maintained just above the M_s temperature. This process has the major advantage of not developing brittle martensite in high-carbon steels; consequently quenching cracks are not so likely to develop from the differential thermal contraction between the surface and the center of the steel. Unfortunately, the isothermal holding times may be rather extended if alloying elements are present.

• *Bainite formation.* The carbide particles within the bainitic microstructure of Fig. 11–21 were nucleated at many locations within the original austenite grain and not primarily at the austenite grain boundaries, as occurs in pearlite formation. Detailed studies have shown that the austenite may also transform to ferrite by a shear displacement of the fcc iron atoms to a bcc arrangement. As this transformation proceeds, it follows specific crystal planes through the original austenite grain, and carbide particles are precipitated at many sites along the transformation path. This means that the isothermal transformation curves of Fig. 11–20 are in reality two sets of curves (Fig. 11–23): one set which indicates the time required for diffusion of the carbon and iron atoms (pearlite formation), and the other set which shows the time required for the combined shear transformation and carbide precipitation (bainite formation). Above 1000°F and in a eutectoid steel, pearlite forms more rapidly than bainite because there is a sufficiently high diffusion rate to permit the movement of carbon over the relatively great distances shown in Fig. 10–3. Below 1000°F, where the shear transformation provides many nucleation sites along various shear planes, the carbon diffusion distances are never very great, and bainite is formed rapidly.

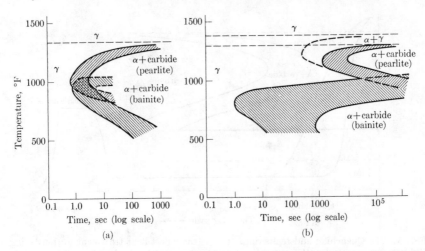

FIG. 11–23. Pearlite and bainite formation: (a) eutectoid steel, (b) 4340 steel. Pearlite forms in less time than bainite above 1000°F, and bainite forms in less time than pearlite below 1000°F.

The two sets of transformation curves are more distinct in a 4340 steel (Fig. 11–23b) than in a 1080 steel because the curves are not tangent to each other. The extra alloying elements of a 4340 steel (1.8% Ni, 0.75% Cr, and 0.25% Mo) reduce the rate of transformation to pearlite more than the rate of transformation to bainite. Undoubtedly this is a reflection of the effect of the alloying elements on the diffusion coefficient of carbon.

11–9 Quenching and tempering processes. The quenching and tempering process may be summarized by the following schematic equation:

$$\gamma \atop \text{(unstable)} \quad \xrightarrow[\text{transformation}]{\text{normal}} \quad \alpha + \text{carbide} \qquad (11\text{–}6)$$

$$\underset{\text{(transition)}}{M}$$

with *quenching* and *tempering* arrows.

In Fig. 11–24, the process of quenching and tempering is diagrammed onto an isothermal transformation curve. The time lag between quenching and tempering may be whatever is compatible with production requirements.

Continuous cooling transformation. The isothermal transformation curve in Fig. 11–24 is appropriate if the cooling is rapid enough to cool both the surface and the center of the steel in less time than is necessary to initiate transformation at the "knee" of the curve. However, in a plain carbon steel the quench can be that rapid only in extremely small-sized pieces. Therefore, in order to take into

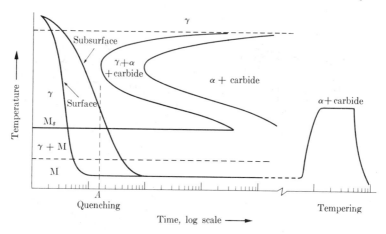

Fig. 11–24. Quenching and tempering. This is the oldest heat treatment for hardening and toughening steel. However, the formation of brittle martensite makes possible cracking of steel in the quenching step.

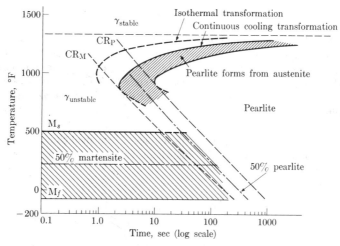

Fig. 11–25. Continuous cooling transformation curve (eutectoid steel). Transformation temperature and times are displaced from the isothermal transformation curve for the same steel. (Cf. Fig. 10–24.) CR_M = minimum cooling rate for 100% martensite. CR_P = maximum cooling rate for 100% pearlite.

account the integrating effect of time *and* temperature on the transformation reaction, it is necessary for us to modify the transformation curve. This is done in Fig. 11–25 for a eutectoid steel, where we note that the *continuous cooling transformation* curve is displaced downward and to the right of the corresponding isothermal transformation curve.

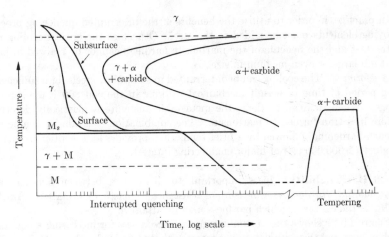

FIG. 11–26. Interrupted quench, or marquenching (schematic). This heat treatment tends to avoid severe stresses in the nonductile martensite because the center and surface transform together. The temperature gradient in the initial quench is not detrimental, inasmuch as the austenite is ductile.

There are two important cooling rates on a continuous cooling transformation curve which are included in Fig. 11–25. The first is the minimum cooling rate which produces *only* martensite; the second is the maximum cooling rate which produces *only* pearlite. At 1300°F these two cooling rates are about 600°F/sec and 200°F/sec, respectively, for a 1080 steel. These critical cooling rates are reduced for steels to which alloying materials have been added. (Again it should be emphasized that alloying elements do not reduce the rate of heat removal during a quench; rather they reduce the critical cooling rates which are required for martensite formation.)

• *Interrupted quench.* Because the temperature drop at the center lags the temperature drop at the surface, the interior steel transforms either to pearlite or to martensite after a brittle martensitic surface has already been developed by the quench. Thus cracks may develop in the surface martensite when the center expands during its transformation (Fig. 12–37). This is particularly true in high-carbon steels that have low toughness (Fig. 11–11), and in parts which have sharp curves or notches that concentrate the resulting stresses.

The danger of cracking may be partially eliminated by a variation of the quenching process, called an *interrupted quench,* or *marquenching.* The temperature changes in this process are shown in Fig. 11–26. As with austempering, the steel is quenched into a bath above the M_s temperature. After the temperature has equalized, the steel is slowly cooled to form martensite. Under these conditions, severe differential cooling stresses are not set up in the brittle martensite. A tempering step must follow the interrupted quench, just as after regular quenching. (The term *martempering* has also been applied to this process. However, the modification comes in the quenching rather than the tempering stage of the process.)

In practice, in order to utilize the benefits of the interrupted quenching process, alloying elements must be added to the steel. Otherwise the critical cooling rate is too fast and the benefits of the martensite hardness cannot be realized in parts that are large or even medium in size.

• *Ausforming.* The cooling can be interrupted in some alloy steels for a sufficiently long period of time to permit mechanical working in the 600–800°F temperature range. When this can be done, the metastable austenite is plastically deformed before it is transformed to martensite. The combination of strain-hardening and quench-hardening, followed by a brief tempering, provides an exceptionally strong product (>300,000 psi) of major engineering interest.

11–10 Hardenability. It is important to distinguish between *hardness* and *hardenability: Hardness* is a measure of resistance to plastic deformation. *Hardenability* is the ease with which hardness may be attained.

Figure 11–27 shows the maximum possible *hardnesses* for increasing amounts of carbon in steels; these maximum hardnesses are obtained only when 100% martensite is formed. A steel that transforms rapidly from austenite to ferrite plus carbide has low *hardenability* because these high-temperature transformation products tend to be formed at the expense of the martensite. Conversely, a steel that is transformed very slowly from austenite to ferrite plus carbide has greater hardenability. Hardnesses nearer the maximum can be developed with less severe quenching in a steel of high hardenability, and greater hardnesses can be developed at the center of a piece of steel even though the cooling rate is slower there.

End-quench test. There is a standardized test, commonly called the *Jominy end-quench test,* to determine the hardenability of steel. In this test, a round bar of a specified size is heated to form austenite and is then end-quenched with a water

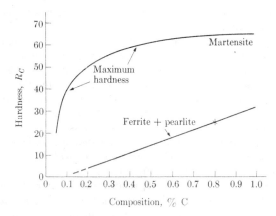

FIG. 11–27. Maximum hardness versus carbon content of plain carbon steels, showing maximum hardnesses arising from martensite compared with hardnesses developed by pearlitic microstructures. To produce maximum hardness, the reaction $\gamma \rightarrow \alpha +$ carbide must be avoided during quenching.

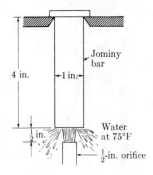

Fig. 11–28. Jominy end-quench test. (A. G. Guy, *Elements of Physical Metallurgy*. Reading, Mass.: Addison-Wesley, 1959.)

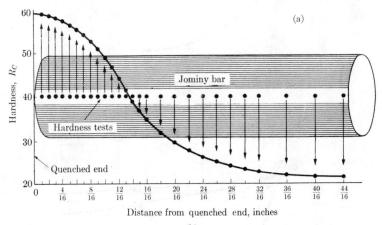

Distance from quenched end, inches

(b)

stream of specified flow rate and pressure, as indicated in Fig. 11–28. Hardness values along the cooling-rate gradient are determined on a Rockwell hardness tester, and a *hardenability curve* is plotted.

The quenched end is cooled very fast and therefore has the maximum possible hardness for the particular carbon content of the specimen. Since the steel behind the quenched surface is cooled at slower rates, its hardness is less than the maximum possible for the particular steel being tested. Figure 11–29 indicates rate of cooling as a function of distance from the quenched end. This curve holds for all *plain carbon* or *low-alloy* steels* for which hardenability data are desired. Since the test is standardized as to temperature, specimen size, procedure, and other variables, the cooling rate at any specific location is almost completely independent of the type of steel.

---

* The properties of steel which would alter the cooling rate are thermal conductivity, specific heat, and density. In *plain carbon* and *low-alloy* steels, these vary so slightly that only very minor differences in cooling rates result. High-alloy, stainless-type steels would be exceptions. However, these steels are seldom quenched for hardness requirements.

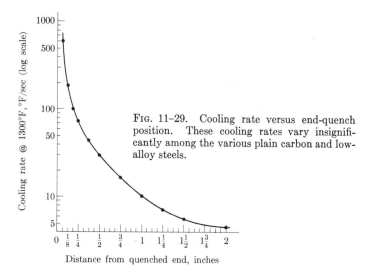

Fig. 11-29.   Cooling rate versus end-quench position.   These cooling rates vary insignificantly among the various plain carbon and low-alloy steels.

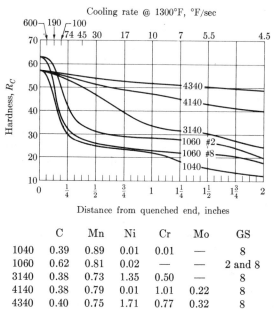

	C	Mn	Ni	Cr	Mo	GS
1040	0.39	0.89	0.01	0.01	—	8
1060	0.62	0.81	0.02	—	—	2 and 8
3140	0.38	0.73	1.35	0.50	—	8
4140	0.38	0.79	0.01	1.01	0.22	8
4340	0.40	0.75	1.71	0.77	0.32	8

Fig. 11-30.   Hardenability curves for six steels with the indicated compositions and austenite grain sizes.   The latitude of normal chemical specifications produces some latitude in the hardenability.   (Adapted from U. S. Steel Corp. data.)

TABLE 11–4

COOLING RATES AT 1300°F IN STEEL BARS
(3-inch diameter)

Position	Agitated water quench, °F/sec	Agitated oil quench, °F/sec
Surface	190	37
$\frac{3}{4}$ radius	45	20
Mid-radius	26	15
$\frac{1}{4}$ radius	22	12
Center	20	10

Hardenability calculations. End-quench hardenability curves are of great practical value because (1) if the cooling rate of a steel in any quench is known, the
hardness may be read directly from the hardenability curve for that steel, and
(2) if the hardness at any point can be measured, the cooling rate at that point
may be obtained from the hardenability curve for that steel.

Figure 11–30 presents the end-quench hardenability curve for an SAE 1040
steel with the grain size and composition indicated.* The quenched end has
maximum hardness for 0.40% carbon steel because the cooling was very rapid
and only martensite was formed. However, close behind the quenched end the
cooling rate was not rapid enough to avoid some ferrite and carbide formation,
and so maximum hardness was not attained at that point. (Compare the maximum hardness shown in Fig. 11–30 with the maximum hardness indicated for this
steel in Fig. 11–27.)

It is also possible to determine the cooling rates within bars of steel. Table 11–4,
for example, shows the cooling rates at eutectoid temperatures for the surfaces,
mid-radii, and centers of three-inch rounds quenched in mildly agitated water and
oil. These cooling rates were determined by thermocouples embedded in the bars
during the quenching operation. Similar data may be obtained for bars of other
diameters. These data are summarized in Fig. 11–31.

By the use of the data of Fig. 11–31 and a hardenability curve, the hardness
which will exist in a steel after quenching may be predicted. For example, the
center of the three-inch round quenched in oil has a cooling rate of 10°F per second.
Since the center of this large round has the same cooling rate as a Jominy test bar
of the same steel at a point one inch from the quenched end, the hardness at the
center of the round will be the same as that at the one-inch point of the Jominy
bar. Thus if the bar is 1040 steel (Fig. 11–30), the center hardness will be 22 R_C.

---

* These data apply to this 1040 composition (and grain size). A slight variation is
possible in the chemical specifications of any steel (e.g., in a 1040 steel, C = 0.37/0.44,
Mn = 0.60/0.90, S = 0.05, P = 0.04, and Si = 0.15/0.25). As a result, two different
1040 steels may have somewhat different hardenability curves.

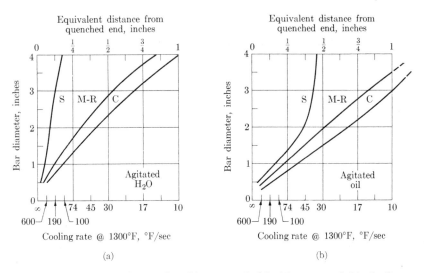

Fig. 11–31. Cooling rates in round steel bars quenched in (a) water, and (b) oil. Bottom abscissa, cooling rates at 1300°F; top abscissa, equivalent positions on an end-quenched test bar. (C, center; M-R, mid-radius; S, surface.)

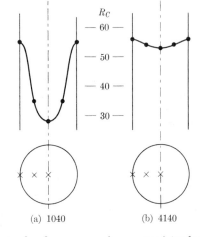

Fig. 11–32. Hardness traverses. See Example 11–2.

Figure 11–30 shows that the following center hardnesses may be expected for bars of the following steels when cooled at 10°F per second:

SAE:	1040	4140	3140	4340	1060 (GS-8)	1060 (GS-2)
R_C:	22	47	34	52	23	29

Example 11–2

Sketch the hardness traverses for two steel rounds quenched in water; each is 1.5 inches in diameter, with SAE 1040 and 4140 compositions, respectively.

Answer:

From Fig. 11–31(a)		From Fig. 11–30		
Position	Approx. cooling rate at 1300°F	Cooling rate at 1300°F	SAE 1040	SAE 4140
Surface	600°F/sec	600°F/sec	55 R_C	56 R_C
Mid-radius	100°F/sec	100°F/sec	35 R_C	54 R_C
Center	65°F/sec	65°F/sec	28 R_C	53 R_C

The hardness traverses for the two steels of Example 11–2 are shown in Fig. 11–32. Although the surface hardnesses of the two are practically identical, the difference in their hardenability produces a higher center hardness for the SAE 4140 steel. As indicated, this steel has a higher alloy content, which slows down the transformation of austenite to ferrite and carbide. Consequently, more martensite may form.

Example 11–3

Figure 11–33 shows the points in the cross section of an irregularly shaped, SAE 3140 steel bar at which the following hardnesses were obtained after oil quenching. What hardness values would be expected for an identically shaped bar of SAE 1060 (GS-8) steel?

Answer:

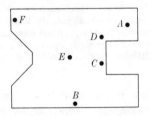

Fig. 11–33. Hardness versus position in a V-bar for two steels.

Point	SAE 3140 From Fig. 11–30		SAE 1060 (GS-8) From Fig. 11–30	
	Hardness	Approx. cooling rate at 1300°F	Cooling rate at 1300°F	Hardness
A	53 R_C	70°F/sec	70°F/sec	32 R_C
B	52 R_C	60°F/sec	60°F/sec	30 R_C
C	51 R_C	45°F/sec	45°F/sec	28 R_C
D	48 R_C	35°F/sec	35°F/sec	27 R_C
E	47 R_C	30°F/sec	30°F/sec	26 R_C
F	56 R_C	600°F/sec	600°F/sec	60 R_C

● 11–11 Graphitization processes. Carbides in iron and steels appear to be quite stable. However, very precise measurements indicate that carbon existing as graphite is more stable in iron and steel than is carbon in the form of carbides. Iron carbide will *dissociate* into iron and graphite if sufficient time, or help, is provided; that is:

$$Fe_3C \rightarrow 3Fe + C_{(gr)}. \tag{11-7}$$

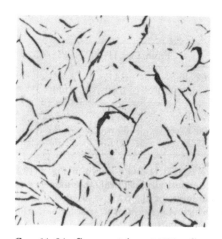

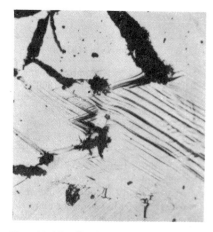

FIG. 11–34. Gray cast iron, ×100. Carbon is present as graphite flakes. The high carbon content permits easy casting, but reduces strength and ductility. (J. E. Rehder, Canada Iron Foundries.)

FIG. 11–35. Crack propagation in gray cast iron, ×350. Stresses are concentrated at the ends of the graphite flakes. (R. A. Flinn and P. K. Trojan, University of Michigan.)

However, in most steels there is no easy way for the carbon in carbide to change to graphite. Therefore, for practical purposes, iron carbide is a metastable phase just like glass (Section 10–5), and will persist almost indefinitely at room temperatures.

Although the dissociation of iron carbide to iron and graphite is usually undetectable, there are methods of accelerating the reaction. For example, higher temperatures permit faster dissociation, and the presence of *silicon* as a positive catalyzer speeds up the reaction considerably. The dissociation reaction can be written as follows:

$$\text{Fe}_3\text{C} \xrightarrow[\text{heat}]{\text{Si}} 3\text{Fe} + \text{C}_{(\text{gr})}. \tag{11–8}$$

Almost all cast irons contain some silicon. With less than 1% silicon present, the solidification of the casting is usually fast enough so that the Fe_3C dissociation reaction does not have time to occur. Larger amounts of silicon make it progressively easier for the dissociation to proceed.

Gray cast iron. The majority of cast irons have sufficient silicon (more than $1\frac{1}{2}\%$) so that graphite forms during the solidification process. The graphite gives the metal a gray color on a fractured surface, hence the name *gray cast iron*. The graphite is quite typically present as *flakes* (plates) within the metal (Fig. 11–34). The effect of these flakes on the mechanical properties is marked. Because graphite has almost no strength, the flakes act as voids within the structure and reduce the effective cross-sectional area of the casting. Furthermore, tensile stresses during loading are concentrated at the ends of the flakes, as shown in Fig. 11–35, and

TABLE 11-5

DUCTILITY OF FERRITIC MATERIALS

Iron type	Percent elongation (2 inches)
Ferritic steel	50
Ferritic nodular iron	15 to 20
Ferritic malleable iron	15±
Ferritic gray iron	1

deformation or fracture can thereby occur more easily. The crack is readily propagated from flake to flake. Thus the presence of the graphite flakes in iron markedly reduces not only the tensile properties but also the ductility and related properties.

In spite of these shortcomings, gray iron castings are used quite extensively where their other beneficial qualities come into play. For example, the low liquidus temperature of gray iron facilitates the pouring of *intricate castings*. Furthermore, the graphite makes the metal readily machinable, and the over-all cost is relatively small. A less apparent advantage of gray cast iron is its *damping capacity*. Because there are "voids" in the iron, the full transfer of vibrations through the metal is prevented. This fact alone encourages the use of cast iron for such applications as heavy machine bases.

Nodular cast iron. The addition of minor amounts of magnesium (or cerium) to molten iron immediately before casting produces *nodular* (actually spherical) rather than flake graphite (Fig. 11–36). The reason for this difference in shape is not yet clear, and it is currently being studied intensively. One possible explanation is that the magnesium affects the interfacial energy between the crystallizing graphite and the molten iron, thus controlling the growth characteristics.

Whatever the explanation, the result is important to the engineer. Because the spherical graphite structure does not produce the severe stress concentrations developed internally in gray cast iron, much greater ductility is available in nodular cast iron (Table 11–5). The 15 to 20% ductility of nodular cast iron

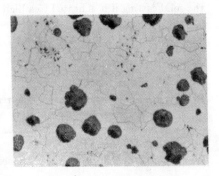

FIG. 11–36. Nodular cast iron, ×100. Carbon is present as graphite *nodules*. Unlike gray cast iron, nodular cast iron is ductile (Table 11–5). Both gray cast iron and nodular cast iron produce graphite *during* solidification. (G. A. Colligan, Dartmouth.)

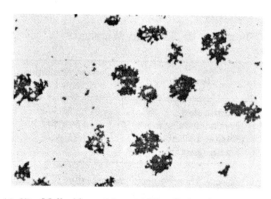

Fig. 11–37. Malleable cast iron, ×100. Carbon is present as graphite clusters (*temper carbon*). As a result, some ductility is obtained (Table 11–5). Temper carbon is formed by the solid reaction $Fe_3C \rightarrow 3Fe +$ carbon. (*Metals Handbook Supplement* 1-*A*. Cleveland: American Society for Metals, 1954.)

permits considerable bending and even some mechanical working, both of which are impossible with the nonductile gray iron. Of course nodular cast iron is not as ductile as a steel which has no graphite. On the other hand, nodular iron may be cast more readily than steel because of its lower melting temperature (Fig. 9–25). Nodular iron may be used in any application where a low melting temperature and moderate ductility are required.

White cast iron. The above two types of iron contain sufficient silicon to dissociate the iron carbide during solidification. When the silicon content is less (approximately 1%), fast cooling can inhibit the dissociation reaction and produce carbides. With no graphite present, a fractured surface of the cast iron appears white rather than gray, hence the name *white cast iron*. The high carbide content makes white cast iron a very brittle, nonductile material, with a wear-resistant surface because of the hard particles. White cast iron is used for such applications as railroad car brakes, which must resist abrasion.

Malleable cast iron. The iron carbide in white cast iron may be dissociated in the solid casting if it is heated to a high temperature for a sufficient period of time for the reaction to occur. Above the eutectoid temperature, the carbide dissociates to austenite and graphite:

$$Fe_3C \xrightarrow{\text{Si}} 3Fe_{(\gamma)} + C_{(gr)}. \tag{11-9}$$

Below the eutectoid temperature, the reaction is

$$Fe_3C \xrightarrow{\text{Si}} 3Fe_{(\alpha)} + C_{(gr)}. \tag{11-10}$$

When the carbon in cast iron is formed by the dissociation of Fe_3C in a solid casting, it develops "clusters" of graphite (Fig. 11–37).* The resulting micro-structures provide some ductility (or malleability) to the otherwise nonductile iron casting, hence the name *malleable cast iron*. The $15\pm\%$ ductility which is possible in properly treated malleable irons results from the removal of most of the brittle carbides and the absence of graphite in flake form, which produces stress concentrations.

• **Example 11–4**

A white cast iron containing 3% carbon receives the following heat treatments. What phases are present after each treatment, and what is the carbon content of each phase?

Answer: (a) White cast iron, as received:

    (1) carbides (in pearlite) with 6.67% carbon;

    (2) ferrite (in pearlite) with less than 0.025% carbon;

    (3) carbides (not in pearlite) with 6.67% carbon.

(b) White cast iron heated at 1600°F for a short period of time:

    (1) austenite with 1.25% carbon (from Fig. 9–26);†

    (2) carbide with 6.67% carbon.

(c) White cast iron heated at 1300°F for a long period of time:

    (1) austenite with approximately 1.25% carbon;

    (2) graphite (as "temper" carbon) with 100% carbon.

(d) White cast iron heated at 1400°F for a long period of time:

    (1) austenite with approximately 0.9% carbon (from Fig. 9–26);

    (2) graphite (as "temper" carbon) with 100% carbon.

(e) White cast iron heated at 1400°F for a long period of time, and then cooled rapidly (not quenched) to room temperature:

    (1) ferrite (in pearlite, from austenite) with 0.02% carbon;

    (2) carbide (in pearlite, from austenite) with 6.67% carbon;

    (3) graphite (as "temper" carbon) with 100% carbon.

Heat treatment (e) produces *pearlitic malleable iron*.

(f) A small piece of white cast iron heated to 1400°F for a long period of time, and then quenched to room temperature:

    (1) martensite (from austenite) with approximately 0.9% carbon;

    (2) graphite (as "temper" carbon) with 100% carbon.

(g) White cast iron heated at 1300°F for a very long period of time:

    (1) ferrite with 0.02% carbon (from Fig. 9–26);

    (2) graphite (as "temper" carbon) with 100% carbon.

Heat treatment (g), or (e) followed by slow cooling, produces *ferritic malleable iron*.

---

* Commonly called *temper carbon* because the clusters are formed in a heat-treating process.

† The carbon solubility in austenite in the presence of graphite is very slightly, but not significantly, lower than it is in the presence of Fe_3C.

The dissociation of iron carbide must occur in the solid state to produce the structure shown in Fig. 11–37. Therefore *malleable iron must start as white cast iron*. However, without special techniques, a large casting (diameter greater than three or four inches) cannot be cooled fast enough to prevent the formation of graphite during solidification and at the same time contain enough silicon to permit the subsequent dissociation of carbide in the solid. Therefore malleable iron castings are usually limited to small castings.

References for Further Reading

11–1. BIRCHENALL, C. E., *Physical Metallurgy*. New York: McGraw-Hill, 1959. Chapters 11–13 present microstructural changes resulting from heat treatments. Supplementary material for this text.

11–2. CLARK, D. S. and W. R. VARNEY, *Physical Metallurgy for Engineers*, second edition. New York: D. Van Nostrand, 1962. Chapters 8 and 9 discuss the heat treatment of steel and the functions of alloying elements, respectively. Chapter 8 presents empirical methods of calculating hardenability and tempering softening. Undergraduate level.

11–3. GROSSMAN, M. A., *Elements of Hardenability*. Cleveland: American Society for Metals, 1952. Chapter 1 discusses various hardenability tests on an introductory level. Chapter 2 considers the microstructural changes which accompany hardening of steel. Chapters 3 and 4 present empirical methods for estimating hardenability from chemical analyses and grain sizes.

11–4. GUY, A. G., *Elements of Physical Metallurgy*. Reading, Mass.: Addison-Wesley, 1959. Chapters 12–14 give a thorough presentation of heat treatments. Advanced undergraduate level.

11–5. GUY, A. G., *Physical Metallurgy for Engineers*. Reading, Mass.: Addison-Wesley, 1962. Chapters 8–10 provide an excellent undergraduate discussion of microstructures and properties.

11–6. KEYSER, C. A., *Materials of Engineering*. Englewood Cliffs, N. J.: Prentice-Hall, 1956. Chapter 10 discusses ferrous alloys and various heat treatments for modifying microstructures. Steels and cast irons are both included. Chapter 9 covers age-hardening. Introductory.

11–7. KINGERY, W. D., *Introduction to Ceramics*. New York: John Wiley & Sons, 1960. Chapter 13 characterizes and discusses the variations in microstructures in ceramic materials.

11–8. National Bureau of Standards, *Microstructure of Ceramic Materials*. NBS Miscellaneous Publication 257, 1964. Washington, DC.: U.S. Government Printing Office. A series of six lectures on ceramic microstructures and their effect on properties of ceramic materials.

11–9. SMITH, C. S., "Grains, Phases, and Interfaces: An Interpretation of Microstructure," *Trans. A.I.M.E.*, **175**, 15, 1948. An advanced but easily read discussion of the factors which control microstructure, and hence certain of the properties of metals.

11–10. VAN VLACK, L. H., *Physical Ceramics for Engineers*. Reading, Mass.: Addison-Wesley, 1964. Chapter 7 describes microstructures of ceramic materials.

Problems

11-1. Calculate the density (lb/in^3) of a glass-reinforced phenol-formaldehyde plastic, in which the glass content is 15 w/o. (A borosilicate glass is used for glass fibers.)
Answer: 0.05 lb/in^3

11-2. If the density of 1080 steel is 7.84 gm/cm^3, estimate the density of Fe$_3$C. (The density of ferrite is 7.87 gm/cm^3.)

11-3. Estimate the thermal conductivity of the reinforced plastic of Problem 11-1. (Assume the glass is randomly dispersed.)
Answer: 0.0005 cal·cm/°C·cm^2·sec

11-4. In commercial practice, a normalized steel is heated an hour 100°F above the lowest temperature of single-phase austenite. Indicate the normalizing temperature for a 1040, a 1080, and a 1% C steel.

11-5. In commercial practice, an annealed steel is heated an hour at 50°F above the highest temperature of α-ferrite. Indicate the annealing temperature for a 1040, a 1080, and a 1% C steel.
Answer: 1550°F, 1385°F, 1385°F

11-6. Explain why the following alloys can (or cannot) be considered for age-hardening. (a) 97% aluminum, 3% copper. (b) 97% copper, 3% zinc. (c) 97% nickel, 3% copper. (d) 97% copper, 3% nickel. (e) 97% aluminum, 3% magnesium. (f) 97% magnesium, 3% aluminum.

11-7. Explain why a 92% copper, 8% nickel alloy can (or cannot) be age-hardened.
Answer: No supersaturation possible

11-8. An aircraft manufacturer receives a shipment of aluminum alloy rivets that have already age-hardened. Can they be salvaged? Explain.

11-9. A slight amount of age-hardening is realized when a steel (99.7 w/o Fe, 0.3 w/o C) is quenched from 1300°F and reheated for 3 hr at 212°F. Account for the hardening.
Answer: Carbon solubility in ferrite decreases.

11-10. The quenched end of a Jominy bar has a hardness of 44 R_c. What is the carbon content of the steel? Explain.

11-11. How hard will the quenched end of AISI 4620 steel be?
Answer: Approximately R_c 50

11-12. A bar of 1040 steel has a surface hardness of 41 R_c and a center hardness of 28 R_c. How fast were the surface and center cooled through 1300°F?

11-13. What hardness would you expect the center of a 2-in. round of 1040 steel to have if it were quenched in (a) mildly agitated oil? (b) mildly agitated water?
Answer: (a) R_c 23 (b) R_c 25

11-14. Sketch a hardness traverse for a 1-in. round of 3140 steel (a) quenched in oil, (b) quenched in water.

11-15. A 2.5-in. round of 1040 steel is quenched in agitated oil. Estimate the hardness 1 in. below the surface of the round. (Show reasoning.)
Answer: R_c 23

11-16. How would the hardness traverse of the 1040 steel shown in Fig. 11-32 vary if (a) it were quenched in still oil? (b) it were quenched in still water? (c) it had a coarser austenite grain size?

11–17. Draw the hardness traverses for two 3-in. rounds of SAE 3140 steel which have been (a) quenched in agitated oil, (b) quenched in agitated water.

Answer: (a) S, R_c 48; M-R, R_c 38; C, R_c 33 (b) S, R_c 55; M-R, R_c 46; C, R_c 42.

11–18. Two 3-in. rounds were quenched, one in agitated water, the other in agitated oil. The following hardness traverses were made:

Distance below surface, inches	Water, R_C	Oil, R_C
0	57	39
$\frac{3}{8}$	46	35
$\frac{3}{4}$	36	32
$1\frac{1}{8}$	34	31
$1\frac{1}{2}$	33	30

Calculate and sketch the hardenability curve which would be obtained from an end-quenched test of the same steel.

11–19. The center hardnesses of 6 bars of the same steel are indicated below. From these data plot the hardenability curve for the steel.

1 inch WQ	58 R_c	2 inch OQ	47 R_c
1 inch OQ	57 R_c	4 inch WQ	34 R_c
2 inch WQ	54 R_c	4 inch OQ	30 R_c

Answer: EQ position $\frac{1}{4}$ in., R_c 57; $\frac{1}{2}$ in., R_c 53; $\frac{3}{4}$ in., R_c 45; 1 in., R_c 34; $1\frac{1}{4}$ in., R_c 30.

11–20. On the basis of Fig. 11–38, show a plot of the effect of carbon on the surface hardnesses of 1-in. and 3-in. round bars when quenched in oil.

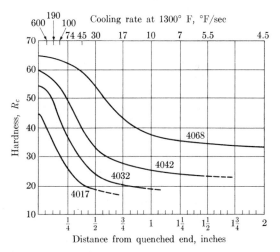

FIG. 11–38. Hardenability curves for 40xx steels. (Composition, other than carbon content, is unchanged.)

11–21. A spline gear had a hardness of 42 at its center when it was made of the 3140 steel shown in Fig. 11–30. What hardness would you expect the same gear to have if it were made of 1040 steel?

Answer: R_c 24

11–22. The hardness of the surface of a round bar of 1040 steel quenched in agitated oil is R_c 40. Determine the hardness of the center of a round bar of 4068 steel quenched in water if this bar is twice the diameter of the 1040 bar. (Indicate all steps in your solution.)

• 11–23. A white cast iron is heated to 1600°F and held there long enough for all the iron carbide to dissociate. It is then cooled in air to room temperature. (a) What were the compositions of the phases present before air-cooling? (b) What microstructures are present after air-cooling?

Answer: (a) Graphite, 100% C, and austenite, 1.2% C; (b) graphite (temper carbon) and pearlite, plus excess carbide.

• 11–24. (a) Two gray cast irons contain (1) ferrite and flake graphite, and (2) pearlite and flake graphite, respectively. What variables in their production could account for this difference? (b) Two malleable irons contain (1) ferrite and "temper" carbon, and (2) pearlite and "temper" carbon, respectively. What variables in their production could account for this difference?

• 11–25. Two malleable irons originally have the same composition. After processing, one is composed of ferrite and "temper" carbon, and the second is composed of pearlite and "temper" carbon. How did the processing procedures differ?

• 11–26. A 100-lb iron casting containing 1% Si and 2% C was cooled *very* slowly after casting. Give the amounts and compositions of the phases present.

11–27. Compare and contrast (a) pearlite, (b) bainite, (c) tempered martensite.

11–28. Draw temperature (ordinate) and time (abscissa) plots for the following heat treatments. Indicate the important temperatures, relative times, and reasons for drawing the curves as you do. (a) Normalizing a 1095 steel, contrasted with annealing the same steel. (b) Solution-treating an aluminum 5% copper alloy, contrasted with aging the same alloy. (c) Austempering a 1045 steel, contrasted with martempering the same steel. (d) Spheroidizing 1080 steel, contrasted with spheroidizing 10105 steel.

• Problems preceded by a bullet are based, in part, on optional sections.

12

stability of materials
in service environments

12-1 Service stability. The stability a material has in its surroundings is of major importance in many engineering applications. It has been estimated that the cost of corrosion alone is between eight and ten billion dollars a year in this country. Automobile deterioration is an example of this type of loss; however, corrosion occurs with all types of equipment. The engineer must also specify materials for his products which provide stability at various elevated temperatures, and resistance to radiation damage in high-energy surroundings.

A stable material is one which can exist in varying environments without undergoing chemical or structural alteration. Therefore, when we evaluate the stability of a material, we shall first consider possible changes in composition and internal structure during service.

CORROSION

12-2 Introduction. Corrosion is the deterioration and loss of material due to chemical attack. The conditions that promote corrosion involve both chemical and electronic changes, and they are constantly with us. Obviously, the engineer must understand the mechanisms of corrosion if its effects are to be minimized. He will then be better able to (1) avoid severely corrosive conditions, or (2) provide protection against corrosion.

12-3 Corrosion by solution. The simplest corrosion is by means of chemical *solution*, illustrated in the familiar examples of sugar or salt in water (Section 9-3). The sugar dissolves as molecules and the salt dissolves as sodium and chloride ions. Materials as soluble as sugar and salt are not ordinarily used for engineering components, of course, but there are occasions when engineering materials come into contact with strong solvents. For example, a rubber hose through which gasoline flows is in contact with hydrocarbon solvents, and silica refractories come in contact with iron oxide slag that dissolves the silica. The following generalizations may be made about chemical solution:

(1) *Small molecules and ions dissolve most readily.* The components of asphalt, for example, dissolve more readily than the components of a highly polymerized plastic. Apparent exceptions are polymers which are easily depolymerized, but here the material goes into solution as small molecules. Similarly, alkali and halide ions have greater solubility than more complex silicate ions. The ready solubility of the simpler salts prohibits their use in engineering construction.

(2) *Solution occurs more readily when the solvent and solute are structurally similar.* Organic materials are most soluble in organic solvents, metals in other metal liquids, and ceramic materials in other ceramic melts. Even within these general categories, a similarity of solvent and solute structures produces greater solubility. For example, polyethylene is more soluble in liquid hydrocarbons than in liquid phenol, and copper is more soluble in liquid zinc than in liquid lead.

(3) *The presence of two solutes may produce greater solubility than the presence of only one.* As an example, the calcium carbonate ($CaCO_3$) of limestone is nearly insoluble in pure water. However, the addition of CO_2 to form carbonic acid in the water markedly increases the $CaCO_3$ solubility. Limestone caverns are the result of the dissolution of $CaCO_3$ by water containing carbonic acid from organic material. The time required for solution in this case is exceedingly long, of course, but the same effect occurs when limestones, or calcium carbonate bonded sandstones, are used as construction materials in an industrial atmosphere containing such gases as SO_3. The solution of SO_3 into atmospheric moisture produces a dilute sulfuric acid solvent which will react directly with $CaCO_3$.

(4) *The rate of solution increases with temperature.* Solution involves diffusion, and since diffusion occurs more rapidly with the greater thermal vibrations at high temperatures, solution corrosion also occurs more rapidly.

Example 12–1

A hundred pounds of slag containing 90% FeO and 10% SiO_2 are placed in a silica crucible at 2900°F. How much silica can the slag dissolve?

Answer: The liquid slag saturated with silica at 2900°F (1595°C) contains 52% FeO and 48% silica (Fig. 9–48).

$$90 \text{ lb FeO} = (0.52)(W).$$
$$W = 173 \text{ lb liquid slag.}$$
$$\text{Pounds } SiO_2 \text{ dissolved} = (0.48)(W) - 10$$
$$= 73 \text{ lb } SiO_2 \text{ dissolved per 100 lb original slag.}$$

12–4 Electrochemical oxidation.

The most common type of corrosion involves the electrochemical process of metal oxidation. Strictly speaking, *oxidation* is the removal of electrons from an atom. For example, Eq. (12–1) is the expression for the oxidation of iron to ferrous ions, and Eq. (12–2) expresses the oxidation of ferrous ions to ferric ions:

$$Fe \rightarrow Fe^{2+} + 2e^-, \tag{12–1}$$

and

$$Fe^{2+} \rightarrow Fe^{3+} + e^-. \tag{12–2}$$

This combination of chemical reaction and electron release leads to other reactions, such as rust formation. Rust is ferric hydroxide, and is formed according to the overall reaction

$$4Fe + 3O_2 + 6H_2O \rightarrow 4Fe(OH)_3. \tag{12–3}$$

For iron to rust, reactions (12–1) and (12–2) must occur, and both oxygen and moisture must be present. Iron will not rust if it is submerged in oxygen-free water, nor will it rust in an atmosphere containing only oxygen. However, in practice, the amount of moisture required to produce the above reaction may be surprisingly small. For example, the moisture content of the air can quickly produce rust on hand tools in a basement.

Different metals have different *oxidation potentials*, inasmuch as the energy required to remove electrons varies from metal to metal. Also electrons are removed more readily in some environments than in others. For example, electrons are removed from iron when oxygen and water are both present (Eq. 12–3), and they are removed more easily from aluminum atoms when chloride ions are present.

12–5 Electrode potential. Most corrosion occurs through the interaction of the two processes of *solution* and *oxidation*. The mechanism of corrosion is somewhat complicated, but an understanding of it is important to the engineer. With simple modifications, the mechanism of the corrosion of iron may be applied to all metals, and even to nonmetals. Equations (12–1) and (12–2) may be rewritten as follows:

$$Fe \rightleftarrows Fe^{2+} + 2e^-, \tag{12–4}$$

and

$$Fe \rightleftarrows Fe^{3+} + 3e^-. \tag{12–5}$$

As iron goes into solution as ions, excess electrons are produced (Fig. 12–1). Equilibrium is usually reached quickly because ions and electrons soon recombine at the same rate at which they form.

The production of ions and electrons builds up an electrical potential, called an *electrode potential*, which depends on (1) the nature of the metal, and (2) the nature of the solution. All metal does not oxidize to ions and electrons with equal facility. For example, atoms along a grain boundary are less stably located than

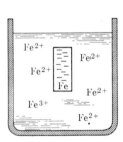

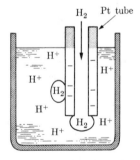

FIG. 12–1. Dissociation of iron into solution. Reaction (12–4) is more prevalent than (12–5). Iron ions are formed. The electrons produce an electrical potential.

FIG. 12–2. Dissociation of hydrogen into solution. The electrical potential of this reaction (12–6) is not as high as that of reaction (12–4).

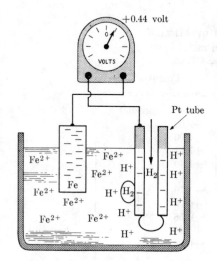
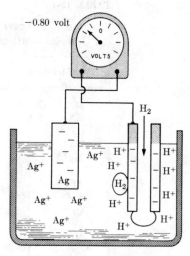

FIG. 12–3.   Potential difference, Fe versus H₂. Iron produces a higher electron potential than does H₂. Therefore iron is the anode and hydrogen the cathode.

FIG. 12–4.   Potential difference, H₂ versus Ag. H₂ produces a higher electron potential than does silver, and is therefore the anode. Silver is the cathode.

those in the crystal lattice (Section 4–9), so they ionize more readily. Furthermore, the reaction in Eq. (12–4) will produce equilibrium with a higher electrode potential if the metal ions enter a solution in which they are relatively stable (the positive iron ions are more stable in a uniformly Cl^- concentrated solution than in a uniformly dilute Cl^- solution).

To measure the electrode potential of any material (and therefore its corroding tendencies), we must first determine the voltage difference between the metal and a standard hydrogen electrode. With hydrogen (Fig. 12–2), equilibrium occurs by means of the following reaction:

$$H_2 \rightleftarrows 2H^+ + 2e^-. \tag{12–6}$$

The potential difference† (measured with a potentiometer) between the iron and hydrogen electrodes is $+0.44$ volt (Fig. 12–3).

Similar measurements for other metals yield the voltage comparisons listed in Table 12–1. The alkali and alkaline earth metals, which hold their outer-shell electrons rather loosely, show a greater potential difference than iron. Conversely, the noble metals such as silver, platinum, and gold produce fewer electrons than hydrogen and therefore are lower on the potential scale (Fig. 12–4 and Table 12–1).

---

† Since the potential *difference* is the only voltage that can actually be measured, all comparisons are made with a standardized hydrogen electrode.

TABLE 12-1

ELECTRODE POTENTIALS OF METALS
(25°C; molar solutions of metal ions)

Metal ion		Potential*	
Li^+	(base)	+2.96	(anodic)
K^+		+2.92	
Ca^{2+}		+2.90	
Na^+		+2.71	
Mg^{2+}		+2.40	
Al^{3+}		+1.70	
Zn^{2+}		+0.76	
Cr^{2+}		+0.56	
Fe^{2+}		+0.44	
Ni^{2+}		+0.23	
Sn^{2+}		+0.14	
Pb^{2+}		+0.12	
Fe^{3+}		+0.045	
H^+		0.000	(reference)
Cu^{2+}		—0.34	
Cu^+		—0.47	
Ag^+		—0.80	
Pt^{4+}		—0.86	
Au^+	(noble)	—1.50	(cathodic)

* These signs are consistent with thermodynamics
and are used by physical chemists. The opposite
signs are still used by many electrochemists and
corrosion experts.

12-6 Galvanic couples (cells). The electrode couples shown in Figs. 12–3 and
12–4 involve iron and silver, respectively. The electrode supplying the electrons
to the external circuit is called the *anode*,* and the electrode receiving the electrons
from the external circuit is called the *cathode*.

If electrical contact is made between the two electrodes, the greater potential at
the anode will permit electrons to flow from the anode to the cathode (Fig. 12–5).

---

* In the original terminology, the anode was the positive pole. This nomenclature was
established before it was known that electrons (which have negative charge) are *supplied*
by the anode. The definitions given here are suitable for the discussion of corrosion,
batteries, circuits, and tubes; i.e., the anode *supplies* electrons to the *external* circuit, and
the cathode *receives* electrons from the *external* circuit.

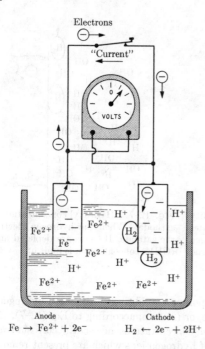

FIG. 12–5. Galvanic corrosion. The reaction represented in Fig. 12–1 soon stops because equilibrium is reached. Here the same reaction proceeds as described because removal of electrons from the iron prevents equilibrium. Galvanic corrosion requires two electrodes. One produces electrons (anode) and the other consumes electrons (cathode) from the external circuit.

The introduction of the excess electrons to the cathode upsets the equilibrium described by Eq. (12–6), driving it to the left. As a result, H_2 is liberated at the cathode from the hydrogen ions in the water. Such a reaction also removes some of the electrons from the iron electrode and upsets the equilibrium of the reactions described by Eqs. (12–4) and (12–5), so that they proceed to the right. Consequently, these reactions continue to occur spontaneously, dissolving the anode metal and producing hydrogen at the cathode.

This example has demonstrated the mechanism of *galvanic corrosion*. The corrosion occurs only at the anode because there the electrical potential is higher than at the cathode. The solution equilibrium is thus upset in the direction of greater solution (corrosion) when electrical contact is made and electrons are removed.

Hydrogen "plates out" at the cathode because it is lower in the electromotive series. The H_2 comes from the hydrogen ions present in the water as a result of the reaction

$$H_2O \rightleftarrows H^+ + OH^-. \tag{12–7}$$

Ordinarily, this reaction produces only a few hydrogen ions.* Consequently, the reaction in Fig. 12–5 does not proceed rapidly. For one thing, the removal of H^+ ions from solution reduces the hydrogen ion concentration adjacent to the

---

* The hydrogen ion concentration in pure water is 10^{-7} gm-atom/liter (i.e., pH = 7).

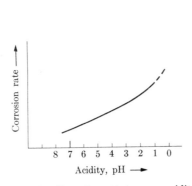

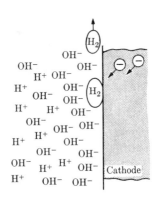

FIG. 12-6. Corrosion rate versus acidity (schematic). Increased acidity accelerates corrosion of metals anodic to hydrogen (assuming homogeneous electrolytes and nonoxidizing conditions).

FIG. 12-7. Hydroxyl concentration at the cathode. When the hydrogen electrode is the cathode, H^+ ions are depleted and the $(OH)^-$ concentration is built up.

cathode surface and establishes temporary equilibrium until more hydrogen ions can (1) diffuse to the cathode surface, or (2) form according to Eq. (12-7). Acidic solutions with greater hydrogen ion concentrations accelerate corrosion at the anode, because the greater number of hydrogen ions which are present remove the electrons supplied through the cathode by the anode (Fig. 12-6).

Cathode reactions. When the reaction expressed by Eq. (12-6) moves to the left, it is a major cathode reaction that is quite noticeable because it evolves a gas. However, there are a number of other important, less obvious cathode changes. The first is the increase in OH^- concentration that accompanies the removal of H^+ ions (Fig. 12-7). The removal of H^+ from solution makes the reaction expressed in Eq. (12-7) move to the right* and produces more $(OH)^-$ ions at the cathode

---

* The *Mass Law* in its simplest form states that the ratio of the product concentration to the reactant concentration is a constant. That is,

$$AB \rightleftarrows A + B,$$

and

$$K = \frac{(\text{conc}_A)(\text{conc}_B)}{(\text{conc}_{AB})},$$

or

$$K = \frac{(\text{conc}_{H^+})(\text{conc}_{OH^-})}{(\text{conc}_{H_2O})}.$$

Thus, if the concentration of H^+ is lowered, the concentration of $(OH)^-$ must increase to maintain a constant ratio, K. (The concentration of H_2O varies insignificantly, because it is the major constituent.)

surface, which permits the formation of *rust* (Fig. 12–8) when Fe^{3+} ions are present:

$$Fe^{3+} + 3(OH)^- \rightarrow Fe(OH)_3. \qquad (12\text{–}8)$$

Because $Fe(OH)_3$ is almost insoluble in most aqueous solutions, it precipitates readily and lets the above reaction proceed to the right as fast as Fe^{3+} and $(OH)^-$ ions come into contact. These two reactants originate at the anode and cathode, respectively, but their combination occurs more commonly at the cathode, because the smaller Fe^{3+} ions (radius = 0.67 A) diffuse more rapidly than the larger $(OH)^-$ ions (radius = 1.32 A). Furthermore, only one Fe^{3+} ion must diffuse to the cathode for each three $(OH)^-$ ions. Significantly, *corrosion occurs at the anode; rust is deposited at the cathode* (Fig. 12–8).

Another important cathode reaction is that shown in Fig. 12–9; this reaction also produces $(OH)^-$ ions:

$$2H_2O + O_2 + 4e^- \rightarrow 4(OH)^-. \qquad (12\text{–}9)$$

An increase in oxygen content has two effects: (1) it forces reaction (12–9) to the right, producing more $(OH)^-$ ions, and (2) it removes more electrons and therefore accelerates corrosion at the anode. Each of these effects increases the supply of the reactants for the rust-forming reaction (Eq. 12–8). The presence of oxygen thus greatly accelerates both corrosion and rusting, with the corrosion occurring at the anode and the rust forming at the cathode.

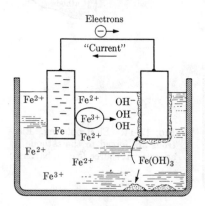

FIG. 12–8.   Rusting. Although corrosion occurs at the anode, rust is more commonly found at the cathode, because electrons and smaller Fe^{3+} ions move to the cathode more readily than the larger OH^- ions can move to the anode.

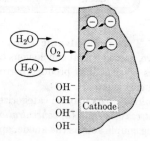

FIG. 12–9.   Hydroxyl formation at the cathode. The speed of the reaction expressed in Eq. (12–9) increases with oxygen content. It occurs at the cathode, where electrons are consumed.

If ions other than H^+ and OH^- are present in the electrolyte, they may also be involved in the reactions at the electrodes. A very simple example is the reaction when Cu^{2+} ions are present (Fig. 12–10):

$$Cu^{2+} + 2e^- \rightleftarrows Cu. \qquad (12–10)$$

This reaction is sensitive to a supply of electrons from an external source (e.g., Eq. 12–4).

Electroplating. Copper plating and other kinds of electroplating are accomplished by means of the reaction described in Eq. (12–10). The part to be plated is used as a cathode in an electrolytic cell and electrons are introduced from an external source (Fig. 12–11). In principle, electroplating is the reverse of corrosion; that is, in electroplating, metal is deposited from solution; in corrosion, metal is dissolved into solution. Corrosion always occurs at the anode and electroplating always occurs at the cathode.

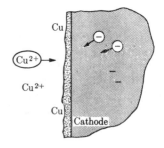

Fig. 12–10. Metal plating at the cathode. A forced supply of electrons to the cathode causes a reversal of the corrosion reaction. (*Corrosion* and *plating* are opposites.)

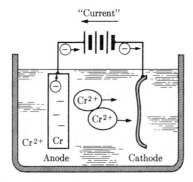

Fig. 12–11. Electroplating. Electrons are forced to the cathode by an external source (e.g., a battery).

12–7 Types of galvanic cells. On the basis of the corrosion principles stated above, some general conclusions can be reached. First we shall discuss the various types of cells that produce corrosion, and then the means of protection against such corrosion.

Galvanic cells may be categorized in three different groups: (1) *composition* cells, (2) *stress* cells, and (3) *concentration* cells. Each produces corrosion because one-half of the couple acts as the anode, and the other half, with a lower electrode potential,

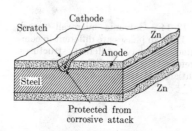
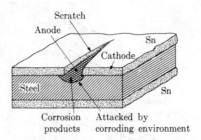

FIG. 12–12. Galvanized steel (cross section). Zinc serves as the anode; the iron of the steel serves as the cathode. Therefore the iron is protected even though it is exposed where the zinc is scraped off.

FIG. 12–13. Tinplate (cross section). The tin protects the iron while the coating is continuous. When the coating is broken, the iron of the steel becomes the anode and is subject to accelerated corrosion.

serves as the cathode. Only the anode is corroded, and then only when it is in electrical contact with a cathode. If the anode were present alone, it would quickly come to equilibrium with its environment [see Eq. (12–4) or (12–5), where only iron is present].

Composition cells. A composition cell may be established between any two *dissimilar* materials. In each case the metal higher in the electromotive series acts as the anode. For example, on a sheet of galvanized steel (Fig. 12–12), the zinc coating acts as an anode and protects the underlying iron even if the surface is not completely covered, because the exposed iron is the cathode and does not corrode. Any corrosion which does occur is on the anodic zinc surface. So long as zinc remains it provides protection to adjacent exposed iron.

Conversely, a *tin* coating on sheet iron or steel provides protection only so long as the surface of the metal is completely covered. Since tin is only slightly above hydrogen in the electromotive series, its rate of corrosion is limited. However, if the surface coating is punctured, the tin becomes the cathode. The exposed iron, which is above tin in the electromotive series, acts as the anode (Fig. 12–13). The galvanic couple which results produces corrosion of the iron. Since the small anodic area must supply electrons to a large cathode surface, very rapid localized corrosion can result.

Other examples of galvanic couples often encountered are (1) steel screws in brass marine hardware, (2) Pb-Sn solder around copper wire, (3) a steel propeller shaft in bronze bearings, and (4) steel pipe connected to copper plumbing. Each of these is a possible galvanic cell unless protected from a corrosive environment. Too many engineers fail to realize that the contact of dissimilar metals is a potential source of galvanic corrosion. Recently, in an actual engineering application, a brass bearing was used on a hydraulic steering mechanism made of steel. Even in an oil environment, the steel acted as an anode and corroded sufficiently to permit leakage of oil through the close-fitting connection.

There is no size limitation for galvanic cells. Furthermore, each phase with its individual properties possesses its own electrode potential, so that galvanic cells

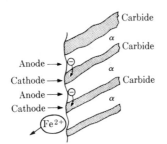

Anode →
Cathode →
Anode →
Cathode →

FIG. 12-14. Galvanic microcell (pearlite). The two phases are different in composition and have different structures. Therefore they have different electrode potentials and produce a small galvanic cell.

FIG. 12-15. Galvanic microcells (Al-Si alloy). Any two-phase alloy is more subject to corrosion than is a single-phase alloy. A two-phase alloy provides anodes and cathodes. (Aluminum Research Laboratories)

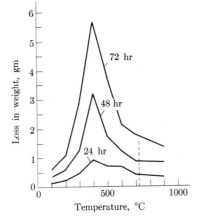

FIG. 12-16. Microcells and corrosion. After quenching, only martensite exists. After intermediate-temperature tempering, many small galvanic cells exist as a result of the fine (α + carbide) structure in tempered martensite. After high-temperature tempering, the carbide is agglomerated and fewer galvanic cells are present. (Adapted from F. N. Speller, *Corrosion: Causes and Prevention.* New York: McGraw-Hill, 1935.)

can be set up in most two-phase alloys when they are exposed to an electrolyte. Figure 12-14 illustrates such a cell on a *microscopic* scale for pearlite; Fig. 12-15 shows galvanic cells in an Al-Si alloy.

Many alloys are subject to galvanic corrosion even though they are used alone, but fortunately the potential difference between two similar phases is usually quite small. Ferrite and iron carbide have electrode potential values sufficiently close together that the corrosion rate for plain carbon steel is ordinarily lower than that for a steel-brass galvanic couple.

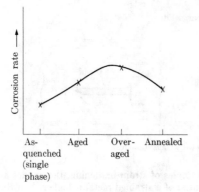

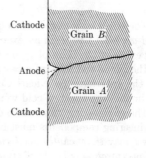

FIG. 12–17. Age-hardening and corrosion (schematic). The single-phase, quenched alloy has a lower corrosion rate than the subsequent two-phase modifications.

FIG. 12–18. Grain-boundary corrosion. The grain boundaries serve as the anode because the boundary atoms have a higher potential.

Heat treatment may affect the corrosion rate by altering the microstructure of the metal. Figure 12–16 shows the effect of tempering on the corrosion of a previously quenched steel. At very low tempering temperatures, the steel contains a single phase, martensite. The tempering of the martensite produces many galvanic cells and grain boundaries of ferrite and carbide, and the corrosion rate is increased. At higher temperatures an agglomeration of the carbides reduces the number of galvanic cells and the number of grain boundaries, which decreases the corrosion rate markedly.

In a single phase the corrosion rate of an age-hardenable aluminum alloy is low (Fig. 12–17), but the corrosion rate is significantly increased with precipitation of the second phase. Still greater agglomeration of the precipitate once again decreases the rate, but never to as low a level as in the single-phase alloy. The maximum corrosion rate occurs after maximum hardness has been attained.

Stress cells. As shown in Fig. 4–17, where the grain boundaries have been etched (i.e., corroded), the atoms at the boundaries have an electrode potential different from that of the atoms in the grain proper; thus an anode and a cathode are developed (Fig. 12–18). One conclusion follows logically: a fine-grained metal will have a higher corrosion rate than a coarse-grained metal, because there is more anode area. The grain boundary zone may be considered to be stressed, since the atoms are not at their positions of lowest energy.

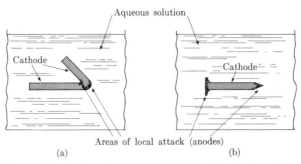

Fɪɢ. 12–19. Stress cells. In these two examples of strain hardening, the anodes are in the cold-worked areas. The electrode potential of a strained metal is higher than that of an annealed metal.

The effect of internal stress on corrosion is also evident after a metal has been *cold-worked*. A very simple example is shown in Fig. 12–19(a), where strain-hardening exists at the bend of an otherwise annealed wire. The cold-worked area serves as the anode and the strain-free area as the cathode. *Corrosion in Action*, published by the International Nickel Company (1955), demonstrates with illustrative experiments the effect of cold work on galvanic corrosion.

The engineering importance of the effects of stress on corrosion is plain. When engineering components must be used in a corrosive environment, the presence of stress may significantly accelerate the corrosion rate.

Concentration cells. In Section 12–5 we remarked that the electrode potential is, among other things, dependent on the concentration of the electrolyte. The reaction expressed in Eq. (12–4), for example, moves farther to the right in a concentrated solution of sodium chloride than in a dilute solution of sodium chloride. However, such is not the case when the electrolyte contains ions of the corroding metal. For example, Eq. (12–11) represents the reactions in Fig. 12–20:

$$Cu \rightleftarrows Cu^{2+} + 2e^-. \tag{12–11}$$

The metal on side (D) is in the solution with the more dilute Cu^{2+} electrolyte. Therefore, its electrode reaction is more strongly to the right than is found on side (C), which has a higher Cu^{2+} content. In fact, when the two electrodes are connected into a galvanic cell, the electrons supplied through the external connection from side (D) and the larger number of Cu^{2+} ions on side (C) combine to force reaction (12–11) back to the left. The electrode in the concentrated electrolyte is protected and becomes the cathode; the electrode in the dilute electrolyte undergoes further corrosion and becomes the anode.

The concentration cell accentuates corrosion, but it accentuates it where the concentration of electrolyte is lower.

Concentration cells of the above type are frequently encountered in chemical plants, and also under certain flow-corrosion conditions. However, in general, they

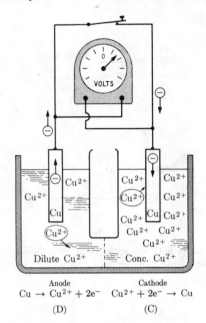

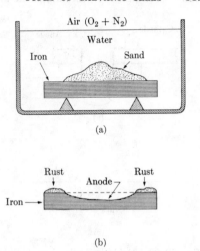

Anode   Cathode
$Cu \rightarrow Cu^{2+} + 2e^-$ $Cu^{2+} + 2e^- \rightarrow Cu$
(D)   (C)

Fig. 12–20. Concentration cell. When the electrolyte is *not homogeneous*, the less concentrated area becomes the anode.

Fig. 12–21. Oxidation cell. This concentration cell produces an anode under the sand in (a) where oxygen is less available. The cathode forms where oxygen is available. (b) After the sand is removed. *Oxygen accelerated corrosion; however, it accelerated it where the oxygen was low.* (Adapted from *Corrosion in Action.* New York: International Nickel Company, 1955.)

are of less widespread importance than are *oxidation-type concentration cells* (Fig. 12–21). When oxygen in the air has access to a moist metal surface, corrosion is promoted. However, the most marked corrosion occurs in the part of the cell with an oxygen deficiency.

This apparent anomaly may be explained on the basis of the reactions at the cathode surface, where electrons are consumed. Equation (12–9) is restated below because it indicates the role of O_2 in promoting corrosion in oxygen-free areas:

$$2H_2O + O_2 + 4e^- \rightarrow 4(OH)^- \qquad (12\text{–}12)$$

Since this cathode reaction, which requires the presence of oxygen, removes electrons from the metal, more electrons must be supplied by adjacent areas which do not have as much oxygen. The areas with less oxygen thus serve as anodes.

The oxidation cell accentuates corrosion but it accentuates it where the oxygen concentration is lower. This generalization is significant. Corrosion may be accelerated in apparently inaccessible places because the oxygen-deficient areas serve as anodes, and therefore cracks or crevices serve as loci of corrosion (Fig. 12–22).

Corrosion is also accelerated under accumulations of dirt or other surface contaminations (Fig. 12–22b). This frequently becomes a self-aggravating situation, because accumulation of rust or scale restricts the access of oxygen and establishes

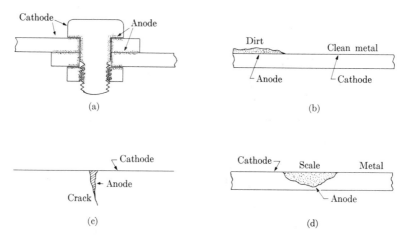

(a)

(b)

(c)

(d)

Fig. 12–22.   Oxidation cells.   Inaccessible locations with low oxygen concentrations become anodic.   This situation arises because the mobility of electrons and metal ions is greater than that of oxygen or oxygen ions.

TABLE 12-2

SUMMARY OF GALVANIC CELLS

Specific examples	Anode	Cathode
	Baser phase	*Nobler phase*
Zn versus Fe	Zn	Fe
Fe versus H_2	Fe	H_2
H_2 versus Cu	H_2	Cu
Pearlite	α	Carbide
	Higher energy	*Lower energy*
Boundaries	Boundaries	Grain
Grain size	Fine-grain	Coarse-grain
Stresses	Cold-worked	Annealed
Stress corrosion	Stressed areas	Nonstressed areas
	Lower conc.	*Higher conc.*
Electrolyte	Dilute solution	Concentrated solution
Oxidation	Low O_2	High O_2
Dirt or scale	Covered areas	Clean areas

an anode, to promote still greater accumulation. The result is localized *pitting* due to nonuniform corrosion (Fig. 12–22d), and the useful life of the product is thereby reduced to a greater extent than the weight loss would indicate.

12–8 Summary of the galvanic corrosion mechanism. Most corrosion is a result of the setting up of galvanic cells and the accompanying electrical currents. Two dissimilar electrodes are required, which may be provided by (1) differences in *composition*, (2) differences in *energy level* (disordered or stressed areas), or (3) differences in electrolytic *environment*. These are detailed further in Table 12–2. The electrode with the higher potential is the anode. More descriptively, the *anode undergoes corrosion,* the *cathode is protected.*

12–9 Corrosion prevention. Only under ideal service conditions can corrosion be completely avoided. The materials would have to be absolutely uniform, with no heterogeneities in either composition or structure, and the environment would also have to be entirely uniform. Although such conditions are impossible to attain, it is possible to minimize corrosion considerably, and the reward in the form of increased life of the product is well worth the effort.

There are three primary methods for preventing corrosion: (1) the isolation of electrolytes from the electrodes by means of *protective surfaces*, (2) the *avoidance of galvanic couples*, and (3) the use of *galvanic protection*. Each of these methods will be considered in detail.

12–10 Protective surfaces. Protecting the surface of an object is probably the oldest of the common procedures for corrosion prevention. A painted surface, for example, isolates the underlying metal from the corroding electrolyte. The only limitation on this method is the service behavior of the protective coating. For example, difficulties arise with organic coatings when the service conditions involve high temperatures or abrasive wear, and the oxidation of organic coatings with time requires periodic resurfacing.

But protective coatings need not be limited to organic materials. For instance, tin can be used as an "inert" coating on a steel base. Copper-plate, nickel-plate, and silver-plate are other examples of corrosion-resistant surfaces. Such metals may also be applied as hot-dip coats. Inert ceramic materials can also be used for protective coatings. For example, true enamels are oxide coatings applied as powdered glass and fused into a vitreous surface layer. A comparison of the advantages and disadvantages of the several categories of protective coatings is given in Table 12–3.

Protection by passivation. In an oxygen concentration cell (Section 12–7) oxygen accentuates corrosion, but it does so where the oxygen concentration is low. In the absence of oxygen concentration differentials, other varied effects may be noted. Specifically, the oxygen may react with ions and electrons from the anode to form a protective surface. This reaction is particularly significant in stainless (Cr-containing) steels where

$$Cr + 2O_2 + 2e^- \rightarrow (CrO_4)^{2-}. \tag{12–13}$$

TABLE 12–3

COMPARISON OF INERT PROTECTIVE COATINGS

Type	Example	Advantages	Disadvantages
Organic	Baked "enamel" paints	Flexible Easily applied Cheap	Oxidizes Soft (relatively) Temperature limitations

Metal	Noble metal electroplates	Deformable
		Insoluble in
		  organic solutions
		Thermally conductive
			Establishes
			  galvanic cell if
			  ruptured

Ceramic	Vitreous enamel oxide coatings	Temperature resistant
		Harder
		Does not produce
		  cell with base
			Brittle
			Thermal
			  insulators

The $(CrO_4)^{2-}$ ions are adsorbed onto the anode surface, and in effect isolate it from further anodic reactions, and thus passivate the metal (Fig. 12–23). A chromium-bearing steel is quite resistant to corrosion under an oxidizing condition; however, in the absence of oxygen, the reaction

$$Cr \rightarrow Cr^{2+} + 2e^- \qquad (12-14)$$

is free to proceed. Hence we find that those steels which are *passive* in the presence of oxygen or oxidizing acids such as HNO_3 or H_2SO_4 become *active* in the presence of HCl, HF, or other oxygen-free acids. A steel is therefore placed within a galvanic series of alloys at one position or another depending on the oxidation level of the electrolyte (Table 12–4).

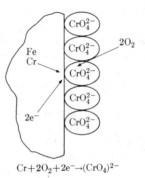

FIG. 12–23.   Passivation of 18% Cr steel. The anode is isolated from the electrolyte by an adsorbed $(CrO_4)^{2-}$ layer.

$$Cr + 2O_2 + 2e^- \rightarrow (CrO_4)^{2-}$$

TABLE 12–4

Galvanic Series of Common Alloys*

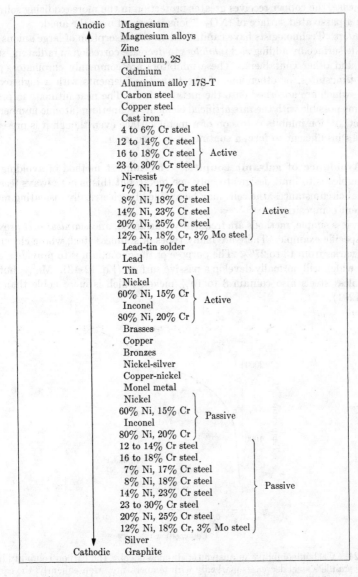

Anodic   Magnesium
          Magnesium alloys
          Zinc
          Aluminum, 2S
          Cadmium
          Aluminum alloy 17S-T
          Carbon steel
          Copper steel
          Cast iron
          4 to 6% Cr steel
          12 to 14% Cr steel ⎫
          16 to 18% Cr steel ⎬ Active
          23 to 30% Cr steel ⎭
          Ni-resist
          7% Ni, 17% Cr steel
          8% Ni, 18% Cr steel
          14% Ni, 23% Cr steel ⎬ Active
          20% Ni, 25% Cr steel
          12% Ni, 18% Cr, 3% Mo steel
          Lead-tin solder
          Lead
          Tin
          Nickel
          60% Ni, 15% Cr ⎫
          Inconel   ⎬ Active
          80% Ni, 20% Cr ⎭
          Brasses
          Copper
          Bronzes
          Nickel-silver
          Copper-nickel
          Monel metal
          Nickel
          60% Ni, 15% Cr ⎫
          Inconel   ⎬ Passive
          80% Ni, 20% Cr ⎭
          12 to 14% Cr steel
          16 to 18% Cr steel
          7% Ni, 17% Cr steel
          8% Ni, 18% Cr steel
          14% Ni, 23% Cr steel ⎬ Passive
          23 to 30% Cr steel
          20% Ni, 25% Cr steel
          12% Ni, 18% Cr, 3% Mo steel
          Silver
Cathodic Graphite

* C. A. Zapffe, *Stainless Steels*, Cleveland: American Society for Metals.

Another, and probably more familiar, example of passivation is encountered with copper, which reacts more slowly with nitric acid than with hydrochloric acid, and is corroded more readily in dilute nitric acid than in concentrated nitric acid. In each case, the copper receives greater protection in the more oxidizing solutions because a passivated surface of $(NO_3)^-$ ions is formed over the anode.

Inhibitors. Technologists have capitalized on the adsorption of large anions onto the anode surface by adding *rust inhibitors* to decrease corrosion in radiators, steam boilers, and other containers. These inhibitors are commonly chromates, phosphates, tungstates, or other ions of the transition elements with a high oxygen content, which are adsorbed onto the metal surface. The near ultimate in protection seems possible with the rare artificial element, technetium (atomic number 43). The $(TcO_4)^-$ ion inhibits corrosion of a metal surface even though it is present in quantities insufficient to form a continuous surface layer.

12–11 Avoidance of galvanic couples. The simplest method of avoiding galvanic couples is to limit designs to only one metal, but this is not always feasible. In special circumstances, the cells may be avoided by electrically insulating metals of different compositions.

Other, less simple, methods are frequently warranted, and *stainless steel* provides a good specific example. There are many types of stainless steel, whose chromium content varies from 13 to 27%. The purpose of the chromium is to provide a composition which will normally develop a passive surface (Eq. 12–13). Many, but not all, stainless steels also contain 8 to 10% nickel, which is more noble than iron (Table 12–1).

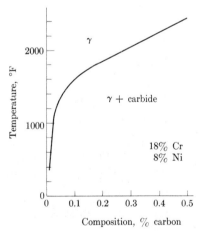

Fig. 12–24.   Carbon solubility in austenitic stainless steel. The carbon solubility in an 18–8 type stainless steel decreases markedly with temperature. Consequently, the carbon will precipitate if cooling is not rapid. The precipitated carbide is rich in chromium. (Adapted from E. E. Thum, *Book of Stainless Steels.* Cleveland: American Society for Metals, 1955.)

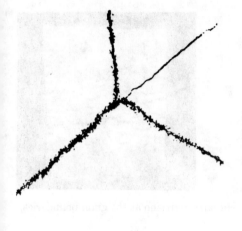

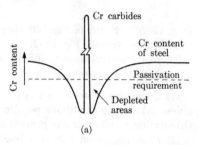

Fig. 12–25. Carbide precipitation at the grain boundaries, ×1500. The small carbon atom readily diffuses to the grain boundary. It will precipitate there as a chromium carbide if sufficient time is available (a few seconds at 1200°F). Galvanic cells are then formed. (P. Payson, *Trans. AIME*, **100**, 306–382, 1932.)

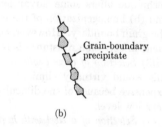

Fig. 12–26. Chromium depletion adjacent to the grain boundary. The carbide precipitation consumes nearly 10 times as much chromium as carbon. Since the larger chromium atoms diffuse slowly, the Cr content of the adjacent areas is lowered below protection levels.

The high alloy content of such a metal as 18–8 stainless steel (so-called because it contains 18% Cr-8% Ni) causes the formation of austenite, which is stable at ambient temperatures (Fig. 9–33). Such a steel is not used primarily for applications requiring high hardness, but rather in corrosive applications. Therefore carbon, which is more soluble in austenite at high than at low temperatures (Fig. 12–24), is kept to a minimum. If steel containing 0.1% carbon is cooled rapidly from 1800°F, a separate carbide does not form and galvanic cells are not established. On the other hand, if the same steel is cooled slowly, or held at 1200±°F for a short period of time, the carbon precipitates as a chromium carbide, usually in the form of a fine precipitate at the grain boundaries (Fig. 12–25). In the latter case, two effects are possible: (1) galvanic cells may be established on a microscopic scale, or (2) the carbon forms chromium carbide (more stable than Fe_3C), which depletes the grain boundary area of chromium and removes its passivating protection locally

FIG. 12–27. Intergranular corrosion. This type of corrosion becomes severe if the steel has been heated into the carbide-precipitation range. (W. O. Binder, "Corrosion Resistance of Stainless Steels," *Corrosion of Metals*. Cleveland: American Society for Metals, 1946.)

(Fig. 12–26). Either of these effects accentuates corrosion at the grain boundaries, and is to be avoided (Fig. 12–27).

There are several ways to inhibit intergranular corrosion; the choice, of course, depends on the service conditions:

(1) *Quenching to avoid carbon precipitation.* This method is commonly used unless (a) service conditions require temperatures in the precipitation range, or (b) forming, welding, or size prevent such a quenching operation.

(2) *Provision for an extremely long anneal in the carbide separation range.* This technique offers some advantage because of (a) agglomeration of the carbides, and (b) homogenization of the chromium content so that there is no deficiency at the grain boundary. However, this procedure is not common because the improvement in corrosion resistance is relatively small.

(3) *Selection of a steel with less than* 0.03% *carbon.* As indicated in Fig. 12–24, this would virtually eliminate carbide precipitation. However, such a steel is expensive because of the difficulty of removing enough of the carbon to attain this very low level.

(4) *Selection of a steel with high chromium content.* A steel which contains 18% chromium corrodes less readily than a plain carbon steel. The addition of more chromium (and nickel) provides additional protection. This, too, is expensive because of the added alloy costs.

(5) *Selection of a steel containing strong carbide formers.* Such elements include titanium, columbium, and tantalum. In these steels, the carbon does not precipitate at the grain boundary during cooling because it is precipitated earlier as titanium carbide, columbium carbide, or tantalum carbide at much higher temperatures. These carbides are innocuous because they neither deplete the chromium from the steel nor localize the galvanic action to the grain boundaries. This technique is used frequently, particularly with stainless steel which must be fabricated by welding.

Although the above examples are somewhat specific, they do indicate methods which are used to reduce the extent of corrosion in metals. The exact choice of procedure depends on the alloy and the service conditions involved.

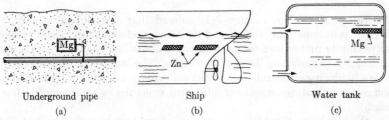

Underground pipe   Ship   Water tank

(a)   (b)   (c)

FIG. 12–28. Sacrificial anodes. (a) Buried magnesium plates along a pipeline. (b) Zinc plates on ship hulls. (c) Magnesium bar in an industrial hot water tank. Each of these sacrificial anodes may be easily replaced. They cause the equipment to become a cathode.

12–12 Galvanic protection. It is possible to restrict corrosion by turning some of the mechanisms of corrosion to protective ends. A good example is the galvanized steel discussed in Section 12–7. The zinc coating serves as a sacrificial anode which itself corrodes instead of the underlying steel. The same method may be used in other applications. Three examples are shown in Fig. 12–28. An advantage of such procedures is that the spent anode can be replaced quite easily. For example, the magnesium plates in Fig. 12–28(a) can be replaced at a fraction of the cost of replacing the underground pipe.

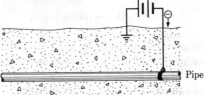

Pipe

FIG. 12–29. Impressed voltage. A small d-c voltage will provide sufficient electrons to make the equipment a cathode.

A second method of galvanic protection is the use of an *impressed voltage* on the metal. This is illustrated in Fig. 12–29. Both the sacrificial anode and the impressed voltage methods involve the same protection principle; that is, extra electrons are supplied so that the metal becomes the cathode and the corrosion reactions do not proceed.

OXIDATION

12–13 Introduction. It was stated in Section 10–9 that many materials release energy and thereby ultimately become more stable if they are oxidized. Examples included the oxidation of iron and other metals to their oxides, and the oxidation of rubber and plastics. Only ceramic materials are immune to significant amounts of oxidation (chiefly because they are already combinations of metallic and non-metallic elements). Fortunately, the oxidation for most metals and organic materials which are used for engineering purposes does not occur rapidly; however, since this reaction does eventually occur, it generally cannot be ignored.

12–14 Aging of rubber. Figure 7–19 showed that cross-linking can occur in rubber by oxidation. This and related reactions produce aging. These reactions occur readily in rubber because most natural and artificial rubbers contain many unsaturated positions along the elastomer chain. The initial consequences of aging include a hardening of the rubber. Additional oxidation actually introduces degradation and eventual decomposition into small molecules, with a complete loss of strength.

The aging stability of rubbers depends on several factors, including heat, light, stresses, and ozone content of the atmosphere. Each of these factors provides a source of energy for bond rupture; therefore, aging rates increase under service conditions in which these conditions are present.

Antioxidants are chemical compounds which are incorporated into the rubber to make it resist aging. Most antioxidants are monofunctional compounds which will not cross-link the adjacent molecular chains. In addition, they combine with the free end of any broken chains to prevent further degradation of the molecule.

12–15 Oxidation of metals. Oxidation may occur at any temperature, but it is particularly important at high temperatures, where a more rapid reaction between metal and air is likely to occur:

$$\text{Metal} + O_2 \rightarrow \text{metal oxide.} \qquad (12\text{–}15)*$$

Oxidation occurs first at the surface of a metal, and the resulting scale forms a barrier that tends to restrict further oxidation. For oxidation to continue, either the metal must diffuse through the scale to the surface, or the oxygen must diffuse through the scale to the underlying metal. Both transfers occur (Fig. 12–30), but the outward diffusion of metal is generally much more rapid than the inward diffusion of oxygen, since the metal ion is appreciably smaller than the oxygen ion ($Fe^{2+} = 0.83$ A, $O^{2-} = 1.32$ A), and consequently has much higher mobility.†

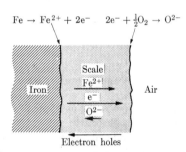

$$Fe \rightarrow Fe^{2+} + 2e^- \qquad 2e^- + \tfrac{1}{2}O_2 \rightarrow O^{2-}$$

FIG. 12–30. Scaling mechanism. Fe^{2+} and electrons diffuse more readily through the scale than do O^{2-} ions. As a result, the reaction $Fe^{2+} + O^{2-} \rightarrow FeO$ is predominant at the scale-air interface.

---

* Generally speaking, oxidation involves a positive increase in the valence of a metal. Thus metals may be oxidized in the absence of air if there is an environment which will remove electrons. (See Section 12–4.)

† The iron and oxygen diffuse in the scale as charged ions rather than as neutral atoms (Fig. 4–9). The net reaction expressed in Eq. (12–15) involves two separate reactions and a transfer of electrons through the scale from the metal to oxygen: $Fe \rightarrow Fe^{2+} + 2e$; $2e + \tfrac{1}{2}O_2 \rightarrow O^{2-}$.

Since the developing scale restricts the oxidation process, the rate of build-up dx/dt of a nonporous scale is an inverse function of the thickness x:

$$\frac{dx}{dt} = f\left(\frac{1}{x}\right),\qquad(12\text{--}16)$$

or

$$x^2 = kt.\qquad(12\text{--}17)$$

The constant k is dependent on temperature and the diffusion coefficients.

The oxidation rates for many metals follow the above parabolic relationship rather closely. However, metals with smaller oxide than metal volumes, such as magnesium, lithium, potassium, and sodium, constitute a major exception. These substances have large radii as metals but small radii as ions. Therefore a shrinkage in volume on oxidation forms a porous scale which permits free access of oxygen to the metal surface, and the rate of oxidation does not decrease with oxide accumulation. Deviations from the normal parabolic relationships also occur when scale does not adhere to the metal and so offers no protection against further oxidation.

Example 12–2

One cubic centimeter of magnesium (specific gravity 1.74) is oxidized to MgO (specific gravity 3.65). What is the volume of the resulting oxide?

Answer:

$$1 \text{ cm}^3 = 1.74 \text{ gm Mg},$$

$$1.74 \text{ gm Mg} = (1.74)\left(\frac{40.31 \text{ mol wt. MgO}}{24.31 \text{ mol wt. Mg}}\right)$$

$$= 2.9 \text{ gm MgO}.$$

$$\text{Volume of MgO} = \frac{2.9 \text{ gm}}{3.65 \text{ gm/cm}^3}$$

$$= 0.79 \text{ cm}^3 \text{ MgO}.$$

The retarding effect of a tightly adhering scale may be illustrated by the oxidation rate of aluminum. The tendency for aluminum to oxidize is even greater than for iron, but because the oxide barrier formed on aluminum is extremely adherent and quite impervious to diffusion, the rate of oxidation is rapidly decreased. Two factors contribute to this effect: (1) unlike many other oxides, the aluminum and the oxygen are very tightly bonded, so that the aluminum ions cannot readily diffuse through the oxide layer toward the surface, and (2) the crystal structures of the aluminum oxide and of the aluminum can be oriented so that there is very little mismatch and considerable continuity from one phase to another (Fig. 12–31). As a result there is a strong *coherency* between the aluminum oxide surface and the aluminum metal.

The presence of this thin oxide coating on aluminum is easily demonstrated by two simple experiments. (1) If aluminum powder, such as is used in aluminum paint, is placed between two electrodes, the electrical resistance is high. Although

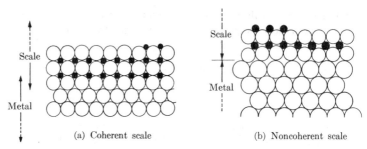

(a) Coherent scale   (b) Noncoherent scale

FIG. 12–31.   Metal-scale coherency (schematic).   The structure of the coherent scale matches the structure of the metal.   In fact, some atoms are part of both structures.

aluminum itself is a good conductor of electricity, each aluminum particle is effectively insulated from its neighbor by an oxide film.   (2) When aluminum is placed in a solution which dissolves aluminum oxide, e.g., one containing a sodium salt, the metal oxidizes very rapidly.

Effect of temperature on oxidation.   Since most metals oxidize at a decreasing rate with time, engineering materials are provided with some scaling protection at low temperatures.   However, diffusion rates increase at higher temperatures, so that the value of k in Eq. (12–17) increases according to the following relationship:

$$k = Ae^{-E/RT}, \qquad (12\text{–}18)^*$$

or

$$\ln k = \ln A - \frac{E}{RT}, \qquad (12\text{–}19)$$

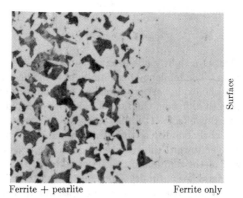

Ferrite + pearlite   Ferrite only

FIG. 12–32.   Decarburization ($\times 100$).   The 1040 steel is softened as the carbon is preferentially oxidized from the surface.

---

* Compare with Eq. (10–5).   Each involves diffusion; therefore each has the same form.

where the values of A and E depend on the phases considered. Thus, for a given time of service, an increase in temperature markedly increases the scaling rate.

• *Decarburization.* When more than one element is present in an alloy, not all will oxidize at the same rate. In steel, carbon may oxidize more rapidly than iron, and since the oxidation product is lost as a gas (CO), decarburization occurs during service (Fig. 12–32), changing the properties of the steel. In this particular material, selective oxidation of the carbon is undesirable because it produces a softening of the surface.

THERMAL STABILITY

12–16 Introduction. The thermal conditions surrounding materials affect them in a variety of ways. Foremost among these effects are the reactions which produce phase and microstructural changes. We have already discussed these in connection with phase equilibria (Chapter 9) and heat treatments (Chapter 11); therefore, we shall give no further attention to them here. We shall, however, discuss the stability of materials in relation to thermal stresses and the accompanying dimensional changes.

12–17 Thermal expansion and internal stresses. Temperature change is the most common cause of volume change in a nonporous material.* Volume changes can arise from two sources when the temperature is altered: (1) *thermal expansion* (and contraction), and (2) *phase changes.* Thermal expansion, which is associated with the increase in thermal vibration of atoms at high temperatures, is usually greater in metals than in nonmetals (Fig. 12–33). The volume changes which ac-

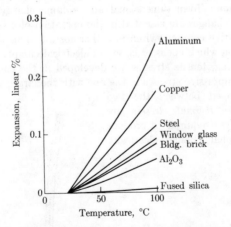

FIG. 12–33. Thermal expansion of solids. In general, the volume changes for metals are greater than those for ceramics.

---

* Volume changes may also be produced by mechanical forces, by electric fields, by magnetic fields, and by irradiation.

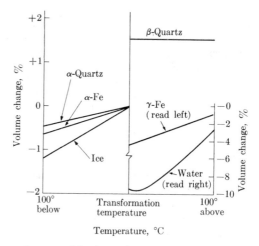

FIG. 12-34. Volume changes with phase changes. (H₂O, solid-liquid; Fe, rearrangement; quartz, bond straightening.) Note that (1) the reference volume is immediately below the transformation temperature, and (2) the water scale is at the right.

company phase changes are illustrated in Fig. 12–34; these may occur within a short temperature range if sufficient time is available.

Each of the possible changes in volume is usually small, amounting to a few percent at the most, and might be neglected if the changes are uniform. However, under normal service conditions, temperature gradients and compositional differences produce nonuniform dimensional and volume changes. For example, differential volume changes are essential in the operation of a bimetallic strip for a temperature-sensitive contact switch in a thermostat. This differential change produces a distortion which opens or closes an electrical circuit. If the strip is restrained from bending, tensile stresses are developed in the component with the smaller volume, compressive stresses in the one with the larger volume, and shear stresses are developed between the two components. These *thermal stresses* are equal to those stresses required to produce the same dimensional change elastically (Fig. 12–35).

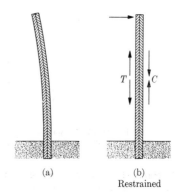

FIG. 12-35. Thermal stresses. Restraint against thermal strain produces stresses. The stresses are equal to those necessary to produce similar mechanical strains.

(a)   (b)
Restrained

Example 12–3

A bimetallic strip composed of iron and a copper alloy is annealed at 770°F to remove all residual stresses. It is then rapidly cooled to room temperature. (a) In which direction will the strip bend? (b) The two elements are the same in thickness. Calculate the stresses in each when the strip is restrained to a straight position at room temperature. (Average coefficients of expansion over this temperature range for the two metals are 14×10^{-6} and 18×10^{-6} cm/cm/°C for iron and copper, respectively. The average moduli of elasticity are 30,000,000 and 16,000,000 psi.)

Answer: (a) The strip will bend in the direction of the copper, since the iron will contract less.

(b) Iron: $\dfrac{14 \times 10^{-6} \text{ cm/cm/°C}}{1.8°\text{F/°C}} = 7.8 \times 10^{-6}$ in/in/°F.

Copper: $\dfrac{18 \times 10^{-6} \text{ cm/cm/°C}}{1.8°\text{F/°C}} = 10.0 \times 10^{-6}$ in/in/°F.

Differential contraction $= (700)(10.0 - 7.8)(10^{-6}) = 1.54 \times 10^{-3}$ in/in.

Since the two elements have the same dimensions:

$$\text{Stress}_{\text{Cu}} = \text{stress}_{\text{Fe}} = \sigma.$$

$$\text{Strain}_{\text{Cu}} = \sigma/(16{,}000{,}000).$$

$$\text{Strain}_{\text{Fe}} = \sigma/(30{,}000{,}000).$$

$$\text{Strain}_{\text{Cu}} + \text{strain}_{\text{Fe}} = 1.54 \times 10^{-3}.$$

$$\sigma \left[\frac{1}{16 \times 10^6} + \frac{1}{30 \times 10^6} \right] = \frac{1.54}{10^3}.$$

$$\sigma = 16{,}000 \text{ psi}.$$

Stresses are similarly developed by *phase changes* in solid materials. These may be either on the microscale indicated in Fig. 12–36, or on a macroscale between surface layers which transform first and the center which transforms later.

Stress relief. The stresses described above are internal (i.e., they do not arise from external application of a load), and so they remain until provision is made for their relief. In the simple case of cooling a single-phase material, *stress relief* comes when the surface and center again become uniform in temperature. Likewise, internal stresses developed at intermediate stages of phase change are relieved at the completion of the phase change.

Internal stresses may also be relieved by atom movements. If, for example, the left-hand component of the strip in Fig. 12–35 were lead, it would gradually de-

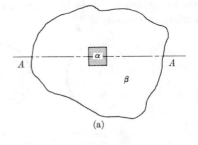

(a)

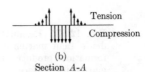

Tension

Compression

(b)
Section *A–A*

FIG. 12–36. Transformation stresses. The reaction $\beta \to \alpha$ is accompanied by a volume expansion. This produces compressive stresses in α and tensile stresses in β.

form under the stresses and relieve the stresses in both the lead and the adjacent metal. Such relief occurs quite rapidly above the recrystallization temperature for metals and above the annealing temperature for ceramics, because the atoms then have sufficient thermal activity to permit adjustment.

• **12–18 Thermal cracking.** Although internal stresses are relieved by atom movements, this cannot always occur, particularly in brittle materials. Thus, cracking is possible whenever thermal variations produce volume changes. As noted earlier, these volume changes may arise from either phase reactions or thermal expansion and/or contraction.

Quench cracking. The residual stresses shown in Fig. 12–37 frequently arise during the quenching of steel to martensite. Because martensite is somewhat less dense than the parent austenite, a slight expansion occurs near the surface. The surface reaches the martensitic transformation range before the central region does. The adjacent austenite which has not yet transformed can be strained to match this change, and when this austenite transforms shortly thereafter, the accompanying expansion places the surface martensite under tension. Such stresses can become important in nonductile materials that will not adjust to volume changes. In fact, the quenching cracks in high-carbon steels arise from such tensile stresses in the surface martensite.

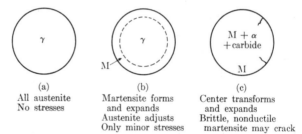

(a)	(b)	(c)
All austenite	Martensite forms	Center transforms
No stresses	and expands	and expands
	Austenite adjusts	Brittle, nonductile
	Only minor stresses	martensite may crack

FIG. 12-37. Residual transformation stresses. Austenite is more, dense than martensite, or $(\alpha + \text{carbide})$. Therefore, its transformation produces tensile stresses in the colder, more rigid, martensitic surface.

Spalling. When thermal cracking occurs without a severe quench, it is usually called spalling. Such cracking most commonly occurs in brittle materials as a result of thermal contractions; however, in certain cases either a phase transformation or thermal expansion is an important causative factor. The spalling behavior of a material is related to several properties other than the thermal expansion coefficient; these properties include strength, modulus of elasticity, and thermal diffusivity. Therefore, it is impossible to consider spalling as a basic property. It is convenient, however, to assign an index to the spalling resistance of a material.

$$\text{Spalling resistance index} = hS/\alpha E, \qquad (12\text{--}20)$$

where the terms and their significance are as follows: S = tensile strength. .A strong material will resist thermal cracking more than a weak material. h = thermal diffusivity. In turn, thermal diffusivity is equal to $k/c_p\rho$ (Eq. 1–5). A higher thermal conductivity k reduces the thermal gradients, and therefore the thermal strains. Together, the heat capacity per gm c_p and density ρ define the amount of heat which can be absorbed by a material. When the $c_p\rho$ product is high, and/or k is low, a steep thermal gradient is established and severe stresses are introduced. α = thermal expansion. A lower coefficient of expansion increases resistance to spalling for the reasons cited earlier. E = modulus of elasticity. A higher modulus of elasticity results in greater stresses for a given strain. Consequently the tensile strength is more readily exceeded.

Comparisons of spalling tendencies among various types of materials are instructive. Most ceramic materials have lower spalling resistance than metals because of their low tensile strengths (Section 8–11) and low thermal conductivities. Plastics, on the other hand, have equally low values of S and k, but have extremely low moduli of elasticity. Consequently, spalling is not common in organic materials, since very little stress is generated by the thermal strains.

Particularly important to spalling resistance is the avoidance of *stress concentrations* (Fig. 8–33) which permit the tensile strength of the materials to be exceeded locally. In the design of components which will undergo sudden temperature changes, just as for components to be used under impact loading, sharp corners should be avoided.

Currently, the effects and the control of thermal spalling are in the forefront of study for the development of automotive gas turbines. Unfortunately, many readily available materials that meet the high-temperature requirements are also brittle, and so offer little resistance to spalling induced by sudden changes in temperature.

Spalling generally produces cracks normal to the surface whenever the stresses arise from thermal contraction. In Fig. 12–38(a), for example, rapid surface cooling introduces tension cracks as the surface contracts around a rigid and still hot center. In contrast, compressive stresses are introduced when the surface of a brick is heated rapidly. Since a material cannot fail in true compression, cracking is commonly resolved into 45° planes as shown in Fig. 12–38(b).

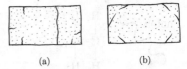

(a)   (b)

FIG. 12–38. Spall cracks in a brick. (a) Tension cracks from rapid cooling. (b) Shear cracks from rapid heating.

RADIATION DAMAGE

12–19 Introduction. In the field of engineering, attention has recently been focused on the effects of radiation on materials. In particular, radiation "damage" has been of concern in the design of nuclear reactors, although irradiation of materials is not unique to this field. That materials are modified by radiation has been recognized for some time. The botanist has watched the effects in photosynthesis.

The photographer has used this fact in the exposure of his films. The physicist has exploited the reaction for fluorescent applications. The doctor has applied radiation in therapy. The effects of visible radiation (light) on materials have even been measured by means of standardized tests (ASTM).

Radiations may be conveniently divided into two categories: (1) *Electromagnetic radiations*, which include *radio, infrared, light, x-ray*, and *gamma-rays* are conveniently considered as energy packets or *photons*. (2) Radiations that are considered to be particulate in nature include accelerated *protons* (H^+), *electrons* (β-rays), *helium nuclei* (α-rays), and *neutrons*. Our attention will be directed toward gamma-rays and neutrons, inasmuch as they are of major importance in nuclear-energy applications.

12–20 Structural alteration. The principal effect of radiation on materials arises from the extra energy it supplies, which assists in the breaking of existing bonds and in the rearrangement of the atoms into new structures. The role of radiation in the branching and crosslinking of polyethylene is an example of this phenomenon. In Table 3–1 it was shown that $99{,}000/(6.02 \times 10^{23})$ or 1.65×10^{-19} cal of energy is required to break each C-H bond. Since each photon of near-visible ultraviolet light contains about 2×10^{-19} cal of energy, the absorption of one of these photons by one of the side hydrogens in polyethylene can free it and open up a site for possible side branching (Fig. 12–39). Commercial use has been made of this effect of radiation on branching of polyethylene (Fig. 12–40) to produce a polyethylene which has stability at the boiling temperature of water.

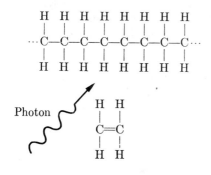

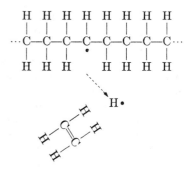

Fig. 12–39. Branching by irradiation. A photon can supply the activation energy necessary to cause branching. A neutron can produce the same effect.

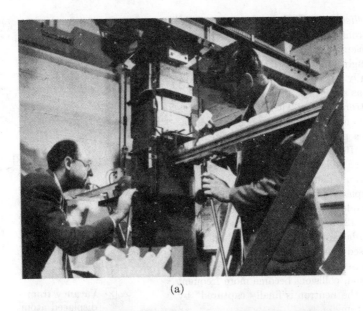

(a)

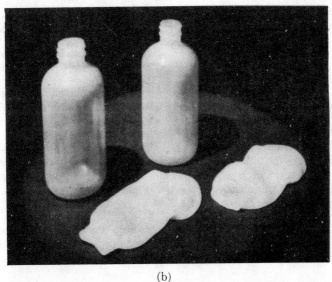

(b)

Fig. 12–40. Irradiation of polyethylene. (a) Equipment for irradiation. (b) Exposure of irradiated and nonirradiated (slumped) polyethylene at 250°F for 20 minutes. Limited irradiation produces sufficient branching of the polyethylene chains to increase the softening temperature to above that of boiling water. Excessive radiation may reverse the effect by rupturing main links in the chains (Fig. 12–42). (General Electric Co.)

Collisions of neutrons with atoms. Since neutrons are not charged, if they are given sufficient energy they can move directly through a material without being preferentially attracted to ions within the material, as are β-rays, protons, or α-particles. Neutrons interact with the atoms in a material only when they happen to "collide" with a nucleus, and such collisions occur only after many atoms have been passed. When a collision does occur in a crystal, a neutron is deflected and the atom (or ion) is displaced from its position in the crystal to produce a vacancy and interstitialcy (Fig. 12–41). A polymer may undergo degradation, or *scission,* when it is exposed to neutron radiation (Fig. 12–42). Because each collision slows down the neutron, collisions become more frequent until the neutron is finally captured* by the atom.

The displacement of an atom produces a defect in the structure of the solid. Several effects may result, depending on the structure of the material:

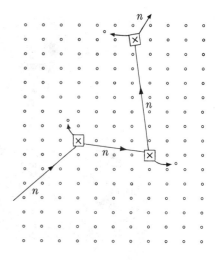

∘ Atom

☒ Vacancy from
    displaced atom

Fig.12–41.   Atom displacements by neutrons. When a neutron collides with an atom, part of the energy may be used to remove the atom from its lattice site into an interstitial site.

(1) The material may be *activated* for further reaction. Commercial use has already been made of this effect to produce branching in polyethylene (Fig. 12–40).

(2) The structure may be *degraded.* This is illustrated in Fig. 12–42 and actually represents the ultimate effect, even in polyethylene. It is more immediately noticeable in other linear plastics. As indicated in Fig. 12–43, such depolymerization degrades the mechanical properties of plastics and also influences the electrical and chemical properties.

(3) The structure may be *distorted* as a result of the vacancy and interstitialcy formation (Fig. 12–41). The resulting changes in properties are somewhat similar to those arising from cold-work and strain-hardening.

---

* Capture entails an isotopic change in the capturing atom. For example, when a manganese nucleus with 30 neutrons and 25 protons captures a neutron, it will contain 31 neutrons and 25 protons. This particular isotope of manganese happens to be unstable and will sooner or later (half-life = 2.59 hr) lose an electron (β-ray) from a neutron in the nucleus to form iron, which contains 30 neutrons and 26 protons: $n \rightarrow p^+ + e^-$.

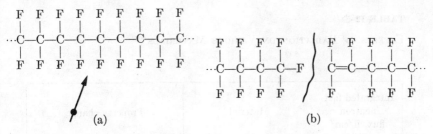

(a)	(b)

FIG. 12–42. Degradation by irradiation (polytetrafluoroethylene). Most polymers react in this manner rather than as shown in Fig. 12–39. As a result, most polymers lose strength through radiation damage.

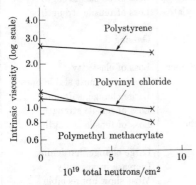

FIG. 12–43. Degradation by neutron exposure. The intrinsic viscosity is lowered because the polymers are ruptured into smaller molecules. (Adapted from L. A. Wall and M. Magot, "Effects of Atomic Radiation on Polymers," *Modern Plastics*, **30**, 111, 1953.)

Example 12–4

Assume that all the energy required to produce scission in a polyethylene molecule comes from a photon (and that none of the energy is thermal). (a) What is the maximum wavelength which can be used? (b) How many ev are involved?

Answer: (a) From Table 3–1,

$$C\!-\!C = \frac{83{,}000 \text{ cal}}{0.6 \times 10^{24} \text{ bond}} = 1.38 \times 10^{-19} \frac{\text{cal}}{\text{bond}}$$

$$= \left(1.38 \times 10^{-19} \frac{\text{cal}}{\text{bond}}\right)\left(4.185 \times 10^{7} \frac{\text{erg}}{\text{cal}}\right)$$

$$= 5.8 \times 10^{-12} \frac{\text{erg}}{\text{bond}}.$$

From Eq. (2–3),

$$\text{Energy} = h\nu = \frac{hc}{\lambda};$$

$$\lambda = \frac{(6.62 \times 10^{-27} \text{ erg·sec})(3 \times 10^{10} \text{ cm/sec})}{(5.8 \times 10^{-12} \text{ erg})}$$

$$= 3.4 \times 10^{-5} \text{ cm} = 3{,}400 \text{ A}.$$

(b)	$$\text{ev} = (5.8 \times 10^{-12} \text{ erg})\left(6.24 \times 10^{11} \frac{\text{ev}}{\text{erg}}\right) = 3.6 \text{ ev}.$$

TABLE 12–5

EFFECTS OF RADIATION ON VARIOUS MATERIALS*

Integrated fast-neutron flux, n/cm^2	Material	Property change
10^{14}	Germanium transistor	Loss of amplification
	Glass	Coloring
10^{15}	Polytetrafluoroethylene	Loss of tensile strength
	Polymethyl methacrylate and cellulosics	Loss of tensile strength
	Water and least stable organic liquids	Gassing
10^{16}	Natural and butyl rubber	Loss of elasticity
	Organic liquids	Gassing of most stable ones
10^{17}	Butyl rubber	Large change, softening
	Polyethylene	Loss of tensile strength
	Mineral-filled phenolic polymer	Loss of tensile strength
10^{18}	Natural rubber	Large change, hardening
	Hydrocarbon oils	Increase in viscosity
	Metals	Most show appreciable increase in yield strength
	Carbon steel	Reduction of notch-impact strength
10^{19}	Polystyrene	Loss of tensile strength
	Ceramics	Reduced thermal conductivity, density, crystallinity
	All plastics	Unusable as structural materials
10^{20}	Carbon steels	Severe loss of ductility, doubled yield strength
	Carbon steels	Increased fracture-transition temperature
	Stainless steels	Yield strength tripled
	Aluminum alloys	Reduced but not greatly impaired ductility
10^{21}	Stainless steels	Reduced but not greatly impaired ductility

* C. O. Smith, ORSORT, Oak Ridge, Tennessee.

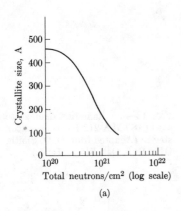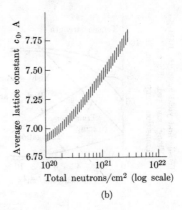

FIG. 12–44.   Radiation damage to graphite. (a) Graphite crystallite size versus exposure.
(b) Lattice spacings versus exposure. Neutron bombardment distorts the lattice and
fragments crystals into smaller grains. (Adapted from J. F. Fletcher and W. A. Snyder,
"Use of Graphite in the Atomic Energy Program," *Bulletin Amer. Cer. Soc.*, **36**, 101, 1957.)

12–21 Property alteration.   Since many, but not all, of the consequences of
neutron irradiation produce deterioration in engineering properties, these consequences are termed *radiation damage*.* Table 12–5 summarizes the extent of radiation exposure necessary to produce noticeable (greater than 10%) changes in
physical properties of some materials. The amount of radiation is based on the total
number of neutrons which pass through a square centimeter of cross-sectional
area of the particular substance.

An example of the irradiation of graphite will serve to indicate the structural
changes that produce alterations in the properties of materials. The destructive
action of neutron bombardment of graphite reduces the average grain dimensions
by a factor of four or five (Fig. 12–44). Also, the average spacing between the lattice
planes is increased because of the localized strains which arise from atomic displacement.

Figure 12–45 shows the effect of neutron exposure on the mechanical properties
of a carbon-silicon steel. Each of the altered properties is a consequence of a decrease in ease of slip in the distorted lattice structure.

Irradiation as a method of hardening or strengthening metals looks attractive at
first sight. However, there are several inherent disadvantages. First, the effect of
irradiation is logarithmic with exposure, as indicated in Fig. 12–46 for type 347
stainless steel. The exposure required for each succeeding increment of hardness
is progressively greater. Secondly, the neutron capture and gamma-ray activation
which accompanies irradiation may produce a radiologically "hot" material.

---

* Important consequences of other than engineering concern may also arise from irradiation. For example, damage can occur in living tissue from changes induced in the
physiological molecular structures.

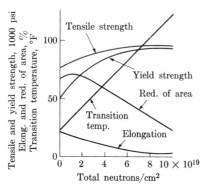

FIG. 12–45. Radiation damage to steel (ASTM A-212-B carbon-silicon steel). (Adapted from C. O. Smith, ORSORT, Oak Ridge, Tenn.)

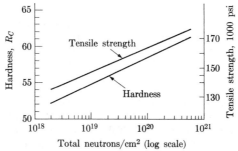

FIG. 12–46. Radiation hardening (Type 347 stainless steel). Neutrons dislodge atoms and therefore restrict slip in metals. Since the neutron flux is plotted on a logarithmic scale, each cycle requires appreciably longer exposures. (Adapted from C. O. Smith, ORSORT, Oak Ridge, Tenn.)

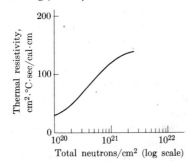

FIG. 12–47. Resistivity versus neutron radiation (graphite parallel to the direction of preferred crystal orientation). (Adapted from J. F. Fletcher and W. A. Snyder, "Use of Graphite in the Atomic Energy Program," *Bulletin Amer. Cer. Soc.*, **36**, 101, 1957.)

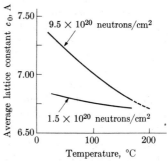

FIG. 12–48. Damage recovery. At high irradiation temperatures, the crystal lattice (Fig. 12–44b) is "annealed" as fast as the distortion proceeds. Therefore, volume changes are nil. (Adapted from J. F. Fletcher and W. A. Snyder, "Use of Graphite in the Atomic Energy Program," *Bulletin Amer. Cer. Soc.*, **36**, 101, 1957.)

REFERENCES FOR FURTHER READING

Thermal and electrical resistivities increase with neutron irradiation. Figure 12–47 illustrates the effect on thermal resistivity. The increase of both resistivities could be predicted from knowledge of the altered electron mobility in distorted solids (Section 6–7).

Recovery from radiation damage. Radiation damage may be erased by appropriate annealing at elevated temperatures. The mechanism of damage removal is identical with the mechanism of recrystallization (Section 6–8). However, the required temperature is usually lower than might be expected, apparently because the distortion of the structure is more extensive than it is in cold-working. Figure 12–48 indicates the role of irradiation temperature in modifying the damage data given in Fig. 12–44(b). At temperatures of only 200°C, the damage is repaired as fast as it is produced.

References for Further Reading

Corrosion

12–1. CARTLEDGE, G. H., "Studies in Corrosion," *Scientific American*, **195**, 35, 1956. For the student who wants supplementary reading on corrosion on a semitechnical level.

12–2. *Corrosion of Metals*. Cleveland: American Society for Metals, 1946. This reference contains five papers entitled: (1) Basic Principles of Metallic Corrosion, (2) Effect of Composition and Environment on Corrosion of Iron and Steel, (3) Corrosion Resistance of Stainless Steels and High Nickel Alloys, (4) Copper and Copper Alloys in Corrosive Environments, (5) Corrosion of Light Metals (Aluminum and Magnesium). Except for the first of the five, these are written for the metallurgical student.

12–3. *Corrosion in Action*. New York: International Nickel, 1955. The best single reference on corrosion for the beginning student. Simply written, excellently illustrated; references and simple experiments included. This is the book form of a three-reel motion picture which is available for educational use from International Nickel Co.

12–4. GUY, A. G., *Physical Metallurgy for Engineers*. Reading, Mass.: Addison-Wesley, 1962. Chapter 11 discusses corrosion and oxidation on an introductory level.

12–5. JASTRZEBSKI, Z. D., *Engineering Materials*. New York: John Wiley & Sons, 1959. Corrosion is introduced in Chapter 9. Introductory level.

12–6. KEYSER, C. A., *Materials of Engineering*. Englewood Cliffs, N. J.: Prentice-Hall, 1956. Chapter 6 discusses corrosion and corrosion testing. The subject is handled at about the same level as it is in this book.

12–7. SPELLER, F. N., *Corrosion: Causes and Prevention*. New York: McGraw-Hill, 1951. Considerable emphasis is placed on the avoidance of corrosion.

12–8. UHLIG, H. H., *Corrosion Handbook*. New York: John Wiley & Sons, 1948. This is the standard reference book on corrosion. For the practicing engineer.

12–9. WULFF, J., et al., *Structure and Properties of Materials*. Cambridge, Mass.: M.I.T. Press, 1962. Chapters 8 and 9 discuss oxidation and corrosion, respectively. Introductory level.

Thermal Behavior

12–10. BALDWIN, W. M., JR., *Residual Stresses*. Philadelphia: American Society for Testing Materials, 1949. An introduction to residual stresses. Recommended because it has illustrative sketches which show the distribution of residual stresses.

12–11. DORN, J. E., *Mechanical Behavior of Materials at Elevated Temperatures*. New York: John Wiley & Sons, 1961. A series of articles which discuss the response of materials to stresses at high service temperatures. Advanced undergraduate level.

12–12. NORTON, F. H., *Refractories*. New York: McGraw-Hill, 1949. Chapter 15 discusses spalling and spall resistance. For the advanced student.

12–13. PARKER, E. R., *Materials for Missiles and Spacecraft*. New York: McGraw-Hill, 1963. A series of articles on the application of materials to the special environments of space.

Radiation Damage

12–14. A.S.T.M., *Radiation Effects on Materials*. Philadelphia: Amer. Soc. for Testing and Materials, Vol. I, 1957; Vol. II, 1958; Vol. III, 1958. The three short volumes contain a series of papers on specific radiation effects. Advanced undergraduate level.

12–15. BILLINGTON, D. S., *et al.*, *How Radiation Affects Materials*; *Nucleonics*, **14,** [9], 1956, page 55. A series of eight articles on how radiation affects materials. For the engineer who is a nonspecialist.

12–16. FRYE, J. H. and J. L. GREGG, "Economic Atomic Power Depends on Materials of Construction," *Metals Progress*, **70,** 92, September 1956. A general article pointing out a new field of engineering interest.

12–17. HARWOOD, J. J., *et al.*, *Effects of Radiation on Materials*. New York: Reinhold, 1958. Symposium on the modifications of physical, chemical, surface, electronic, and optical properties. Advanced-level presentation.

12–18. LEESER, D. O., "Engineering Materials in Nuclear-Fueled Power Plants," *Materials and Methods*, **41,** 98, May 1955. Discusses cross-sectional absorption requirements and effects of radiation.

12–19. SUN, K. H., "Effects of Atomic Radiation on High Polymers," *Modern Plastics*, **32,** 141, September 1954. A good summary article on the effects of irradiation on plastics.

Problems

12–1. Two pieces of metal, one copper and the other zinc, are immersed in sea water and connected by a copper wire. Indicate the galvanic cell by writing the half reaction (a) for the anode, (b) for the cathode; also by indicating (c) the direction of electron flow in the wire, and (d) the direction of the "current" flow in the electrolyte. (e) What metal might be used in place of copper so that the zinc changes polarity?

12–2. A zinc-coated nail is cut in half and placed in an electrolyte. (a) What couples must be considered in judging where the anode will be? (b) Cite the location which will be corroded initially.

12–3. A portion of an old iron pipe in a basement has been replaced by copper tubing. (a) The union (i.e., the coupling) which the plumber used to connect the new to the old contained a plastic insulator. Comment. (b) In order to ensure that the plumbing system could be used as a ground, a "jump" was placed across the connection. Comment.

12–4. An iron sheet is placed in water taken from a lake. Each of the following actions is taken (individually). How will each affect the corrosion reactions? (a) $FeSO_4$ is added to the water. (b) $CuSO_4$ is added to the water. (c) HCl is added to the water. (d) HCl is added to the water and O_2 is bubbled through it. (e) HCl is added to the water and N_2 is bubbled through it. (f) The iron is connected to the center electrode of a dry cell. (g) The iron is connected to the edge electrode of a dry cell. (h) Step (f), plus a copper wire connected from the edge electrode to the electrolyte.

12–5. Zinc and copper are connected in water. (a) Some $ZnSO_4$ is added. Will corrosion increase or decrease? (b) Some $CuSO_4$ is added. Will corrosion increase or decrease?

12–6. Compare and contrast the nature of the protection given to steel by (a) cadmium, (b) zinc, and (c) tin coatings.

12–7. Cite three examples of corrosion from your experience. Describe the nature of the deterioration, and account for the corrosion.

12–8. Refer to figures in Chapter 9 and this chapter. What phases are present in the following stainless steels at room temperature: (a) Fe with 12.5 Cr, (b) Fe with 18 Cr, (c) Fe with 18 Cr and 0.6 C, (d) Fe with 13 Cr and 0.5 C, (e) Fe with 18 Cr, 8 Ni, and 0.1 C, (f) Fe with 18 Cr, 8 Ni, and 0.5 C?

12–9. For each of the analyses in the previous problem indicate the phases at 2000°F.
Answer: (a) $\gamma + \alpha$ (b) α (c) $\gamma +$ carbide   (d) γ (e) γ (f) $\gamma +$ carbide

12–10. A stainless steel sheet is welded into a circular duct. After a period of time, rust appears along a band extending about 0.5 in. on each side of the weld. Why did this occur and what could have been done to avoid it?

12–11. Stainless steels are frequently divided into three categories: austenitic, ferritic, and martensitic. Cite the compositional differences that determine into which category a steel is placed.

12–12. An 18% Cr–8% Ni stainless steel is austenitic at room temperature. (a) Why? (b) Cite distinctive thermal, electrical, and magnetic properties that are consequences of this composition and structure.

12–13. Cutlery is made of martensitic stainless steels for obvious reasons. How does the corrosion resistance of these steels compare with that of austenitic stainless steels?

12–14. Aluminum boats are more satisfactory in fresh-water lakes than in sea water. Explain.

12–15. The coherency of Al_2O_3 to aluminum involves a close match of (a) the Al-to-Al distances in the (111) planes of the metal and (b) the (0001) plane of Al_2O_3. What are these distances?
Answer: (a) 2.86 A   (b) 2.67 A

12–16. How much volume change occurs when iron is oxidized to Fe_3O_4? (Specific gravity of $Fe_3O_4 = 5.18$.)

12–17. How much volume change occurs when calcium is oxidized to CaO? (Specific gravity of CaO = 3.4.)
Answer: 36% contraction

12–18. Show why potassium oxidation occurs rapidly. (Specific gravity of $K_2O = 2.32$.)

12-19. A piece of 1080 steel bar is heated from 70°F to 150°F, but restrained from any longitudinal expansion. What stresses are developed? [*Hint:* The stress developed is the same as the stress required to compress the material to give the same strain.]
Answer: 14,400 psi

12-20. Some iron wire is not allowed to contract as it is transformed from α to γ. Assuming no plastic strain, what stresses would be developed? [*Note:* The modulus of elasticity at 1670°F is *not* 3×10^7 psi. (*See* Fig. 6-8).]

12-21. An annealed copper wire with a yield strength of 8000 psi is restrained from thermal contraction. How much can its temperature be changed before plastic adjustments are made within the wire?
Answer: 56°F

12-22. A bimetallic strip is composed of copper and iron, with cross-sectional areas of 0.005 in² and 0.002 in², respectively. How much stress would be developed in each of these metals if they were handled as described in Example 12-3 (page 361)?

12-23. What will be the strain in each part of the strip in Problem 12-22?
Answer: Copper, 0.00066 in/in; iron, 0.00088 in/in

12-24. A bar of 70-30 brass and a bar of steel are securely attached to two rigid walls which are 3 ft apart. The bars are 2 in. in diameter and without stress at 100°F. What stresses would be present in each bar at 50°F? What would be the change in length of each bar at 50°F if they were not held rigidly?

12-25. (a) What frequency and wavelength must a photon have to supply the energy necessary to break an average C—H bond in polyethylene? (b) Why can some bonds be broken with longer electromagnetic waves? (See Appendix A for an erg-to-cal conversion factor. The values in Table 3-1 are for an Avogadro's number of bonds.)
Answer: (a) 1.04×10^{15} cps, 2900 A; (b) thermal energy is present.

12-26. A neutron breaks a C—C bond in polystyrene. How many ev were used?

12-27. Compare the wavelengths of the electromagnetic photons required to supply all the energy for branching in (a) polyethylene, (b) polyvinyl chloride, and (c) polyvinyl alcohol.
Answer: C—H, 2900 A; C—Cl, 3550 A; C—OH, 3300 A

12-28. A photon breaks a C—C bond in polystyrene. What must the minimum energy of the photon be and what wavelength radiation would supply photons having this energy? (Assume that all the energy came from the photon.)

12-29. Other things being equal, which will *spall more readily:* (a) a material with a high modulus of elasticity and a low thermal conductivity, (b) a material with a low modulus of elasticity and a high thermal conductivity, (c) a material with a low modulus of elasticity and low thermal conductivity, (d) a material with a high modulus of elasticity and high thermal conductivity? Why?

13

composite materials

13–1 Macrostructures. The internal heterogeneities of materials considered up to this point have been those resulting from solidification or from solid-phase reactions, and have been microscopic in dimension. The engineer is not limited to materials with these compositional variations, however, because he can intentionally integrate two or more distinct materials into one composite. He is therefore able to design materials which incorporate a combination of properties that would not be available in one material alone. Examples are glass-reinforced plastic or vitreous-coated (enameled) sheet steel. In the former, the glass provides tensile strength and dimensional stability, while the plastic supplies coherency and eliminates porosity. Enameled sheet steel contains a metal which is easily shaped and has a high modulus of elasticity, both features which are desirable in many applications. However, metals have a major weakness of being subject to oxidation and corrosion; therefore a metal with a protective glass coating is a useful composite (and one which can be colored as desired).

We shall categorize composite materials into three groups, more or less according to processing procedures: agglomerated materials, surface coatings, and reinforced materials. If we consider the internal structures of composite materials, as we did for various materials in previous chapters, it is possible to make comparisons among them. Since the structural and compositional heterogeneities are coarser than those considered so far, and in fact may often be observed with an unaided eye, the term *macrostructure* (literally, coarse structure) is applied. We shall not attempt, however, to make a sharp distinction between microstructures and macrostructures.

AGGLOMERATED MATERIALS

13–2 Introduction. Many engineering materials are formed by the agglomeration of small particles into a usable product. Probably the most obvious example is concrete, in which gravel, sand, portland cement, and water are mixed into a monolithic (literally, one-stone) engineering material. The current achievements in highway construction would be impossible were it not for the substitution of concrete for the former brick and stone pavements (Fig. 13–1). Agglomerations of asphalt and stone are also used for highway surfaces (Fig. 13–2), and in such cases the soils or similar aggregates on which they rest must be taken into account.

Many other agglomerated materials are equally important for modern industry. Unlike concrete, which is bonded by hydraulic cement, the abrasive grains of grinding wheels are bonded together by either a glass or a resin; brick depends

375

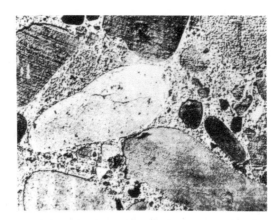

FIG. 13–1. Cross section of concrete (×1.5). The pores within the gravel are filled with sand. The pores within the sand are filled with a hydrated portland cement paste. (Portland Cement Association.)

FIG. 13–2. Cross section of asphalt pavement. Like concrete, this is an aggregate, but viscous asphalt, rather than a hydrated silicate, serves as the bond. (The Asphalt Institute.)

entirely on a vitreous bond, and powdered metals (Fig. 13–3) depend on solid sintering at high temperatures for bonding. One of many recent industrial applications of agglomerated materials is for shell molds for the foundry industry (Fig. 13–4). Here, thin sand molds are bonded with a resin which is polymerized by a hot pattern.

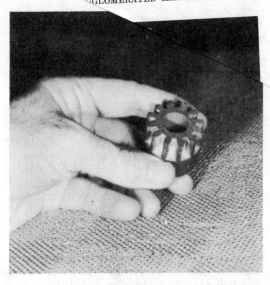

FIG. 13–3. Powdered metal gear. The metal particles are sintered into a coherent structure.

FIG. 13–4. Shell mold. This mold for metal castings is composed of sand bonded with a phenolformaldehyde resin. (Link Belt Co.)

TABLE 13-1

TYLER SCREE~

Mesh number	Opening, inches	Mesh number	Opening, inches
—	1.050	20	0.0328
—	0.742	28	0.0232
—	0.525	35	0.0164
—	0.371	48	0.0116
3	0.263	65	0.0082
4	0.185	100	0.0058
6	0.131	150	0.0041
8	0.093	200	0.0029
10	0.065	270	0.0021
14	0.046	400	0.0015

13–3 Particle size. If all the particles used in agglomerated materials were perfect spheres, the determination of particle size would be a relatively simple matter of measuring diameters. In practice, most particles vary considerably from perfect sphericity, but it is still desirable to have a measure of the size. For this purpose sand and gravel, for example, are sifted through screens with standardized openings. Large openings are measured directly in inches, but openings less than $\frac{1}{4}$ inch in size are expressed in *mesh numbers* which indicate the number of openings per linear inch. Table 13–1 shows the most commonly used mesh series. Openings for successive mesh numbers vary by a factor of $\sqrt{2}$.

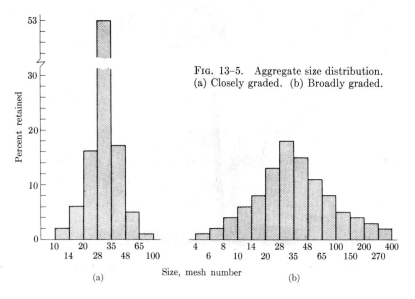

FIG. 13–5. Aggregate size distribution. (a) Closely graded. (b) Broadly graded.

Size, mesh number

Any aggregate mixture will be composed ~ ange of mesh sizes, and it is usually insufficient to rely on the average size of an ~ ate. Figure 13–5 shows the percent of aggregate retained by successively finer scre~. 'n one case, the particles are very closely graded and are all about the same size. In t.~ *her case, however, there is a wide variation in size. Because the mean and the meu~ sizes are approximately the same in each case, the engineer usually specifies a size u.~ribution based on the percent aggregate retained on screens of more than one mesh siz~.

13–4 Bulk characteristics. A uniformly sized material cannot be packed into a large container without the presence of considerable porosity in the container. The largest possible *packing factor* for spheres is only 74%; that is, only 74% of the total volume is occupied by the spheres (Fig. 13–6):

$$\text{Packing factor} = \frac{\text{particle volumes}}{\text{bulk volume}}$$

$$= 1 - \text{porosity}.$$

$$(13-1)$$

For a material of uniform size and shape in a large container, the packing factor is independent of actual dimensions. The following calculation makes this clear.

FIG. 13–6. Densest packing of uniform spheres. Only 74% of the cube is occupied by spheres. With the data of Fig. 3–16 as a basis, this factor can be calculated.

Example 13–1

Determine the packing factor for uniform spheres (a) 1 inch in diameter and (b) 0.01 inch in diameter, when they are most densely packed. [*Note:* Spheres are packed most densely when they are arranged in either fcc or hcp arrays. We shall use the fcc array for this calculation. See Fig. 3–16.]

Answer: (a) Cube volume (fcc): $\left(\dfrac{(4)(0.5)}{\sqrt{2}}\right)^3 = (1.414 \text{ in})^3 = 2.828 \text{ in}^3$.

Sphere volume in cube: $(4)(\frac{4}{3}\pi r^3) = \frac{16}{3}\pi(0.5)^3 = 2.094 \text{ in}^3$.

$$\text{Packing factor} = \frac{\text{true volume}}{\text{total volume}} = \frac{2.094}{2.828} = 74\%.$$

(b) Cube volume: $\left(\dfrac{(4)(0.005)}{\sqrt{2}}\right)^3 = (0.01414)^3 = 2.828 \times 10^{-6} \text{ in}^3$.

Sphere volume in cube: $\frac{16}{3}\pi(0.005)^3 = 2.094 \times 10^{-6}$.

$$\text{Packing factor} = \frac{2.094 \times 10^{-6}}{2.828 \times 10^{-6}} = 74\%.$$

In a small container, where ᷒_ .ᴵᴵncant percentage of the particles is in contact with the walls, this calcuᴵᵗ does not hold. At these peripheral locations the walls of the containeᴿ ᷒ᷓ erfere with the packing arrangement, so that the packing cannot be so deᴿ ᷓ

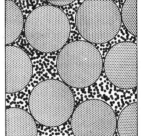

Fig. 13–7. Mixed packing of particles. The packing factor may be increased by introducing small particles into the pore spaces among the large particles.

Packing factors may be increased by two methods: (1) By using nonspherical particles with matching surfaces. The packing factor for a pile of bricks, for example, can be nearly 100% if they are carefully stacked. (2) By mixing particle sizes (Fig. 13–7). For example, a mixture of sand and gravel has a greater packing factor than either sand or gravel alone because the sand fills the pore spaces among the pieces of gravel. Figure 13–8 shows typical variations of the packing factor for mixtures of sand and gravel; this relationship determines the optimum ratio of sand to gravel for a mixture that will fill a given volume with least porosity. If, for example, a ratio of 25% sand and 75% gravel were used in a concrete mixture, only 15–20% of the volume would be pore space to be filled by a cement-water paste. On the other hand, a 50-50 mixture would leave 25–30% pore space and would require half again as much of the more expensive cement to develop the same strength in the concrete.

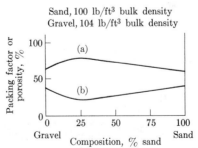

Sand, 100 lb/ft^3 bulk density
Gravel, 104 lb/ft^3 bulk density

Fig. 13–8. (a) Packing factor versus composition of aggregate mixtures. (b) Porosity versus composition of aggregate mixtures. The densest packing and the lowest porosity occur when there is just enough sand to fill the pore spaces within the gravel.

Density and porosity. The interconnecting pore channels of Fig. 13–7 are called *open pores.* An agglomerated material may also have internal or *closed pores* which do not contribute to the permeability of the material.

The choice of method for calculating the density and specific gravity of a mixture depends on whether the pores are open or closed, as indicated by the following relationships:

$$\text{True density} = \frac{\text{mass}}{\text{true volume}} = \frac{\text{mass}}{\text{bulk volume} - \text{total pore volume}} . \quad (13\text{--}2)$$

$$\text{Apparent density} = \frac{\text{mass}}{\text{apparent volume}} = \frac{\text{mass}}{\text{bulk volume} - \text{open pore volume}} .$$
$$(13\text{--}3)$$

$$\text{Bulk density} = \frac{\text{mass}}{\text{bulk volume}} = \frac{\text{mass}}{\text{true volume} + \text{total pore volume}} . \quad (13\text{--}4)$$

$$\text{True porosity} = \frac{\text{total pore volume}}{\text{bulk volume}} = 1 - \text{true packing factor}. \quad (13\text{--}5)$$

$$\text{Apparent porosity} = \frac{\text{open pore volume}}{\text{bulk volume}} = 1 - \text{apparent packing factor}. \quad (13\text{--}6)$$

Relationships among the above values determine the bulk behavior of a material. The absorption characteristics of a sponge, of concrete, or of cellular wall insulation depend on the *apparent porosity*. The *bulk density* of a material determines its construction weight and also markedly affects thermal conductivity. The number of open pores, as well as their size and shape, contributes to permeability and strength characteristics.

Example 13–2

The true specific gravity of a concrete to which an air-entraining agent was added is 2.80. However, a dry core (6 in. × 4 in. in diameter) of this concrete weighs 6.56 lb. The same core weighs 6.775 lb when saturated with water. What are the volumes of the open and closed pores?

Answer: Basis: 1 ft³ concrete.

$$(62.4)(2.80) = 174.7 \text{ lb/ft}^3, \text{ true density};$$

$$\frac{6\pi(2)^2}{1728} = 0.0436 \text{ bulk ft}^3, \text{ in core};$$

$$\frac{6.56 \text{ lb}}{0.0436 \text{ bulk ft}^3} = 150.4 \text{ lb/ft}^3, \text{ bulk density};$$

$$\frac{174.7 - 150.4}{174.7} = 13.9\%, \text{ total porosity};$$

$$\frac{6.775 - 6.56 \text{ lb}}{62.4 \text{ lb/ft}^3} = 0.00343 \text{ ft}^3, \text{ open pore space in core};$$

$$\frac{0.00343}{0.0436} = 7.9\%, \text{ apparent porosity (open pores)};$$

$$13.9 - 7.9 = 6.0\%, \text{ closed pores}.$$

13–5 Concrete. To state the matter simply, let us say that concrete is gravel with an admixture of sand to fill the pores. The space still remaining in the sand is then filled with a "paste" of cement and water. The cement hydrates (it does not dry) to form a bond within the concrete. Experience has indicated that, in addition to the aggregate and cement "paste," it is advantageous to entrain a few percent (by volume) of small air bubbles into the concrete. This entrained air improves the workability of the concrete during placement; but more important, these small air bubbles increase the resistance of the concrete to deterioration resulting from freezing and thawing. The reasons for this are not fully understood as yet.

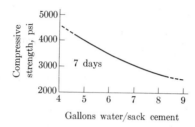

Gallons water/sack cement

FIG. 13–9. Strength of concrete versus water content. Seven-day job curve for one lot of portland cement. (Compare with a similar 28-day job curve in Fig. 1–12.)

Assuming that the aggregate is much stronger than the cement, it is the property of the cement paste which governs the properties of the concrete. Consequently, concrete with a *low water-to-cement ratio* is stronger than concretes with higher ratios. With the low ratio, there is more hydrated cement and less excess water in the spaces between the sand and gravel particles. This indirect relationship between the strength of concrete and its water-cement ratio is not fully appreciated even by many engineers. Figure 13–9 shows this variation for one lot of portland cement.

Example 13–3

A concrete mix consists of 2.75 ft³ of gravel, 2.00 ft³ of sand, and 6 gal of water per sack of cement (94 lb), plus 5 v/o entrained air. How many sacks of cement would be required to make a retaining wall containing 329 ft³ of concrete?

Data	Specific gravity	Bulk density, lb/ft³
Gravel	2.60	110
Sand	2.65	105
Cement	3.25	94

Answer: Basis: 1 sack cement.

$$\text{True volume of gravel} = \frac{(2.75)(110)}{(62.4)(2.60)} = 1.86 \text{ ft}^3.$$

$$\begin{array}{c} \text{True volume of sand} \\ \text{(in pores within gravel)} \end{array} = \frac{(2.00)(105)}{(62.4)(2.65)} = 1.27 \text{ ft}^3.$$

$$\begin{array}{c} \text{True volume of cement} \\ \text{(in pores within sand)} \end{array} = \frac{94}{(62.4)(3.25)} = 0.46 \text{ ft}^3.$$

$$\begin{array}{c} \text{True volume of water} \\ \text{(in pores among all solids)} \end{array} = \frac{(6)(8.33)}{62.4} = 0.80 \text{ ft}^3.$$

$$\frac{\text{Total ft}^3 \text{ concrete}}{\text{sack cement}} = \frac{4.39 \text{ ft}^3}{0.95} = 4.62.$$

$$\text{Sacks of cement} = \frac{329}{4.62} = 71 \text{ sacks.}$$

Portland cement. The preceding examples of concrete referred to a cement paste which serves as a bond for the aggregate. The bonding occurs because the portland cement, which initially is a mixture of calcium aluminate and calcium silicate, undergoes hydration:

$$Ca_3Al_2O_6 + 6H_2O \rightarrow Ca_3Al_2(OH)_{12}, \tag{13-7}$$

$$Ca_2SiO_4 + xH_2O \rightarrow Ca_2SiO_4 \cdot xH_2O. \tag{13-8}*$$

In each reaction the hydrated product is less soluble than the original cement. Therefore, in the presence of water the above reactions are really ones of solution and precipitation.

Other cements. There is a wide variety of other cements, both organic and inorganic. In general, these may be categorized as (1) hydraulic, (2) polymeric, and (3) reaction. *Hydraulic* cements include those which have hydration reactions similar to those of portland cement. An inorganic example of a *polymeric* cement is silicic acid:

$$x Si(OH)_4 \rightarrow \left(\begin{array}{c} OH \\ | \\ Si-O \\ | \\ OH \end{array} \right)_x + xH_2O. \tag{13-9}$$

---

* This reaction may be more correctly stated as:

$$2Ca_2SiO_4 + (5 - y + x)H_2O$$
$$\rightarrow Ca_2[SiO_2(OH)_2]_2 \cdot (CaO)_{y-1} \cdot xH_2O + (3 - y)Ca(OH)_2,$$

where x varies with the partial pressure of the water and y is approximately 2.3. (See Reference 13-3.)

Although a linear chain is indicated, considerable cross-linking is possible. *Reaction cements* are typified by the phosphate bonds:

$$Al_2O_3 + 2H_3PO_4 \rightarrow 2AlPO_4 + 3H_2O. \tag{13–10}$$

The interaggregate bond is the $AlPO_4$ which may be compared directly with SiO_2, in which Al and P atoms have replaced two Si atoms, i.e., $AlPO_4$ versus $SiSiO_4$.

13–6 Sintered products. *Sintering* is a process of heating in order to agglomerate small particles into bulk materials. For sintering to occur, a bond must develop (1) through the formation of a liquid phase, or (2) by solid diffusion.

Although bonding may be achieved by the formation of a liquid phase, it is mandatory that the liquid lose its fluidity before the material goes into service. Tools made of sintered carbides are bonded with alloys containing cobalt or nickel. In the sintering process the metal binder melts and forms a continuous matrix between the carbide particles (Fig. 13–10), but the metal binder crystallizes after sintering to provide a strong and rigid tool. Likewise, when resins are used to bond small particles (Fig. 13–4), the resin must be able to flow onto the particle surface. However, instead of crystallizing, the resin polymerizes and becomes less fluid, producing a strong bond.

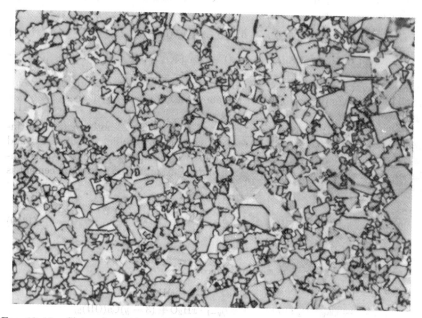

FIG. 13–10.   Sintered carbides, ×1500. Powdered carbide and powdered metal particles were compacted and heated. The metal (cobalt) melted during sintering and formed a continuous matrix between the hard tungsten carbide particles. (Metallurgical Products Department, General Electric Co.)

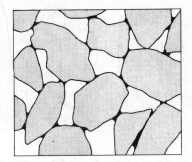

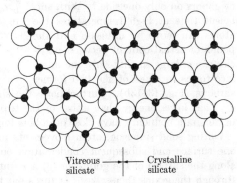

FIG. 13–11. Vitreous sintering (schematic). A glassy silicate (black) starts to form when the material is heated above the solidus. The glass does not crystallize on cooling, but does form a strong bond between the remaining particles.

FIG. 13–12. Coherency of glass and crystals (schematic). The vitreous, glassy structure is contiguous with the repetitive crystalline structure. This continuity of primary bonding produces a strong material.

Vitreous ——————— Crystalline
silicate   silicate

The most widely employed sintering process is the *firing* of silicate materials, sometimes called *vitreous sintering*. The brick, porcelain, spark plug, or similar silicate object is heated to a temperature above the solidus at which some liquid forms. The liquid in a silicate material is a glass which may be cooled to room temperature without crystallizing. However, even though not crystallized, it is extremely viscous and provides a very hard and strong glassy bond. Figure 13–11 shows schematically the microstructure of such a bond between adjacent particles. The adherence of the glass to the particles can be very strong because there may be continuity (coherency) in the atomic structures (Fig. 13–12).

The properties of a vitreous (i.e., glassy) bonded material depend, among other things, upon the amount of glass present. Because it must take mechanical wear, a paving brick must contain a relatively high percentage of glass, unlike a "soft-fired" drain tile which lies statically below the frost line in a field. Some processing difficulties are encountered in "hard-firing." Although more glass makes the material harder, it also produces a semifluid phase in the kiln, with a greater possibility of distortion. It is therefore necessary to maintain close firing control.

Solid sintering. Sintering without the formation of a liquid phase requires diffusion and therefore occurs most rapidly at temperatures just below the solidus. Many powdered metal parts and various magnetic and dielectric ceramic materials are produced by *solid sintering*. These ceramic materials cannot be made by melting or by vitreous sintering because the properties are then altered. Also, because no feasible crucible or mold is available for the required pouring temperatures, such refractory metals as tungsten and columbium (niobium) are commonly formed by solid sintering.

The principle involved in solid sintering is illustrated in Fig. 13–13. As shown in part (a), there are two surfaces between any two particles. These are high-energy regions because the atoms at the surfaces of the particles have neighbors on only one side.* With sufficient time at high temperatures the atoms can move by diffusion and the points of actual contact between particles can enlarge so that only one interface forms in place of the two former

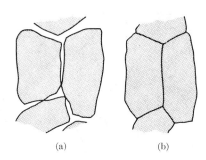

FIG. 13–13. Solid sintering. (a) Particles before sintering have two adjacent surfaces. (b) Grains after sintering have one boundary. The driving force for the sintering is the reduction of surface area (and therefore of surface energy).

surfaces (Fig. 13–13b). Furthermore, the single interface (now a grain boundary) has lower energy than either of the two former surfaces because the atoms in the grain boundary have close neighbors (although not perfectly aligned).

During solid sintering, atom movements may occur by (1) vaporization from one surface and subsequent condensation onto another surface, (2) a diffusion along the surface of the grains, or (3) a counter-diffusion of vacancies and atoms through the grains themselves. It turns out that the latter mechanism, depicted in Fig. 13–14, is the most common, because it can directly involve many more atoms. This counter-diffusion brings the center of the grains closer together and induces shrinkage during sintering.

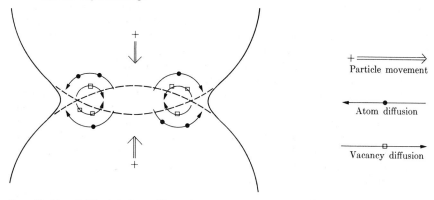

FIG. 13–14. Solid sintering. There is a counter-movement of atoms and vacancies. Shrinkage occurs as a result of this sintering.

* Although two particles may be close together, the gap between them may still be many atomic distances, so that interatomic attractions are extremely weak.

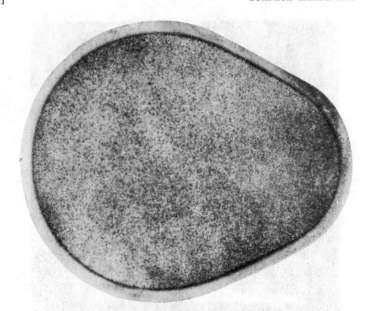

Fig. 13–15. Induction-hardened steel. High-frequency currents were induced into the surface of the steel, and there was localized heating at the desired positions. (H. B. Osborn, Jr., The Ohio Crankshaft Co.)

SURFACE MODIFICATIONS

13-7 Surface hardening. An engineer often wants a material with a very hard surface which will resist a great amount of wear. Two simple procedures to obtain such a surface call for either welding a hard metal onto the existing metal, or spraying an abrasion-resistant coating onto metal or ceramic surfaces. Other procedures call for actual surface alteration.

Surface alteration. Commercially, surface alterations are frequently made by means of heat treatments of the surface. This may be done in two ways: (1) the surface zone may receive a heat treatment different from that given the material farther below the surface, or (2) the composition of the surface zone may be changed. The former is illustrated by *induction* and *flame* hardening (Figs. 13–15 and 13–16), where the surface is heated so quickly that the center is not appreciably affected. Subsequent quenching can occur much faster because heat does not have to be conducted from the center through the surface zone. In fact, the cold center may actually help quench the surface. Consequently, a high percentage of martensite may be developed in the surface zone around a tougher core.

The second method of surface alteration involves the diffusion of elements into the surface. *Nitriding* is one example. In this process, steel containing aluminum is placed in an atmosphere of dissociated ammonia. At about 950°F, nitrogen diffuses into the crystal lattice and precipitates in the surface zone as aluminum

Fig. 13–16. Flame-hardening of steel. Heat is applied only where hardness is desired. The remainder of the piece remains tough. (Farrel-Birmingham Co.)

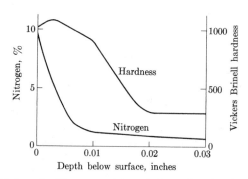

Fig. 13–17. Nitrided steel. The composition of the surface has been changed by the introduction of nitrogen, which reacts with aluminum in the steel. The AlN (R_C 75) is harder than martensite. (Adapted from B. Jones and H. E. Morgan, "Investigations into the Nitrogen Hardening of Steels," *Iron and Steel Institute, Carnegie Schol. Mem.*, **31**, 39–86, 1932.)

nitride. Because this phase is harder than martensite, a wear-resistant surface is produced (Fig. 13-17).

Carburizing differs from nitriding in the nature of the surface alteration. If a low-carbon steel is exposed to a carbonaceous atmosphere at high temperatures, the small carbon atoms can be diffused into the subsurface of the solid metal to produce a high-carbon *case* (Fig. 13-18). Subsequent quenching will produce a hard, wear-resistant, martensitic surface and a tough ferritic *core*. Such a combination is particularly useful in mechanical components of machinery.

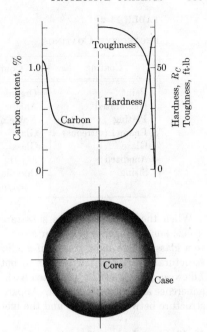

FIG. 13-18. Carburized steel. Carbon has been diffused into the surface. A hard case may thus be formed around a tougher core.

13-8 Compressive surfaces. Inasmuch as many fractures start at the surfaces of materials, it is often desirable to place the surface under compression. This may be accomplished by shot-peening in metals. In glass, compression is commonly produced by volume changes (Figs. 8-36 and 8-37). It may also be accomplished by compositional changes in glass, a procedure which requires the application of several of the principles cited earlier in this text. For example, if a glass is exposed to a hot Li_2SO_4 solution, lithium ions diffuse into the surface zone of the glass, depolymerizing the framework structure of SiO_4 units (Fig. 8-23). The presence of Li^+ ions thus permits rather rapid crystallization in the surface zone during subsequent heat-treatments, and since there is a volume expansion as the lithium silicate glass crystallizes, the surface zone of the glass is placed under compression. A stress pattern is developed which is similar to that shown in Fig. 8-37.

• **13-9 Protective coatings.** A coating of paint on a metal, polymer, or ceramic produces the simplest of all composite materials. Although paint may be applied primarily for the appearance of the product, the engineering significance of any coating is usually that of protection. Various types of coatings are listed in Table 13-2.

For a coating to adhere, continuity must be established between the surface layer and the substrate material. When the two are similar, the bonds are similar to those between phases within a microstructure. Thus Fig. 13-12 could indicate the bond between a glaze and an electrical insulator; likewise, galvanized coating adheres to sheet steel through a metal-to-metal bond.

TABLE 13–2

PROTECTIVE COATINGS

Coating	Composition	Substrate
Paint	Organic vehicle	Metal or polymer
Galvanized	Anodic metal	Metal
Plating	Noble metal	Metal
Enamel (vitreous)	Glass	Metal
Glaze	Glass	Ceramic
Anodized	Al_2O_3	Aluminum
Sizing	Organic or silicone polymers	Organic or glass fibers

When the coating and the substrate are less similar, it is often necessary to utilize bonding agents or primer coats. For example, an organic paint will adhere to a glass surface more readily if a silicone is added first, because the silicone has structural characteristics similar to both the glass and the vehicle of the paint. Likewise, glass must be saturated with the oxide of the substrate metal for good adherence as a vitreous enamel. Apparently the oxide serves to provide a transition structure between the glass and the metal.

13–10 Electrical surfaces. Surface coatings are used functionally in electrical applications. An insulating coating, such as bakelite varnish, is most obvious in this respect because we can see it and its effects. However, recently surface coatings have been used for conductive purposes. For example, a layer of aluminum a few angstroms thick can be placed on an n-type semiconductor by vapor deposition. A subsequent thermal treatment, which permits diffusion of the aluminum atoms into the structure, produces a p-type surface and a p-n junction just below the surface.

Other examples of conductive surfaces include printed circuits produced by vapor deposition, electroplating, or a true printing operation. Also, transparent conductors for electroluminescence glasses require a surface coating of SnO or other defect semiconductor compound.

REINFORCED MATERIALS

13–11 Dispersion-strengthened materials. In Chapter 11 we encountered materials such as bainite, tempered martensite, and age-hardened aluminum alloys which were strengthened by the presence of fine particles of harder phases. For example, the tensile strength of the ferrite plus carbide in bainite can be more than 200,000 psi, whereas ferrite alone has a tensile strength of less than 40,000 psi. Likewise, pure aluminum has a tensile strength of less than 15,000 psi, as compared with more than 60,000 psi for certain age-hardened aluminum alloys. Therefore it is only natural that the engineer has turned to the idea of particle reinforcement of materials as a means of improving their mechanical properties. However, when we examine each of the above examples we find a shortcoming. At higher temperatures the reinforcing phase dissolves in the matrix. Of course, this should not be surprising, since a precipitation reaction was originally used to produce the multiphase microstructure. In order to obtain a *dispersion-strengthened* alloy which does not revert to a single phase at elevated temperatures, it is necessary to mechanically mix or chemically precipitate the reinforcing phase.

SAP alloys. Alumina (Al_2O_3) has low solubility in metallic aluminum. A technique which utilizes this fact, developed in the research laboratories of an aluminum company in Switzerland (*Aluminium-Industrie-Aktien-Gesellschaft*), has been quite successful in providing additional strength to aluminum and other alloys. To produce this alloy, aluminum powder is finely ground under controlled oxygen pressure so that a thin film of oxide is formed on the metal surface. Although originally on the surface, the oxide film is broken by the grinding and entrapped within the deformed metal particles. This powder is then compacted and sintered by powder-metallurgy techniques. The sintered aluminum powder of Fig. 13–19, which contains about 6% Al_2O_3, has a significant tensile strength when heated to within a few degrees of the melting point of aluminum. It is possible, with higher Al_2O_3 contents ($\sim$20%), to retain some strength above the melting point of the metal, even though most of the material is liquid. With these higher contents, the Al_2O_3 present forms a continuous network of refractory solid through the material.

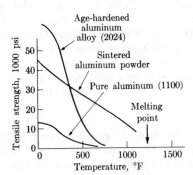

Fig. 13–19.   SAP (sintered aluminum powder) and other aluminum alloys. The powder contains Al_2O_3, which does not dissolve in the aluminum at higher temperatures.

TD-nickel. A second method of intimately mixing a refractory oxide and a ductile metal, developed in this country at Du Pont, employs a colloidal mixture of ThO_2 and NiO. The NiO can be reduced to metal and the powders compacted and sintered to give a ThO_2-reinforced nickel alloy with behaviors quite similar to those in Fig. 13–19, but with higher strengths at higher temperatures.

Internal oxidation. Insoluble precipitates for dispersion strengthening may be produced by still another procedure, opposite in approach to that of TD-nickel. For example, an alloy containing silver and a small amount of aluminum is heated slowly, so that oxygen diffuses into the metal. The oxygen selectively oxidizes the aluminum to yield Al_2O_3. The strengthening of silver by this procedure, illustrated in Fig. 13–20, is quite effective at low temperatures; however, at higher temperatures the effect of the Al_2O_3 is partially lost.

FIG. 13–20. Reinforced-silver alloys. Alumina (Al_2O_3), either as dispersed particles or as microscopic fibers (whiskers), increases the strength of silver. At higher temperatures, the fibers are more effective than the particles. [Adapted from W. H. Sutton and J. Chorné, "Development of High-Strength, Heat-Resistant Alloys by Whisker Reinforcement," *Metals Engineering Quarterly*, **3** (February 1963), pages 44–51.]

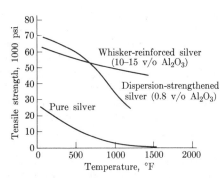

13–12 Fiber reinforcement. Engineers have tried to use the concept of fiber reinforcement in a number of materials. Although glass fibers can reinforce plastics when used at ambient temperatures, the glass quickly loses its strength at higher temperatures because of its viscous behavior. Therefore, the concept of reinforcement of metals by fibers was not realistic until it became possible to produce Al_2O_3 whiskers. The term *whisker* is applied to single crystals of various types, grown by means of vapor deposition. These crystals have diameters of a few microns and lengths of several millimeters. Not only are these vapor-grown whiskers single crystals, but they are also free of dislocations. Therefore, they develop high strengths (in excess of 1,000,000 psi for Al_2O_3). For this reason, when Al_2O_3 whiskers are incorporated in a ductile metal, they strengthen the metal considerably without displaying, as glass fibers do, a sensitivity to temperature. However, there are limits due to production methods and to the fact that the very high strengths cited above for whiskers are applicable only until plastic deformation occurs. During plastic deformation, dislocations are introduced, and the resistance to stresses declines.

13–13 Conclusion. Mention could also be made of glass-reinforced plastics, nylon-reinforced tires, and steel-reinforced concrete. However, these items, unlike our previous microstructures, have components sufficiently coarse so that the engineer may analyze the contributions of each component separately and then synthesize them into composite materials, as he does, for example, in the case of a prestressed concrete beam (Fig. 13–21). Therefore, let us end our consideration of the structures of engineering materials here, and leave grosser properties to the design engineer.

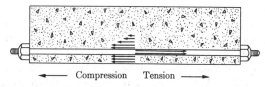

◄——— Compression   Tension ———►

FIG. 13–21. Prestressed concrete beam. The initial compressive stresses in the concrete must be exceeded before the concrete is subjected to tensile stresses.

References for Further Reading

13-1. *Surface Treatment of Metals.* Cleveland: American Society for Metals, 1941. A collection of technical papers covering topics from diffusion coatings to shot-peening.

13-2. BOGUE, R. H., *Chemistry of Portland Cement.* New York: Reinhold, 1955. The most complete technical book on portland cement. For the advanced student and the instructor.

13-3. BRUNAUER, S., "Tobermorite gel—The Heart of Concrete," *American Scientist,* **50,** March 1962, pp. 210–229. Detailed attention is given to portland cement hydration. For the cement specialist.

13-4. FISHER, J. C., "Synthetic Microstructures," *Trans. ASM,* **55,** 916–933, 1962. Discusses "tailor-made" materials such as SAP-alloys, TD-nickel, and Lodex magnets. Easily read by the student.

13-5. GUARD, R. W., "Mechanisms of Fine-Particle Strengthening," *Strengthening Mechanisms in Solids.* Metals Park, Ohio: Amer. Soc. for Metals, 1962. Dispersion hardening is discussed. Specialized, but readable by the undergraduate student.

13-6. KEYSER, C. A., *Materials of Engineering.* Englewood Cliffs, N. J.: Prentice-Hall, 1956. Chapter 15 discusses concrete mixtures and testing procedures.

13-7. KINGERY, W. D., *Ceramic Fabrication Processes.* New York: John Wiley & Sons, and Cambridge, Mass.: The Technology Press, 1958. Chapter 15, "Recrystallization and Sintering in Ceramics," and Chapter 16, "Sintering in the Presence of a Liquid Phase," summarize the mechanisms of sintering. Advanced level.

13-8. OLCOTT, J. S., "Chemical Strengthening of Glass," *Science,* **140,** June 14, 1963, pp. 1189–1193. Describes procedures for introducing compressive stresses into glass without heat treatment. For the educated layman.

13-9. SONNEBORN, R. H., *Fiberglas-Reinforced Plastics.* New York: Reinhold Publishing Co., 1954. Covers a variety of applications in which two dissimilar materials may be used together to give improved properties to each.

13-10. SUTTON, W. H., and J. CHORNÉ. "Development of High-Strength, Heat-Resistant Alloys by Whisker Reinforcement," *Metals Engineering Quarterly,* **3,** February 1963, pp. 41–51. Describes current progress in the new area of fiber reinforcement.

13-11. TINKLEPAUGH, J. R. and W. B. CRANDALL, *Cermets.* New York: Reinhold, 1960. Gives a centralized location for information on cermet-type composite materials.

13-12. WHITE, A. H., *Engineering Materials.* New York: McGraw-Hill, 1948. Chapter 20 discusses the silicate cements at an introductory level. Brief discussions are presented on the different types of portland cement.

Problems

13-1. The bulk volume of a sack of cement is 1 ft^3. Using the data in Problem 13-5, calculate the porosity of the dry cement.

Answer: 52%

13-2. The bulk density of crushed limestone is 114 lb/ft^3. What is its porosity if its specific gravity is 2.7?

13–3. A box 6 in. × 4 in. × 9 in. contains 12 lb of SiO_2 sand when it is level full. (a) What is the packing factor? (Specific gravity = 2.65.) (b) What is the maximum weight of water which could be added to just fill the pores of the sand in this box?

Answer: (a) 0.58 (b) 3.28 lb

13–4. A "two-yard" truck body holds 6000 lb of gravel when level full. The true density of this gravel is measured by placing 10 lb of gravel into a 3-gal pail full of water. The water plus the gravel has a net weight of 31.2 lb. (a) What is the apparent specific gravity of the gravel? (b) How many cubic feet of bulk sand should be added to the 54 ft³ of gravel to obtain the greatest packing factor?

13–5. A unit mix of concrete comprises one sack of cement, 2.25 ft³ of sand, and 2.85 ft³ of gravel. Using the data given below, calculate the number of cubic feet of concrete from this mix if 6 gal of water are used.

	Bulk density	Specific gravity
Sand	110 lb/ft³	2.65
Gravel	108 lb/ft³	2.62
Cement	94 lb/sack	3.15
H_2O	62.4 lb/ft³	1.00

Answer: 4.656 ft³

13–6. A unit mix of concrete comprises one sack of cement, 2.5 ft³ of sand, 3.25 ft³ of gravel, and 5.5 gal of water. Using the data in Problem 13–5, calculate the number of sacks of cement required for a driveway 6 in. thick, 112 ft long, and 8 ft wide.

13–7. In a certain construction project the builder uses a concrete mix composed of dry cement, sand, and gravel in volume proportions of 1:2:3.5, respectively, plus 6 gal of water for each sack of cement. The densities of the constituents are as follows:

	Bulk density	Specific gravity
Dry cement	94 lb/ft³	3.10
Sand	105 lb/ft³	2.65
Gravel	95 lb/ft³	2.60
Water	62.4 lb/ft³	1.00
	(8.33 lb/gal)	

Air-entraining agents are added to give 4.5 v/o closed pore space. (a) Calculate the bulk density of the wet concrete mix. (b) What is the ratio of the bulk volume of the paste (water–cement mixture plus closed pore space) to the interparticle space of the aggregate (sand and gravel mixture) in this concrete mix?

Answer: (a) 142 lb/ft³ (b) 2.06

13–8. A carbon black formed by burning benzene consists of spherical particles averaging 1000 A in diameter. Calculate the surface area in cm² for 100 gm of this powder. (The true density of the carbon black is 2.0 gm/cm³.)

13–9. Sand ($\rho = 2.65$ gm/cm^3) has an average diameter of 0.06 in. Its surface area is _____ in^2 per pound.

Answer: 1045 in^2

13–10. A brick weighs 6.6 lb dry, 6.9 lb when saturated with water, and 3.8 lb when suspended in water. (a) What is its porosity? (b) Its bulk density? (c) Its apparent density?

13–11. The rate of burning of powdered coal is proportional to the fineness of grinding (other factors being constant). Based on average surface area, what would be the rate of burning of −20+28 mesh coal relative to −8+10 mesh coal?

Answer: 2.8 times faster

13–12. An insulating brick weighs 3.9 lb dry, 4.95 lb when saturated with water, and 2.3 lb when suspended in water. (a) What is its porosity? (b) Its bulk specific gravity? (c) Its apparent specific gravity?

13–13. A polystyrene foam having a bulk density of 4 lb/ft^3 is made of a polymer whose specific gravity is 1.05. One pound of the foam absorbs 1 lb of water. Calculate (a) the percent expansion of the polymer on foaming; (b) the total porosity of foam; (c) the percent of open pore space; (d) the density of the foam when saturated with water.

Answer: (a) 1530% (b) 94% (c) 6.4% (d) 8 lb/ft^3

13–14. A certain type of rubber has a true specific gravity of 1.40. This type of rubber is used in the manufacture of a foamed rubber which weighs 0.015 lb/in^3 when dry, and 0.025 lb/in^3 when saturated with water. (a) What is the apparent porosity of the foamed rubber? (b) What is the true porosity?

13–15. A piece of tile 10 cm × 20 cm × 40 cm absorbs 400 gm of water. What is the porosity of the tile?

Answer: 5%

13–16. Birchwood veneer is impregnated with bakelite to ensure water resistance and to increase strength in the final form of the plywood. Dry birch weighs 35 lb/ft^3. The specific gravity of bakelite is 1.30 and the specific gravity of the wood substance (the material forming the cellular structure of the wood) is 1.53. How many pounds of bakelite would be required to impregnate 1 ft^3 of dry birch?

13–17. A powdered metal part has a porosity of 23% after compacting and before sintering. What linear shrinkage allowance should be made if the final porosity is expected to be 2%?

Answer: 8% (sintered basis)

13–18. A magnetic ferrite for an oscilloscope component is to have a final dimension of 0.621 in. Its volume shrinkage during sintering is 33.1% (unfired basis). What initial dimension should the powdered compact have?

13–19. A 4017 steel bar 2.9 in. in diameter has been carburized so that the case has 0.7% carbon at the surface and 0.4% carbon 0.2 in. below the surface. On the basis of the hardenability data in Fig. 11–38, draw a hardness traverse for this steel after oil quenching.

Answer: S, R_c 57; (0.2 in.), R_c 32; M-R, R_c 17; C, R_c 16

13–20. A bar of 4032 steel 2.0 in. in diameter must have a surface hardness of at least R_c 50 and a midradius hardness of less than R_c 27. Prescribe a method for obtaining these specifications.

appendix a

SELECTED CONSTANTS

$\sqrt{2}$	$= 1.414\ldots$
$\sqrt{3}$	$= 1.732\ldots$
$\cos 30°$	$= 0.866\ldots$
$\cos 45°$	$= 0.707\ldots$
$\cos 60°$	$= 0.500\ldots$
π	$= 3.1416\ldots$
e	$= 2.718\ldots$
$\log_e 10$	$= 2.303\ldots$
$\log_{10} 2$	$= 0.3010\ldots$
Avogadro's number	$= (6.02\ldots)(10^{23})$
Fe-C eutectoid temperature	$= 1333°F\ (723°C)$
Fe-C eutectoid composition	$= 0.8\%\ C$
Electron charge	$= 1.6 \times 10^{-19}$ coulomb
	$= 4.803 \times 10^{-10}$ esu
	$= 4.803 \times 10^{-10}\ (\text{erg} \cdot \text{cm})^{1/2}$
Boltzmann's constant	$= (1.38\ldots)(10^{-16})$ ergs/°K
Planck's constant	$= (6.62\ldots)(10^{-27})$ erg · sec
Velocity of light	$= (3)(10^{10})$ cm/sec
Volume of gas	$= 378\ \text{ft}^3/\text{lb} \cdot \text{mole at } 60°F \text{ and } 760 \text{ mm Hg}$
	$= 22.4\ \text{l/gm} \cdot \text{mole at } 0°C \text{ and } 760 \text{ mm Hg}$
Gas constant	$= 1.987$ cal/mole · °K
	$= 0.082$ liter · atm/mole · °K
Density of water	$= 62.4\ \text{lb/ft}^3 = 8.34\ \text{lb/gal}$
1 psi	$= 0.703\ \text{gm/mm}^2$
1 kcal	$= (4.185..)(10^{10})$ ergs
1 ev	$= (1.602\ldots)(10^{-12})$ erg
	$= (0.386\ldots)(10^{-19})$ cal

appendix b

GLOSSARY OF TERMS AS APPLIED TO MATERIALS*

Abrasive — Hard, mechanically resistant material used for grinding or cutting; commonly made of a ceramic material.

Absorption — Volume assimilation (cf. *ad*sorption).

Acetic acid — *See* Appendix F.

Acetone — *See* Appendix F.

Acceptor levels — Energy levels of *p*-type (electron-hole) carriers.

Acrylonitrile — *See* Appendix F.

Activation energy — Recoverable energy required to initiate a chemical reaction.

Activators — Components added to start a reaction.

Addition polymerization — Polymerization by sequential addition of monomers.

Adipic acid — *See* Appendix F.

Adsorption — Surface adhesion (cf. *ab*sorption).

Age-hardening — Hardening with time by incipient precipitation.

Agglomerate — Small particles bonded together into an integrated mass.

Aggregate — Coarse particles used in concrete; for example, sand and gravel.

Aging — Process of age-hardening.

Allotropism — *See* Polymorphism.

Alloy — A metal containing two or more elements.

Alloying elements — Elements added to form an alloy (sometimes referred to as alloys).

Alpha iron — Iron with a body-centered cubic structure which is stable at room temperature.

Ammonia — *See* Appendix F.

Amorphous — Noncrystalline and without long-range order.

Anion — Negative ion.

Anisotropic — Having different properties in different directions.

Annealing — Heating and cooling to produce softening; see Table 11–1.

Anode — The electrode which supplies electrons to an external circuit.

Anodized — Surface-coated with an oxide layer; achieved by making the component an anode in an electrolytic bath.

Antioxidant — Inhibitor to prevent oxidation of rubber and other organic materials by molecular oxygen.

Apparent density — Mass divided by apparent volume.

Apparent porosity — Porosity which includes open pores only (in contrast to true porosity).

Apparent volume — Bulk volume minus open pores, or true volume plus closed pores.

Asbestos — A fibrous silicate mineral.

Atactic — Lack of long-range repetition in a polymer (as contrasted to isotactic).

Ausforming — Process of strain-hardening austenite prior to transformation.

---

* Additional terms are defined in the glossary of the *Metals Handbook*. Cleveland: American Society for Metals, 1961.

Austempering — Process of isothermal transformation to form bainite.

Austenite — Face-centered cubic iron or iron alloy based on this structure.

Avogadro's number — Number of molecules per gram-molecular weight (6.02×10^{23}).

Axial ratio (crystals) — c unit length divided by a unit length.

Axis (crystals) — One of three principal crystal directions.

Bakelite — *See* Appendix G.

Bainite — Microstructure of carbide dispersed in ferrite, obtained by low-temperature isothermal transformation.

Banded structure — A segregated structure which has been mechanically worked.

Benzene — *See* Appendix F.

Body-centered (crystals) — A unit cell with center positions equivalent to corner positions.

Boundary (microstructures) — Surface between two grains or between two phases.

Bragg equation (in x-ray diffractions) — $n\lambda = 2d \sin \theta$.

Branching — Bifurcation in addition polymerization.

Brass — An alloy of copper and zinc.

Bravais lattices — The 14 basic crystal lattices.

Brazing — Joining metals at temperatures above 800°F but below the melting point of the joined metals.

Brinell — A hardness test utilizing an indenter. The hardness is measured by the diameter of the indentation.

Bronze — An alloy of copper and tin (unless otherwise specified; e.g., an aluminum bronze is an alloy of copper and aluminum).

Bulk density — Mass divided by bulk volume.

Bulk modulus — Modulus of compressibility by hydrostatic pressures.

Bulk volume — Total volume, including open and closed pores.

Buna — *See* Appendix G.

Burgers vector — Displacement vector around a dislocation. It is parallel to a screw dislocation and perpendicular to an edge dislocation.

Butadiene — *See* Appendix F.

Butylene — *See* Appendix F.

Butyric acid — *See* Appendix F.

Calcination — Solid dissociation to a gas and another solid, e.g., $CaCO_3 \rightarrow CaO + CO_2$

Calcite — The most common phase of $CaCO_3$.

Carbon steel — Steel in which carbon is the chief variable alloying element (other alloying elements may be present in nominal amounts).

Carborundum — A trade name for silicon carbide.

Carburizing — Introduction of carbon to the surface of the steel to change the surface properties.

Case — Subsurface zone (usually of a carburized steel).

Case-hardening — Hardening by forming a case of higher carbon content.

Casting — The process of pouring a liquid or suspension into a mold, or the object produced by this process.

Cast iron — Castings of iron-carbon alloys.

Catalyst — A reusable agent for activating a chemical reaction.

Cathode — The electrode which receives electrons from an external circuit.

Cation — Positive ion.

C-curve — Isothermal transformation curves.

Cell — A combination of two electrodes in an electrolyte (cf. Unit cell).

Celluloid — *See* Appendix G.

Cellulose — *See* Appendix F.

Cement — A material (usually ceramic) for bonding solids together.

Cement, portland — A hydraulic calcium silicate cement.

Cementite — Iron carbide (Fe_3C).

Center-of-gravity method — Calculation method for determining phases.   The over-all composition is at the center of gravity of the weighted components.

Ceramic (phases) — Compounds of metallic and nonmetallic elements.

Charpy — One of two standardized impact tests utilizing a square notched bar.

Chloroprene — *See* Appendix F.

Cis- (polymers) — A prefix denoting unsaturated positions on the same side of the polymer chain.

Cleavage — Plane of easy splitting.

Close-packed — Structure with the highest possible packing factor.

Closed pores — The internal pores without external access.

Coercive force — The opposing magnetizing force which is necessary to remove previous magnetization.

Coherency (phases) — A matching structure of two phases.

Cold-working — Deformation below the recrystallization temperature.

Compact — Compressed shapes of powders prior to sintering.

Component (design) — The individual parts of a machine or similar engineering design.

Component (phases) — The basic chemical substances required to create a chemical mixture or solution.

Compound — A phase composed of two or more elements in a given ratio.

Concentration cell — Galvanic cell established by differences in electrolyte concentration.

Concrete — Agglomerate of an aggregate and a hydraulic cement.

Condensation polymerization — Polymerization by chemical reaction which also produces a by-product.

Conductivity — Transfer of thermal or electrical energy along a potential gradient.

Constituent (microstructure) — A distinguishable part of a multiphase mixture.

Constitution diagram — *See* Phase diagram.

Continuous cooling transformation — Transformation during cooling (cf. isothermal transformation).

Coordination number — Number of closest atomic neighbors.

Copolymerization — Addition polymerization involving more than one type of mer.

Core (heat-treating) — Center of a bar, inside the case.

Corrosion — Deterioration and removal by chemical attack.

Corundum — The commonest phase of Al_2O_3.

Coulombic attraction — Attraction between unlike charges.

Couple — Two dissimilar electrodes in electrical contact.

Covalent bond — Atomic bonding by sharing electrons.

Creep — A slow deformation at stresses below the normal yield strength.

Creep rate — Creep strain per unit of time.

Cristobalite — A high-temperature crystal phase of SiO_2.

Critical point — *See* Transformation temperature.

Critical shear stress — Yield stress in a direction parallel to a crystal plane.

Cross-linking — The tying together of adjacent polymer chains.

Crystal — A physically uniform solid, in three dimensions, with long-range repetitive order.

Curie temperature (magnetic) — Transition temperature between ferromagnetism and paramagnetism.

Dacron — *See* Appendix G.

Decarburization — Removal of carbon from the surface of a steel.

Deep-drawing — The process of forming cup-shaped articles out of sheet metal by punching.

Degradation — Reduction of polymers to smaller molecules.

Degree of polymerization — Mers per average molecular weight.

Delta iron — Bcc iron, which is stable above the temperature range of austenite.

Dendrite — Skeleton crystal.

Depolymerization — Degradation of polymers into smaller molecules.

Diamagnetic — Less magnetic permeability than in a vacuum.

Diamond cubic (crystals) — The cubic crystal structure possessed by diamond.

Die — A forming tool.

Dielectric constant — The ratio in which the numerator is the quantity of electricity stored in the presence of an insulator and the denominator is the quantity of electricity stored in the presence of a vacuum.

Dielectric strength — Electrical breakdown potential of an insulator per unit thickness.

Diffraction (x-rays) — Deviation of an x-ray beam by regularly spaced atoms.

Diffusion — The movement of atoms or molecules in a material.

Diffusion coefficient — Diffusion flux per unit concentration gradient.

Dimethylsilanediol — *See* Appendix F.

Dipole — An electrical couple with positively and negatively charged ends.

Dislocation, edge — Linear defect at the edge of an extra crystal plane. The Burgers vector is perpendicular to the defect line.

Dislocation, screw — Linear defect with Burgers vector parallel to the defect line.

Dislocation loop — Combination of screw and edge dislocations.

Dispersion effects — Induced dipoles by atomic or electronic displacement.

Dolomite — A rock composed of $MgCa(CO_3)_2$.

Domains (magnetic) — Small crystalline areas of aligned ferromagnetic atoms.

Donor levels — Energy levels of n-type (electron) carriers.

Drawing — *See* Forming, and also Tempering.

Driving force — ΔF, or difference in free energy between the reactants and the products.

Drying shrinkage — Volume contraction accompanying water removal.

Ductility — Permanent deformation before fracture.

Durez — *See* Appendix G.

Elasticity — Nonpermanent deformation.

Elastic limit — Stress limit of elastic deformation.

Elastomer — Polymer with high elasticity due to its coiled structure.

Electrode potential — Voltage developed at an electrode (as compared with a standard reference electrode).

Electrolyte — Ionic solute.

Electromotive force series — A sequential list of electrode potentials.

Electron hole — Unoccupied energy level. Acts as a positive charge carrier.

Elongation — The amount of permanent strain prior to fracture.

Emf — *See* Electromotive force series.

Enamel (ceramics) — A protective coating of glass on metal.

Enamel (paints) — A paint which has a gloss like glass.

End-quench — A test for determining hardenability.

Endurance limit — The maximum stress allowable for unlimited cycling.

Energy band — Permissible energy levels for valence electrons.

Energy gap — Nonpermissible energy levels for valence electrons.

Engineering stress — Force per unit of original area (in contrast to physical stress).

Equiaxed — Shapes with approximately equal dimensions.

Equicohesive temperature — The temperature of equal strength for grains and grain boundaries.

Equilibrium (chemical) — Condition of dynamic balance. Compositions of lowest free energy.

Equilibrium diagram — *See* Phase diagram.

Erosion — Mechanical abrasion by solids suspended in a fluid.

Etching — Controlled chemical corrosion to reveal structure.

Ethane — *See* Appendix F.

Ethanol — *See* Appendix F.

Ethylene — *See* Appendix F.

Eutectic (binary) — A thermally reversible reaction:

$$\text{liquid} \xrightleftharpoons[\text{heating}]{\text{cooling}} \text{solid}_1 + \text{solid}_2$$

Eutectoid (binary) — A thermally reversible reaction:

$$\text{solid}_1 \xrightleftharpoons[\text{heating}]{\text{cooling}} \text{solid}_2 + \text{solid}_3$$

Extrusion — Shaping operation accomplished by forcing a plastic material through a die.

Face-centered — A unit cell with face positions equivalent to corner positions.

Fatigue — Tendency to fracture under cyclic stresses.

Fatigue limit — *See* Endurance limit.

Ferrite (ceramics) — Compounds containing trivalent iron; commonly magnetic.

Ferrite(metals) — Body-centered cubic iron, or iron alloy based on this structure.

Ferrimagnetism — Magnetism with unbalanced antiparallel magnetic alignment.

Ferroelectric — Materials with spontaneous dipole alignment.

Ferromagnetic — Materials with spontaneous magnetic alignment.

Fiber structures — Heterogeneous, anisotropic materials.

Fictive temperature — Transition temperature between supercooled liquids and glassy solids.

Fillet — A rounded internal corner between two surfaces.

Fireclay — A refractory (rather pure) clay.

Firing (ceramics) — High-temperature treatment for agglomeration.

Firing shrinkage — Shrinkage accompanying sintering.

Flakes (graphite) — Two-dimensional graphite sheets in cast iron.

Flakes (steel) — Internal fissures.

Flame-hardening — Hardening by surface heating with appropriate flames.

Flow structure — Fiber structure arising from deformation.

Fluidity — Coefficient of flowability; reciprocal of viscosity.

Fluorescence — Luminescence which occurs immediately after excitation.

Formaldehyde — *See* Appendix F.

Forming — An operation which shapes by deformation.

Framework structure — A phase structure with primary bonds in all three dimensions.

Free energy — Energy available for chemical reaction.

Frenkel defect — Atom or ion displacement (combined vacancy and interstitialcy).

Frequency — Cycles per unit time; commonly cycles per second.

Functionality — Number of available reaction sites for polymerization.

Fused quartz — *See* Fused silica, which is a more correct term.

Fused silica — SiO_2 glass.

Galvanic cell — A cell containing two dissimilar metals and an electrolyte.

Galvanic corrosion — Chemical corrosion occurring at the anode in a galvanic cell.

Galvanic protection — Protection given to a material by making it the cathode to a sacrificial anode.

Gamma iron — *See* Austenite.

Geon — *See* Appendix G.

Glass — An amorphous material with three-dimensional primary bonds.

Globars — Trade name for silicon carbide resistors.

Glycerol — *See* Appendix F.

Glyptol — *See* Appendix G.

Grains — Individual crystals.

Grain size — Statistical grain diameter in a random cross section. (Austenite grain size is reported as the number of former austenite grains within a standardized area. See text.)

Graphite — Most common phase of carbon (sheetlike).

Graphitization — Carbide dissociation to graphite.

Gray cast iron — Cast iron with flake graphite which was formed during solidification.

Gutta percha — *See* Appendix G.

Gypsum — The most common natural phase of hydrated calcium sulfate.

Hard-drawn — Cold worked to high hardnesses by drawing.

Hardenability — The ability to develop maximum hardness.

Hardening — Heat treatment to increase hardness.

Hardness — Resistance to penetration.

Heat of formation — Energy required for a compound to be formed from elements. (Negative values indicate energy is released.)

Hexamethylenediamine — *See* Appendix F.

Hole — Vacancy in a crystal or in an electronic structure.

Homogenization — Heat treatment to produce uniformity by diffusion.

Homopolar — *See* Covalent.

Hot-working — Shaping above the recrystallization temperature.

Hydration — Chemical reaction consuming water:

$$\text{solid}_1 + H_2O \rightarrow \text{solid}_2.$$

Hydrogen bridge — Van der Waals bond in which the hydrogen atom (proton) is attracted to electrons of neighboring atoms.

Hypereutectoid — A steel with a higher carbon content than the eutectoid composition.

Hypoeutectoid — A steel with a lower carbon content than the eutectoid composition.

Hysteresis — A lagging, not completely reversible change.

Ideal fluid — A fluid with a flow rate proportional to an applied stress.

Ideal solid — A solid with elastic strain proportional to stress.

Impact test — A test which measures the energy absorbed during fracture.

Inclusions — Particles of impurities contained by a material.

Induction hardening — Hardening by high-frequency induced currents for surface heating.

Ingot — A large casting which is to be subsequently rolled or forged.

Inhibitor (corrosion) — An additive to the electrolyte which promotes passivation.

Inoculation — Addition of nucleators to liquids to induce solidification.

Internal stresses — *See* Residual stresses.

Interrupted quench — Two-stage quenching of steel which involves heating to form austenite and an initial quench to a temperature above the start of martensite formation, followed by a second cooling to room temperature.

Interstices — Open pore spaces between particles.

Interstitialcy — Atom in a nonlattice site.

Ion — An atom which carries a charge because it has had electrons added or removed.

Ion exchange — Solid solution by ion substitution.

Ionic bond — Atomic bonding by coulombic attraction of unlike ions.

Iso- — Prefix indicating "the same."

Isomer — Molecules with the same composition but different structures.

Isoprene — *See* Appendix F.

Isotactic (polymers) — Long-range repetition in a polymer chain (in contrast to atactic).

Isothermal transformation — Transformation with time by holding at a specific temperature.

Isotope — The same element with a different number of neutrons.

Isotropic — Having the same properties in all directions.

Izod — One of two standardized impact tests with notched specimens which have a round cross section.

Jominy bar — *See* End-quench.

Kaolin — A soft rock composed primarily of kaolinite.

Kaolinite — The most common clay mineral.

Kel-F — *See* Appendix G.

Kiln — A furnace for firing ceramic materials (pronounced *kil*).

Laser — Light amplification by stimulated emission of radiation.

Lattice (crystal) — The space arrangement of atomic nuclei in a crystal.

Laue pattern — Diffraction pattern of a single crystal.

Ledeburite — Eutectic microstructure of austenite and cementite.

Lever rule — Calculation method for determining phases. The over-all composition is at the fulcrum of the lever.

Liquidus — The locus of temperatures above which only liquid is stable.

Long-range order — A repetitive pattern over many atomic distances.

Low-alloy steels — Steels containing up to 10% alloying elements.

Lubricant — A soft, readily deformed material with weak secondary bonds.

Lucite — *See* Appendix G.

Luminescence — Light emission by the reradiation of photons after initial activation.

Lustron — *See* Appendix G.

Macroscopic — Visible to the unaided eye (or up to 10× magnification).

Macrostructure — Structure with macroscopic heterogeneities (cf. *Micro*structure).

Magnet, permanent — Magnet with a large ($-BH$) energy product so that it maintains domain alignment.

Magnet, soft — Magnet which requires negligible energy for domain randomization.

Magnetic force — A magnetic field which induces magnetization.

Magnetic saturation — The maximum magnetization which can occur in a material.

Magnetostriction — Volume changes accompanying magnetization.

Malleability — The property that permits shaping by deformation.

Malleabilization — *See* Graphitization.

Malleable iron — Cast iron in which the graphite was formed by solid graphitization.

Marquenching — *See* Interrupted quench.

Martempering — *See* Interrupted quench, and also Tempering.

Martensite — Metastable body-centered phase of iron supersaturated with carbon, produced through a diffusionless phase change by quenching austenite.

Matrix — The enveloping phase in which another phase is embedded.

Mechanical properties — Those properties associated with stress and strain.

Mechanical working — Shaping by the use of forces.

Melamine — *See* Appendix F.

Melmac — *See* Appendix G.

Mer — The smallest repetitive unit in a polymer.

Mesh — The screen size for particle measurement.

Metallic bond — Atomic bonding in metals (*See* Section 2–9).

Metals — Materials containing elements which readily lose electrons.

Metastable — Temporary equilibrium.

Methane — *See* Appendix F.

Methanol — *See* Appendix F.

Methyl methacrylate — *See* Appendix F.

Mho — Unit of conductance; reciprocal of ohm.

Mica — A family of silicate minerals with sheetlike structures.

Microhm — 10^{-6} ohm.

Micron — 10^{-4} centimeter; 10^4 angstroms.

Microstructure — A structure with heterogeneities as shown by a microscope (cf. *macrostructure*).

Mil — 10^{-3} inch.

Miller indices — *See* Section 3–15.

Mineral — A rock phase or a ceramic phase.

Mixture — Combination of two phases.

Mobility (change) — Drift velocity per unit of potential gradient.

Modulus of elasticity — Elastic stress per unit of elastic strain.

Modulus of rupture — Breaking strength in a nonductile solid as measured by bending.

Modulus of shear — Elastic shear stress per unit of elastic shear strain.

Mole — Mass equal to the molecular weight of a material.

Mold — A shaped cavity for casting.

Molecules — Groups of atoms with strong mutual attraction.

Monel — An alloy of copper and nickel.

Monoclinic (crystals) — Three unequal axes, two of which are at right angles to each other.

Monolithic — Massive cemented units (literally, one stone).

Monomer — A molecule with a single mer.

Monotectic (binary) — A thermally reversible reaction:

$$\text{liquid}_1 \underset{\text{heating}}{\overset{\text{cooling}}{\rightleftharpoons}} \text{liquid}_2 + \text{solid}.$$

Mortar — A cement or plaster used to bond large blocks.

Mullite — A phase containing $Al_6Si_2O_{13}$.

Mylar — *See* Appendix G.

Natural rubber — *See* Appendix G.

Neoprene — *See* Chloroprene, Appendix F.

Nitriding — Introduction of nitrogen to the surface of a steel to change the surface properties.

Noble — Nonreactive.

Nodular cast iron — A cast iron with spherical graphite microstructure.

Normal directions — Directions perpendicular to the cross section.

Normal stresses — Stresses perpendicular to the cross section.

Normalizing — Heat treatment for homogenization; see Table 11–1.

Notch sensitivity — A reduction in properties by the presence of stress concentrations.

n-type semiconductor — A semiconductor with excess electrons for the first two valence energy bands.

Nucleation — The start of the growth of a new phase.

Number average molecular weight — Molecular weight average based on numbers of molecules.

Nylon — *See* Appendix G.

Octahedron — An eight-sided volume.

Open pores — Interstices with surface connections.

Ordered (crystal) — Structure with a long-range repetitive pattern.

Orientation — Angular relationships between crystal or molecular alignment and external reference directions.

Organic materials — Polymeric materials composed of carbon compounds.

Orthorhombic — A crystal with three unequal but perpendicular axes.

Overaging — Continued aging until softening occurs.

Oxidation (general) — Increased valence by removing electrons.

Oxidation cell — A galvanic cell established by differences in oxidation potential.

Packing factor — True volume per unit of bulk volume.

Paramagnetic — Slightly more magnetic permeability than in a vacuum.

Parameter — Arbitrarily selected constants.

Passivity — The condition in which normal corrosion is impeded by an adsorbed surface film on the electrode.

Pearlite — A microstructure of ferrite and lamellar carbide of eutectoid composition.

Peritectic (binary) — A thermally reversible reaction:

$$\text{solid}_1 + \text{liquid} \underset{\text{heating}}{\overset{\text{cooling}}{\rightleftharpoons}} \text{solid}_2.$$

Peritectoid (binary) — A thermally reversible reaction:

$$\text{solid}_1 + \text{solid}_2 \underset{\text{heating}}{\overset{\text{cooling}}{\rightleftharpoons}} \text{solid}_3.$$

Permeability (magnetic) — Ratio of magnetic induction to the intensity of the magnetizing field.

Permeability (porous solids) — Coefficient of transfer through interstices.

Phase (materials) — A physically homogeneous part of a material system.

Phase diagram — Graph of phase relationships with composition and environmental coordinates.

Phase rule — $P + V = C + E$. (*See* Section 9–15.)

Phenol — *See* Appendix F.

Phosphorescence — Luminescence which is delayed until a period of time elapses after excitation.

Photoconductor — Photon-activated semiconductor.

Photon — A quantum of light.

Phthalic acid — *See* Terephthalic acid, Appendix F.

Physical stress — The force per unit of actual area (as contrasted to engineering stress).

Piezoelectric — Electric charges developed by pressure.

Plain carbon steel — Iron-carbon alloys with only nominal amounts of other elements.

Plaster — A covering material capable of being spread before hardening.

Plaster of Paris — A plaster composed of partially dehydrated gypsum.

Plastics — Moldable organic resins.

Plasticity — Ability to be permanently deformed without fracture.

Plasticizer — An additive to commercial resins to induce plasticity.

Plexene — *See* Appendix G.

Plexiglas — *See* Appendix G.

p-n junction — Rectifying junction of *p*- and *n*-type semiconductors.

Poisson's ratio — $\dfrac{\text{Change in transverse dimension during elastic strain}}{\text{Change in longitudinal dimension during elastic strain}}$.

Polarization (molecules) — Displacement of centers of positive and negative charges.

Polyelectrolyte — Polymers capable of (limited) ionization.

Polyethylene — Polymer of $(C_2H_4)_n$.

Polymer — Molecules with many units or mers.

Polymerization — Process of growing large molecules from small ones.

Polymorphism — The existence of a composition in more than one crystal structure.

Polythene — *See* Appendix G.

Porcelain (ceramics) — Characterized by a high glass content.

Portland cement — A hydraulic calcium silicate cement.

Powder metallurgy — The technique of agglomerating metal powders into engineering components.

Precipitation-hardening — *See* Age-hardening.

Preferred orientation — A nonrandom alignment of crystals or molecules.

Prestressed concrete — A beam or similar concrete component which is given initial compressive stresses prior to receiving tensile stresses in service.

Process annealing (steel) — Annealing close to, but below, the eutectoid temperature.

Proeutectoid cementite — Cementite which separates from hypereutectoid austenite above the eutectoid temperature.

Proeutectoid ferrite — Ferrite which separates from hypoeutectoid austenite above the eutectoid temperature.

Propane — *See* Appendix F.

Propanol — *See* Appendix F.

Proportional limit — Limit of proportionality between stress and strain.

Propylene — See Isopropylene, Appendix F.

p-type semiconductor — Semiconductor with a deficiency of electrons in the first two valence energy bands.

Quantum — A discrete unit of energy.

Quartz — The most common phase of SiO_2.

Quench and temper — Heat treatments for hardening and toughening steel.

Radiation damage — Structural defects arising from exposure to radiation.

Recovery — Removal of residual stresses

Recrystallization — The formation of new annealed grains from previously strain-hardened grains.

Recrystallization temperature — Temperature at which recrystallization is spontaneous. Usually about $\frac{1}{3}$ to $\frac{1}{2}$ of absolute melting temperature.

Reduction in area — Decrease of area in terms of the original area.

Refractory (ceramics) — A heat-resistant material.

Relaxation (mechanical) — Relief of stresses by creep.

Relaxation time — Time required to reduce stresses to $1/e$ of their original values.

Residual stresses — Internal stresses which are retained following thermal or mechanical straining.

Resilience — The ability of a material to absorb and return energy without permanent deformation.

Resins — Polymeric materials.

Resistivity — Reciprocal of conductivity (usually expressed in ohm·cm).

Resolved shear stress — Stress vector in slip plane.

Rhombohedral — Crystals with three equal axes not at right angles.

Rigidity — The property of resisting elastic deformation.

Rockwell hardness — A test utilizing an indenter; the depth of indentation is a measure of the hardness.

Rubber — A polymeric material with a high elastic yield strain.

Rupture stress — True stress at the time of fracture.

Rutile — The most common phase of TiO_2.

Saran — See Appendix G.

Scale — An oxide layer on metals.

Schottky defect — Ion pair vacancies.

Scission — Degradation of polymers by radiation.

Segregation — Heterogeneities in composition.

Self-diffusion — Diffusion of solvent atoms.

Semiconduction, extrinsic — Semiconduction from impurity sources. The electrons are excited to acceptor levels (p-type), or from donor levels (n-type).

Semiconduction, intrinsic — Semiconduction of pure material. The electrons are excited across the energy gap.

Semiconductor — A material with controllable conductivities, intermediate between insulators and conductors.

Shear — Relative displacement by sliding.

Shear modulus — See Modulus of shear.

Short-range order — Specific first-neighbor arrangements of atoms, but random long-range arrangements.

Shrinkage — Dimensional decrease in a manufacturing process.

Silicones — See Appendix G.

Simple cell (crystals) — A unit cell with only corner atoms.

Sintering — Agglomeration by thermal means.

Slate — An indurated rock composed of sheetlike mineral phases.

Slip (deformation) — A relative displacement along a structural direction.

Slip (ceramics) — A slurry for casting.

Slip planes — Crystal planes along which slip occurs.

Slurry — A thick suspension of solid particles in a liquid.

Small-angle boundary — Boundary of aligned edge dislocations.

Soldering — Joining metals below 800°F. The joined metals are not melted.

Solidification — Freezing of a melt.

Solid solution — *See* Sections 4-3 and 4-4.

Solidus — The locus of temperatures below which only solids are stable.

Solute — The minor component of a solution.

Solution treatment — A heat treatment to produce solid solution.

Solvent — The major component of a solution.

Solvus — Solid solubility curves in a phase diagram.

Spalling — Cracking originating from stresses accompanying volume changes.

Specific gravity — Ratio of density of a material to the density of water.

Specific heat — Ratio of heat capacity of a material to the heat capacity of water.

Specific surface — Surface area per unit mass.

Specific viscosity — Ratio of viscosity of a material to the viscosity of water.

Specific volume — Volume per unit mass.

Spheroidite — Microstructure of coarse spherical carbides in a ferrite matrix.

Spheroidizing — Process of making spheroidite; see Table 11-1.

Spin (magnetism) — The assumed rotational movement of an electron in its orbit within an atom.

Spinel — Cubic [AB_2O_4] compounds in which A is divalent and B is trivalent. These compounds are commonly used in ceramic magnets and for refractory purposes.

Sterling silver — An alloy of 92.5 Ag and 7.5 Cu. (This corresponds to nearly the maximum solubility of copper and silver.)

Strain — Change in length per unit of original length.

Strain-hardening — Increased hardness accompanying deformation.

Stress — Force per unit area.

Stress rupture — Time-dependent rupture resulting from constant stress (usually at elevated temperatures).

Structure — Geometric relationships of material components.

Styrene — *See* Appendix F.

Styron — *See* Appendix G.

Superconductivity — Property of negligible electrical resistivity and magnetic permeability near absolute zero.

Supercooling — Cooling below the solubility limit without precipitation.

Supersonic — Faster than sound (cf. Ultrasonic).

Surface — Boundary between a condensed phase and gas.

Symmetrical — Duplication, as in a mirror image.

Syndiotactic — Intermediate between atactic and isotactic.

System (phase diagram) — Compositions of equilibrated components.

Talc — Magnesium alumino-silicate with a sheetlike crystal structure.

Teflon — *See* Appendix G.

Temper (hardness) — Extent of strain-hardening.

Temper carbon — In cast iron, carbon that is a product of graphitization.

Temper glass — Glass with residual compressive surface stresses.

Tempered martensite — A microstructure of ferrite and carbide obtained by heating martensite.

Tempering — A toughening process of heating martensite to produce tempered martensite.

Tenite — *See* Appendix G.

Tensile strength — Maximum resistance to deformation (based on original area).

Tetragonal (crystal) — Two of three axes equal; all three at right angles.

Tetrahedron — A four-sided solid.

Texalite — *See* Appendix G.

Texture — Macroscopic structures.

Thermal diffusivity — Diffusion coefficient for thermal energy; $k/\rho C_p$.

Thermal growth — Expansion arising from thermal cycling.

Thermistors — Temperature-sensitive resistor.

Thermocouple — A temperature-measuring device utilizing the thermoelectric effect of dissimilar wires.

Thermoplastic resin — A polymeric material that softens with increased temperature.

Thermosetting resin — A polymeric material which does not soften, but rather polymerizes further with increasing temperature.

Tilt boundary — *See* small-angle boundary.

Titanates (electrical) — Ferroelectric materials composed of titanium compounds.

Toluene — *See* Appendix F.

Toughness — The property of absorbing energy before fracture.

Trans- — A prefix indicating "across" (cf. *Cis*).

Transducer — A device for transforming mechanical vibrations into electrical or magnetic energy (or vice versa).

Transformation temperature — Temperature of an equilibrium phase change.

Transistor — An electrical device utilizing semiconductors and performing some of the functions of electron tubes.

Transition temperature (steels) — Temperature (range) of change from ductile to nonductile fracture.

Transverse — Section perpendicular to the elongated direction of an anisotropic material (in contrast to longitudinal).

Triclinic (crystals) — Three unequal axes, none of which are at right angles to each other.

Tridymite — An intermediate temperature phase of SiO_2.

True porosity — Porosity including open and closed pores.

True volume — Volume excluding open and closed pores.

T-T-T curve — Isothermal transformation curve (Temperature-Time-Transformation).

Twins — Crystals related by mirror-image reflections.

Tygon — *See* Appendix G.

Ultimate strength — *See* Tensile strength.

Ultrasonic — Sounds with higher than audible frequency (cf. Supersonic).

Unit cell — The smallest repetitive volume that comprises the complete pattern of a crystal.

Upsetting — Impact forging by axial compression.

Urea — *See* Appendix F.

Vacancy — Unfilled lattice site.

Van der Waals forces — Secondary bonds arising from structural polarization.

Variance (phase rule) — Unassigned variables. (*See* Section 9–15.)

Variance (statistics) — The square of the standard deviation.

Vinyl compounds — *See* Appendix F.
Vinylite — *See* Appendix G.
Viscosity — Coefficient of resistance to flow (reciprocal of fluidity).
Vitreous — Glasslike.
Vulcanization — Treatment of rubber with sulfur to cross-link the elastomer chains.

Wavelength — Distance between like positions of a wave (speed/frequency).
Weight-average molecular weight — Molecular-weight average based on class-interval weights.
Welding — A joining operation involving the melting of the joined metals.
White case iron — Case iron with all the carbon as cementite rather than as graphite.

x-rays — Electromagnetic radiations with wavelengths approximately 1 angstrom unit in length.

Yield point — The point on a stress-strain curve of sudden plastic yield at the start of plastic deformation (common only in low-carbon steels).
Yield strength — Maximum resistance to elastic deformation.
Young's modulus — *See* Modulus of elasticity.

Zeolite — A silicate with exchangeable ions.

appendix c

COMPARISON OF HARDNESS SCALES

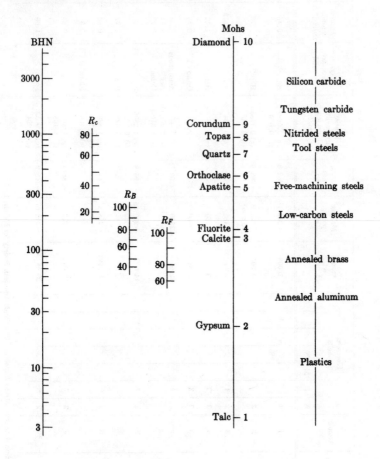

appendix d

TABLE OF ELEMENTS

Element	Symbol	Atomic no.	Electrons in shells K	L	M	N	Atomic wt. (C¹² = 12.000)	Melting point, °C	Boiling point, °C	Density (g) gm/liter (l) gm/cm³ (s) gm/cm³	Crystal structure of solid	Approx. atomic radius,* A	Valence (most common)	Approx. ionic radius, A (Coord. No. = 6)
Hydrogen	H	1	1				1.008	−259.18	−252.8	(g) 0.0899 (l) 0.070	Hex	0.46	+	Very small
Helium	He	2	2				4.003	−272.2 (26 atm)	−268.9	(g) 0.1785 (l) 0.147	Hcp (?)	1.76	Inert	—
Lithium	Li	3	2	1			6.94	186	1609	(s) 0.534	Bcc	1.519	+	0.78
Beryllium	Be	4	2	2			9.01	1350	1530	(s) 1.85	Hcp	1.12	2+	0.34
Boron	B	5	2	3			10.81	2300	2550	(s) 2.3	Ortho (?)	0.46	3+	~0.25
Carbon	C	6	2	4			12.01	~3500	4200(?)	(s) 2 ± (s) 2.25(gr) (s) 3.51(d)	Amorphous Hex Cubic	0.71 0.77	4+	~0.2
Nitrogen	N	7	2	5			14.007	−209.86	−195.8	(g) 1.2506 (l) 0.808 (s) 1.026	Hex	0.71	3−	
Oxygen	O	8	2	6			15.9994	−218.4	−183.0	(g) 1.429 (l) 1.14 (s) 1.426		0.60	2−	1.32
Fluorine	F	9	2	7			19.00	−223	−188.2	(g) 1.69 (l) 1.108	Rhombic (?)	0.5	−	1.33
Neon	Ne	10	2	8			20.18	−248.67	−245.9	(g) 0.9002 (l) 1.204	Fcc	1.60	Inert	—

* Atomic radii are based on data from *Metals Handbook*. Cleveland: American Society for Metals, 1961.

412

Element	Symbol	At. No.	K	L	M	N	At. Weight	M.P. (°C)	B.P. (°C)	Density	Structure	Atomic radius	Valence	Ionic radius
Sodium	Na	11	2	8	1		22.99	97.5	880	(s) 0.97	Bcc	1.857	+	0.98
Magnesium	Mg	12	2	8	2		24.31	650	1110	(s) 1.74	Hex	1.594	2+	0.78
Aluminum	Al	13	2	8	3		26.98	660.2	2060	(s) 2.699	Fcc	1.431	3+	0.57
Silicon	Si	14	2	8	4		28.09	1430	2300	(s) 2.4	Diamond cubic	1.176	4+	0.41
Phosphorus	P	15	2	8	5		30.97	44.1	280	(s) 1.82	Cubic	—	5+	0.2-0.4
Sulfur	S	16	2	8	6		32.06	119.0	246.2	(s) 2.07; (l) 1.803	Fe ortho	1.06	2-; 6+	1.74; 0.34
Chlorine	Cl	17	2	8	7		35.45	-101	-34.7	(g) 3.214; (l) 1.557; (s) 1.9		0.905	—	1.81
Argon	Ar	18	2	8	8		39.95	-189.4	-185.8	(g) 1.784; (l) 1.40; (s) 1.65	Tetra	1.920	Inert	—
Potassium	K	19	2	8	8	1	39.10	63	770	(s) 0.86	Fcc	2.312	+	1.33
Calcium	Ca	20	2	8	8	2	40.08	850	1440	(s) 1.55	Bcc	1.969	2+	1.06
Scandium	Sc	21	2	8	9	2	44.96	1200		(s) 2.5	Fcc	1.605	3+	0.83
Titanium	Ti	22	2	8	10	2	47.90	1820	3400	(s) 4.54	Fcc	1.458	4+	0.64
Vanadium	V	23	2	8	11	2	50.94	1735		(s) 6.0	Hcp	1.316	3+; 5+	0.65; ~0.4
Chromium	Cr	24	2	8	13	1	52.00	1890	2500	(s) 7.19	Bcc	1.249	3+	0.64
Manganese	Mn	25	2	8	13	2	54.94	1245	2150	(s) 7.43	Cubic comp.	1.12	2+	0.91
Iron	Fe	26	2	8	14	2	55.85	1539	2740	(s) 7.87	Bcc	1.24	2+; 3+	0.83; 0.67
Cobalt	Co	27	2	8	15	2	58.93	1495	2900	(s) 8.9	Hcp	1.248	2+	0.82

(Continued)

TABLE OF ELEMENTS (*Continued*)

Element	Symbol	Atomic no.	K	L	M	N	O	P	Atomic wt. (C¹² = 12.000)	Melting point, °C	Boiling point, °C	Density (g) gm/liter (l) gm/cm³ (s) gm/cm³	Crystal structure of solid	Approx. atomic radius, A	Valence (most common)	Approx. ionic radius, A (Coord. No. = 6)
Nickel	Ni	28	2	8	16	2			58.71	1455	2730	(s) 8.90	Fcc	1.245	2+	0.78
Copper	Cu	29	2	8	18	1			63.54	1083	2600	(s) 8.96	Fcc	1.278	+	0.96
Zinc	Zn	30	2	8	18	2			65.37	419.46	906	(s) 7.133	Hcp	1.332	2+	0.83
Gallium	Ga	31	2	8	18	3			69.72	29.78	2070	(s) 5.91	Fc ortho	1.218	3+	0.62
Germanium	Ge	32	2	8	18	4			72.59	958		(s) 5.36	Diamond cubic	1.224	4+	0.44
Arsenic	As	33	2	8	18	5			74.92	814 (36 atm.)	610	(s) 5.73	Rhombic	1.25	3+ 5+	0.69 ~0.4
Selenium	Se	34	2	8	18	6			78.96	220	680	(s) 4.81	Hex	1.16	2—	1.91
Bromine	Br	35	2	8	18	7			79.91	−7.2	19.0	(l) 3.12	Ortho	1.13	1—	1.96
Krypton	Kr	36	2	8	18	8			83.80	−157	−152	(g) 3.708 (l) 2.155 (s)	Fcc	2.01	Inert	
Rubidium	Rb	37	2	8	18	8	1		85.47	39	680	(s) 1.53	Bcc	2.44	+	1.49
Strontium	Sr	38	2	8	18	8	2		87.62	770	1380	(s) 2.6	Fcc	2.15	2+	1.27
Yttrium	Y	39	2	8	18	9	2		88.91	1490		(s) 5.51	Hcp	1.79	3+	1.06
Zirconium	Zr	40	2	8	18	10	2		91.22	1750		(s) 6.5	Hcp	1.58	4+	0.87

Element	Symbol	At. No.							At. wt.	M.P.	B.P.	Density	Crystal		Valence	
Niobium (Columbium)	Nb (Cb)	41	2	8	18	12	1		92.91	2415		(s) 8.57	Bcc	1.429	5+	0.69
Molybdenum	Mo	42	2	8	18	13	1		95.94	2625	4800	(s) 10.2	Bcc	1.36	4+	0.68
Technetium	Tc	43	2	8	18	14	1		99	2700		(An artificial element only)				
Ruthenium	Ru	44	2	8	18	15	1		101.07	2500	4900	(s) 12.2	Hcp	1.352	4+	0.65
Rhodium	Rh	45	2	8	18	16	1		102.91	1966	4500	(s) 12.44	Fcc	1.344	3+	0.68
Palladium	Pd	46	2	8	18	18			106.4	1554	4000	(s) 12.0	Fcc	1.375	+	
Silver	Ag	47	2	8	18	18	1		107.87	960.5	2210	(s) 10.49	Fcc	1.444	+	1.13
Cadmium	Cd	48	2	8	18	18	2		112.40	320.9	765	(s) 8.65	Hcp	1.489	2+	1.03
Indium	In	49	2	8	18	18	3		114.82	156.4		(s) 7.31	Fc tetra	1.625	3+	0.92
Tin	Sn	50	2	8	18	18	4		118.69	231.9	2270	(s) 7.298	Bc tetra	1.509	4+	0.74
Antimony	Sb	51	2	8	18	18	5		121.75	630.5	1440	(s) 6.62	Rhombic	1.452	5+	0.90
Tellurium	Te	52	2	8	18	18	6		127.6	450	1390	(s) 6.24	Hex	1.43	2−	2.11
Iodine	I	53	2	8	18	18	7		126.9	114	183	(s) 4.93	Ortho	1.35	−	2.20
Xenon	Xe	54	2	8	18	18	8		131.3	−112	−108	(g) 5.851 (l) 3.52 2.7	Fcc	2.21	Inert	
Cesium	Cs	55	2	8	18	18	8	1	132.9	28	690	(s) 1.9	Bcc	2.62	+	1.65
Barium	Ba	56	2	8	18	18	8	2	137.3	704	1640	(s) 3.5	Bcc	2.17	2+	1.43
Rare earths	La → Lu	57 → 71	2	8	18	18 → 32	8 → 9	2	138.9 → 175.0						3+	1.22 → 0.99
Hafnium	Hf	72	2	8	18	32	10	2	178.5	1700		(s) 11.4	Hcp	1.59	4+	0.84

(Continued)

TABLE OF ELEMENTS (*Continued*)

Element	Symbol	Atomic no.	Electrons in shells							Atomic wt. (C¹² = 12.000)	Melting point, °C	Boiling point, °C	Density (g) gm/liter (l) gm/cm³ (s) gm/cm³	Crystal structure of solid	Approx. atomic radius, A	Valence (most common)	Approx. ionic radius, A (Coord. No. = 6)
			K	L	M	N	O	P	Q								
Tantalum	Ta	73	2	8	18	32	11	2		180.95	2996		(s) 16.6	Bcc	1.429	5+	0.68
Tungsten	W	74	2	8	18	32	12	2		183.9	3410	5930	(s) 19.3	Bcc	1.369	4+	0.68
Rhenium	Re	75	2	8	18	32	13	2		186.2	3170	—	(s) 20	Hcp	1.370		
Osmium	Os	76	2	8	18	32	14	2		190.2	2700	5500	(s) 22.5	Hcp	1.367	4+	0.67
Iridium	Ir	77	2	8	18	32	17			192.2	2454	5300	(s) 22.5	Fcc	1.357	4+	0.66
Platinum	Pt	78	2	8	18	32	17	1		195.1	1773	4410	(s) 21.45	Fcc	1.387		
Gold	Au	79	2	8	18	32	18	1		197.0	1063	2970	(s) 19.32	Fcc	1.441	+	1.37
Mercury	Hg	80	2	8	18	32	18	2		200.6	-38.87	357	(s) 13.55	Rhombic	1.552	2+	1.12
Thallium	Tl	81	2	8	18	32	18	3		204.4	300	1460	(s) 11.85	Hcp	1.704	3+	1.05
Lead	Pb	82	2	8	18	32	18	4		207.2	327.4	1740	(s) 11.34	Fcc	1.750	2+ 4+	1.32 0.84
Bismuth	Bi	83	2	8	18	32	18	5		209.0	271.3	1420	(s) 9.80	Rhombic	1.556		
Polonium	Po	84	2	8	18	32	18	6		210	600			Monoclinic	1.7		
Astatine	At	85	2	8	18	32	18	7		210							
Radon	Rn	86	2	8	18	32	18	8		222	-71	-61.8				Inert	

Francium	Fa	87	1	8	18	32	18	8	2	223					+	
Radium	Ra	88	2	8	18	32	18	8	2	226	700	(s) 5.0				
Actinium	Ac	89	2	9	18	32	18	8	2	227	1600					
Thorium	Th	90	2	10	18	32	18	8	2	232	1800	(s) 11.5	Fcc	1.800	4+	1.10
Protactinium	Pa	91	2	9	20	32	18	8	2	231	3000					
Uranium	U	92	2	9	21	32	18	8	2	238	1130	(s) 18.7	Ortho	1.38	4+	1.05
Neptunium	Np	93.	2	9	22	32	18	8	2	237						
Plutonium	Pu	94	2	9	23	32	18	8	2	239						
Americium	Am	95	2	9	24	32	18	8	2	241						
Curium	Cm	96	2	9	25	32	18	8	2	242						
Berkelium	Bk	97	2	9	26	32	18	8	2	249						
Californium	Cf	98	2	9	27	32	18	8	2	252						
Einsteinium	E	99	2	9	28	32	18	8	2	254						
Fermium	Fm	100	2	9	29	32	18	8	2	253						
Mendelevium	Md	101	2	9	30	32	18	8	2	256						

appendix e

PROPERTIES OF SELECTED ENGINEERING MATERIALS

PART 1 — METALS (Taken from numerous sources)

Material	Specific gravity	Thermal conductivity, $\frac{\text{cal·cm}}{\text{°C·cm}^2\text{·sec}}$ at 68°F*	Thermal expansion, in/in/°F at 68°F†	Electrical resistivity, ohm·cm at 68°F‡	Average modulus of elasticity, psi at 68°F
Aluminum (99.9+)	2.7	0.53	12.5×10^{-6}	2.9×10^{-6}	10×10^6
Aluminum alloys	2.7(+)	0.4(±)	12×10^{-6}	$3.5 \times 10^{-6}(+)$	10×10^6
Brass (70Cu–30Zn)	8.5	0.3	11×10^{-6}	6.2×10^{-6}	16×10^6
Bronze (95Cu–5Sn)	8.8	0.2	10×10^{-6}	9.6×10^{-6}	16×10^6
Cast iron (gray)	7.15	—	5.8×10^{-6}	—	30×10^6
Cast iron (white)	7.7	—	5×10^{-6}	—	30×10^6
Copper (99.9+)	8.9	0.95	9×10^{-6}	1.7×10^{-6}	16×10^6
Iron (99.9+)	7.87	0.18	6.53×10^{-6}	9.7×10^{-6}	29×10^6
Lead (99+)	11.34	0.08	16×10^{-6}	20.65×10^{-6}	2×10^6
Magnesium (99+)	1.74	0.38	14×10^{-6}	4.5×10^{-6}	6.5×10^6
Monel (70Ni–30Cu)	8.8	0.06	8×10^{-6}	48.2×10^{-6}	26×10^6
Silver (sterling)	10.4	1.0	10×10^{-6}	1.8×10^{-6}	11×10^6
Steel (1020)	7.86	0.12	6.5×10^{-6}	16.9×10^{-6}	30×10^6
Steel (1040)	7.85	0.115	6.3×10^{-6}	17.1×10^{-6}	30×10^6
Steel (1080)	7.84	0.11	6.0×10^{-6}	18.0×10^{-6}	30×10^6
Steel (18Cr–8Ni stainless)	7.93	0.035	5×10^{-6}	70×10^{-6}	30×10^6

* Multiply by 0.806 to get Btu·in/°F·ft²·sec.   † Multiply by 1.8 to get cm/cm/°C   ‡ Divide by 2.54 to get ohm·in.

PROPERTIES OF SELECTED ENGINEERING MATERIALS

PART 2 — CERAMICS (Taken from numerous sources)

Material	Specific gravity	Thermal conductivity, $\frac{cal \cdot cm}{°C \cdot cm^2 \cdot sec}$ at 68°F*	Thermal expansion, in/in/°F at 68°F†	Electrical resistivity, ohm·cm at 68°F‡	Average modulus of elasticity, psi at 68°F
Al_2O_3	3.8	0.07	5×10^{-6}	—	50×10^6
Brick					
Building	2.3(±)	0.0015	5×10^{-6}	—	—
Fireclay	2.1	0.002	2.5×10^{-6}	1.4×10^8	—
Graphite	1.5	—	3×10^{-6}	—	—
Paving	2.5	—	2×10^{-6}	—	—
Silica	1.75	0.002	—	1.2×10^8	—
Concrete	2.4(±)	0.0025	7×10^{-6}	—	2×10^6
Glass					
Plate	2.5	0.0018	5×10^{-6}	10^{14}	—
Borosilicate	2.4	0.0025	1.5×10^{-6}	—	10×10^6
Silica	2.2	0.003	0.3×10^{-6}	10^{20}	10×10^6
Vycor	2.2	0.003	0.35×10^{-6}	—	—
Wool	0.05	0.0006	—	—	—
Graphite (bulk)	1.9	—	3×10^{-6}	10^{-3}	1×10^6
MgO	3.6	—	5×10^{-6}	10^5 (2000°F)	30×10^6
Quartz (SiO_2)	2.65	0.03	7×10^{-6}	2.5 (2000°F)	45×10^6
SiC	3.17	0.029	2.5×10^{-6}	50×10^{-6}	—
TiC	4.5	0.07	4×10^{-6}		50×10^6

(Continued)

* Multiply by 0.806 to get Btu·in./°F·ft²·sec.   † Multiply by 1.8 to get cm/cm/°C.   ‡ Divide by 2.54 to get ohm·in.

appendix e

PROPERTIES OF SELECTED ENGINEERING MATERIALS

PART 3 — ORGANIC MATERIALS (Taken from numerous sources)

Material	Specific gravity	Thermal conductivity, cal·cm / °C·cm²·sec at 68°F*	Thermal expansion, in/in/°F at 68°F†	Electrical resistivity, ohm·cm at 68°F‡	Average modulus of elasticity, psi at 68°F
Melamine-formaldehyde	1.5	0.0007	15×10^{-6}	10^{13}	1.3×10^{6}
Phenol-formaldehyde	1.3	0.0004	40×10^{-6}	10^{12}	0.5×10^{6}
Urea-formaldehyde	1.5	0.0007	15×10^{-6}	10^{12}	1.5×10^{6}
Rubbers (synthetic)	1.5	0.0003	—	—	500–10,000
Rubber (vulcanized)	1.2	0.0003	45×10^{-6}	10^{14}	0.5×10^{6}
Polyethylene	0.9	0.0008	100×10^{-6}	10^{13}	0.5×10^{6}
Polystyrene	1.05	0.0002	35×10^{-6}	10^{18}	0.4×10^{6}
Polyvinylidene chloride	1.7	0.0003	105×10^{-6}	10^{13}	0.05×10^{6}
Polytetrafluoroethylene	2.2	0.0005	55×10^{-6}	10^{16}	—
Polymethyl methacrylate	1.2	0.0005	50×10^{-6}	10^{16}	0.5×10^{6}
Nylon	1.15	0.0006	55×10^{-6}	10^{14}	0.4×10^{6}

* Multiply by 0.806 to get Btu·in/°F·ft²·sec.   † Multiply by 1.8 to get cm/cm/°C.   ‡ Divide by 2.54 to get ohm·in.

appendix f

SELECTED ORGANIC STRUCTURES

Acetic acid:

$$H-\overset{\overset{\displaystyle H}{|}}{\underset{\underset{\displaystyle H}{|}}{C}}-\overset{\overset{\displaystyle O}{\|}}{C}-OH$$

Acetone:

$$H-\overset{\overset{\displaystyle H}{|}}{\underset{\underset{\displaystyle H}{|}}{C}}-\overset{\overset{\displaystyle O}{\|}}{C}-\overset{\overset{\displaystyle H}{|}}{\underset{\underset{\displaystyle H}{|}}{C}}-H$$

Acetylene:

$$H-C\equiv C-H$$

Acrylonitrile:

$$\overset{\overset{\displaystyle H}{|}}{\underset{\underset{\displaystyle H}{|}}{C}}=\overset{\overset{\displaystyle H}{|}}{\underset{\underset{\displaystyle C\equiv N}{}}{C}}$$

Adipic acid:

$$HO-\overset{\overset{\displaystyle O}{\|}}{C}-\overset{\overset{\displaystyle H}{|}}{\underset{\underset{\displaystyle H}{|}}{C}}-\overset{\overset{\displaystyle H}{|}}{\underset{\underset{\displaystyle H}{|}}{C}}-\overset{\overset{\displaystyle H}{|}}{\underset{\underset{\displaystyle H}{|}}{C}}-\overset{\overset{\displaystyle H}{|}}{\underset{\underset{\displaystyle H}{|}}{C}}-\overset{\overset{\displaystyle O}{\|}}{C}-OH$$

Ammonia:

$$\overset{\overset{\displaystyle H}{|}}{\underset{\underset{\displaystyle H}{|}}{N}}-H$$

Benzene:

$$
\begin{array}{c}
H \\
| \\
C \\
H-C \quad\quad C-H \\
\| \quad\quad\quad | \\
C \quad\quad\quad C \\
H-C \quad\quad C-H \\
| \\
C \\
| \\
H
\end{array}
$$

Butadiene:

$$\overset{\overset{\displaystyle H}{|}}{\underset{\underset{\displaystyle H}{|}}{C}}=\overset{\overset{\displaystyle H}{|}}{C}-\overset{\overset{\displaystyle H}{|}}{C}=\overset{\overset{\displaystyle H}{|}}{\underset{\underset{\displaystyle H}{|}}{C}}$$

Butylene (iso): *see* isobutylene.

Butyric acid:

$$H-\overset{\overset{\displaystyle H}{|}}{\underset{\underset{\displaystyle H}{|}}{C}}-\overset{\overset{\displaystyle H}{|}}{\underset{\underset{\displaystyle H}{|}}{C}}-\overset{\overset{\displaystyle H}{|}}{\underset{\underset{\displaystyle H}{|}}{C}}-\overset{\overset{\displaystyle O}{\|}}{C}-OH$$

421

Cellulose acetate:

```
        Ac      Ac
        C———C
        |       |
        H       H
  —C—H          H—C—O—
        H
        C———O
  H—C—Ac
        H
```

Cellulose nitrate:

```
        NO₃     NO₃
        C———C
        |       |
        H       H
  —C—H          H—C—O—
        H
        C———O
  H—C—NO₃
        H
```

Chloroprene:

```
  H  Cl  H  H
  |  |   |  |
  C==C—C==C
  |         |
  H         H
```

Dimethylsilanediol:

```
        H
        |
   H—C—H
        |
 HO—Si—OH
        |
   H—C—H
        |
        H
```

Divinyl benzene:

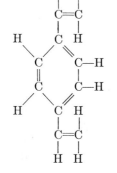

Ethane:

```
   H  H
   |  |
 H—C—C—H
   |  |
   H  H
```

Ethanol:

```
   H  H
   |  |
 H—C—C—OH
   |  |
   H  H
```

Ethylene dichloride: *see* vinylidene.

Ethylene:

```
   H  H
   |  |
   C==C
   |  |
   H  H
```

Ethylene glycol:

```
     H  H
     |  |
 HO—C—C—OH
     |  |
     H  H
```

Formaldehyde:

```
   H
   \
    C==O
   /
   H
```

Glycerol:

```
        H
        |
 H—C—OH
        |
 H—C—OH
        |
 H—C—OH
        |
        H
```

Hexamethylenediamine:

```
 H      H   H   H   H   H   H      H
  \     |   |   |   |   |   |     /
   N—C—C—C—C—C—C—N
  /     |   |   |   |   |   |     \
 H      H   H   H   H   H   H      H
```

Isobutylene:

```
            H
            |
    H   H—C—H
     \      |
      C====C
     /      |
    H   H—C—H
            |
            H
```

Isoprene:

```
            H
            |
    H   H—C—H   H       H
     \      |    |      |
      C====C—C====C
     /              |      |
    H              H      H
```

Isopropyl alcohol:

```
            H
     H   O   H
     |   |   |
 H—C—C—C—H
     |   |   |
     H   H   H
```

Linoleic acid:

```
    H  /H\  H  H   H  H  H  /H\  O
    |  | |  |  |   |  |  |  | |  ‖
 H—C—(C)—C=C—C—C=C—(C)—C—OH
    |  | |              |  | |
    H  \H/₄   H         \H/₇
```

Linolenic acid:

```
    H  H  H  H  H  H  H  H  H  H  /H\  O
    |  |  |  |  |  |  |  |  |  |  | |  ‖
 H—C—C—C=C—C—C=C—C—C=C—(C)—C—OH
    |  |     |        |        | |
    H  H     H        H        \H/₇
```

Maleic anhydride:

```
    H           H
    |           |
    C========C
   /            \
  C              C
  ‖              ‖
  O    O    O
```

Melamine:

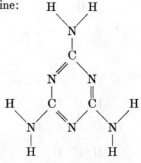

Methane:

```
      H
      |
  H—C—H
      |
      H
```

Methanol:

```
      H
      |
  H—C—OH
      |
      H
```

Methyl chloride:

```
      H
      |
  H—C—Cl
      |
      H
```

Methyl ethyl ketone:

```
      H   O   H   H
      |   ||  |   |
  H—C—C—C—C—H
      |       |   |
      H       H   H
```

Methyl methacrylate:

```
            H
            |
  H    H—C—H   O        H
  |        |   ||        |
  C══C═══════C—O—C—H
  |                      |
  H                      H
```

Neoprene: *see* chloroprene.

Oleic acid:

```
      H  /H\      H  H  /H\    O
      |  | |      |  |  | |    ||
  H—C—( C )—C══C—( C )—C—OH
      |  \ /      |  |  \ /
      H  \H/₇          \H/₇
```

Phenol:

```
         OH
         |
   H     C     H
    \   / \   /
     C     C
     ‖     ‖
     C     C
    /   \ /   \
   H     C     H
         |
         H
```

Phthalic acid: *see* terephthalic acid.

Phthalic anhydride:

```
          H
          |
   H      C        O
    \    / \      ‖
     C      C—C
     ‖      ‖     \
     C      C      O
    /    \ / \    /
   H      C   C—C
          |        ‖
          H        O
```

Propane:

```
      H  H  H
      |  |  |
  H—C—C—C—H
      |  |  |
      H  H  H
```

Propanol:

```
      H  H  H
      |  |  |
  H—C—C—C—OH
      |  |  |
      H  H  H
```

Propylene:

Stearic acid:

Styrene:

Terephthalic acid:

Tetrafluoroethylene:

Toluene:

Trifluorochloroethylene:

Trinitroglycerine:

Urea:

Vinyl acetate:

Vinyl alcohol:

$$
\begin{array}{cc}
H & H \\
| & | \\
C & = C \\
| & | \\
H & OH
\end{array}
$$

Vinyl benzene: *see* styrene.

Vinyl chloride:

$$
\begin{array}{cc}
H & H \\
| & | \\
C & = C \\
| & | \\
H & Cl
\end{array}
$$

Vinylidene chloride:

$$
\begin{array}{cc}
H & Cl \\
| & | \\
C & = C \\
| & | \\
H & Cl
\end{array}
$$

appendix g

Name	*General composition*†

1. Bakelite — Commonly a condensation polymer of phenol-formaldehyde.
2. Buna-N — Copolymer rubber of butadiene and acrylonitrile.
3. Buna-S — Copolymer rubber of butadiene and styrene.
4. Celluloid — Cellulose nitrate.
5. Dacron — Condensation polymer fiber of phthalic acid and ethylene glycol, or related compounds.
6. Durez — Commonly a condensation polymer of phenol-formaldehyde.
7. Geon — Commonly a polyvinyl chloride, or polyvinyl chloride copolymer.
8. Glyptol — Condensation polymer of phthalic acid and ethylene glycol, or related compounds.
9. GR-I — Copolymer rubber of isobutylene and isoprene.
10. GR-M — Polychloroprene rubber.
11. GR-S — Copolymer rubber of butadiene and styrene.
12. Gutta-percha — Polymer of *trans*-isoprene.
13. Kel-F — Polytrifluorochloroethylene.
14. Lucite — Polymethyl methacrylate.
15. Lustron — Polystyrene.
16. Melmac — Condensation polymer of melamine and formaldehyde.
17. Mylar — Condensation polymer film of phthalic acid and ethylene glycol, or related compounds.
18. Natural rubber — Polymer of *cis*-isoprene.
19. Neoprene — Polychloroprene rubber.
20. Nylon — Condensation polymer of hexamethylamine and adipic acid, or related compounds.
21. Plexene — Copolymer of styrene and acrylonitrile.
22. Plexiglas — Polymethyl methacrylate.
23. Plioflex — Copolymer of vinyl chloride and vinylidene chloride.
24. Polythene — Polyethylene.
25. Saran — Polyvinylidene chloride.
26. Silicones — Polymers containing silicon in place of part or all of the carbon.
27. Styron — Polystyrene.
28. Teflon — Polytetrafluoroethylene.
29. Tenite — Commonly cellulose acetate.
30. Texalite — Condensation polymer of phenol and formaldehyde.
31. Tygon — Polymer or copolymer including vinyl chloride and vinyl acetate.
32. Vinylite — Polymer or copolymer including vinyl chloride and vinyl acetate.

---

* Many of these names are trade names.

† Almost every commercial plastic is compounded to include fillers, plasticizers, and other additives to modify or control the properties.

index

index

---

* Letters indicate appendix references.

431

PRINTED IN JAPAN
TOKYO